Microprocessor Syst
An Introduction

Other Macmillan titles of related interest

Introductory Digital Design – A Programmable Approach
Mark S. Nixon

Microprogrammed Systems Design
J. S. Florentin

Mini and Microcomputer Systems
M. G. Hartley, M. Healey and P. G. Depledge

Microprocessor Systems
An Introduction

R. J. Mitchell

Department of Cybernetics
University of Reading

MACMILLAN

First published 1995 by
MACMILLAN PRESS LTD
Houndmills, Basingstoke, Hampshire RG21 2XS
and London
Companies and representatives
throughout the world

ISBN 0–333–64190–6

A catalogue record for this book is available from the British Library.

10   9   8   7   6   5   4   3   2
04 03 02 01 00 99 98 97 96

Printed in Great Britain by
Antony Rowe Ltd, Chippenham, Wiltshire

Contents

Preface

The aim of this book is to provide a coherent introduction to microprocessor systems, their operation and design. It covers those topics needed by engineers and computer scientists who are interested in applying microprocessors in practical situations, namely computer hardware including logic and interfacing, software, in particular high level and assembly language programming, as well as the design and testing of such systems.

In this book the fundamental principles of such systems are described and these are illustrated with reference to two microprocessors: the 32-bit MC68020 from Motorola, which is widely used in the teaching of microprocessors; and a single chip microcomputer, the 8051 from Intel, which is a simpler system much used in industry. In addition, interfacing to the general purpose STE bus is also described; its standard has just been reaffirmed by the IEEE. The two processors were chosen as they differ greatly being appropriate to different situations, and a bus system differs from a dedicated microprocessor system. The details of the processors and the bus are concentrated in three chapters, so presentation of the material can be made independent of the microprocessors if that is desired, and so that the specific details can be found easily.

The book is based on a 40 lecture course given to first year Cybernetists, Computer Scientists and Engineers at the University of Reading, together with second year courses in assembly language programming, computer interfacing and logic design, in which the more advanced features of the book are used. The book should be suitable for similar courses at other institutions.

One problem with this subject is that details of computer hardware require knowledge of software, which in turn requires knowledge of the hardware; where, therefore should the descriptions begin? In an attempt to solve this problem, a top down approach to the description of microprocessors is given.

Chapter 1 gives an overview of the complete system and then chapters 2 to 4 give a more detailed overview of software, hardware and logic. Chapters 5 to 7 then consider how logic circuits can be designed and used in computers. Chapters 8 to 11 describe hardware in more detail, first the logic circuits in microprocessors, then the principles of interfacing and then the interfaces to the 68020, 8051 and STE. Chapters 12 to 14 consider the software in more detail, starting with general principles, then code specific to the two microprocessors, and finally describing the mixing of high level and assembly language programs. The final chapter describes testing of hardware and software. Appendices are provided giving more details of the 68020, the 8051, STE and logic circuits, an explanation of the new logic symbols, and answers to the exercises.

The author wishes to thank everyone who has commented on the various drafts of the book. In this jargon strewn field, the author hopes to have defined each *alphabetic concoction randomly organised negating your mind* (acronym)!

Reading, September 1994.

1 Introduction

Microprocessors are found in many computer systems, from complex workstations with enhanced graphics facilities, to simple controllers inside household products like washing machines. Although the precise configuration and facilities of each system differ, many of the features are common. The aim of this book, therefore, is to introduce various microprocessor systems and describe how they operate. The intention is to be quite general, introducing fundamental concepts which are common to most microprocessor systems, and then to describe how they are implemented in two particular microprocessors, thereby providing comparisons of many features which are found in practice. The first stage is to consider what a microprocessor is, and what it does.

1.1 What is a computer?

It is a common misconception that a computer is a device which performs arithmetic operations; it is said to be a number cruncher. (Some perhaps have a different view; a computer is a device on which to play games.) However, a word processor system is also a computer, so a computer can process characters, and a modern system will not only allow the user to enter text, but it can also inform the user as to any errors in spelling or even report grammatical or stylistic errors. In addition, computers are used to control various devices, from something as simple as a washing machine, to a complex system like an aircraft.

Many of these systems do indeed require arithmetic operations, but a much better description of a computer is that it is a device which processes information. If the information is numerical, then the processing will be arithmetical, but in a word processor the information is a series of characters. In a washing machine, the computer controller reads the control panel to determine which program to obey, and then controls devices such as water pumps and heaters. For example, to ensure that the water temperature is correct, the computer must monitor the temperature and keep heating the water until it reaches the correct temperature. A calculator is a device which can only perform calculations, a computer is a more general device which can perform calculations, but it can also do other operations.

So it is better to describe a computer as an information processor. To be more specific, a computer is a device which obeys a series of instructions telling it to process data in an appropriate manner. These instructions are called a *program*, and for any given task a suitable program must be generated for reading by the computer.

At the heart of a computer is the circuitry which performs these processing operations. However, for a computer to do a useful job, it must be connected to the outside world. For example, a word processor needs a keyboard so the human can type in the words, a screen on which to display the words, and perhaps a disk drive which allows the words to be stored and a printer on which the results can be printed. Whereas the computer controlling the washing machine needs facilities which allow it to control the valves, measure temperatures, and read the control panel.

Another way of describing a computer is to say that it is a tool to assist the human in solving a particular problem. To allow the computer to solve a given problem two things are required; the particular program appropriate to the problem, and the necessary facilities which allow the computer to be connected, that is interfaced, to the 'real world'. A complete system thus includes the information processor and the associated interfaces.

This book is about microprocessor systems, whereas the discussion above talks about computers. There are various forms of computer, including analog and digital computers, and a microprocessor is part of a particular type of a digital computer. To see how the ideas about computers developed, how microprocessors came into being, and also why computers are erroneously thought of as calculators, a brief historical survey is needed.

1.2   History of computers

Some computer historians would start at the invention of the abacus, others would begin with the mechanical calculators produced in the 17th century by the likes of Schickard and Pascal (see Hollingdale and Tootill). However, computers really began with the engines designed by Charles Babbage (see P and E Morrison). The first of these was the *Difference Engine* first proposed in 1820.

At that time various arithmetical tables were being produced for people such as astronomers, navigators and engineers. These were calculated and printed by hand and so they often contained errors. Babbage decided to try to make a machine to calculate and print these tables; the result was the Difference Engine.

The Difference Engine could calculate the values for tables for a variety of functions; for simple functions like $y = x^2$ the operations were simple, but for more complex functions, a more involved sequence of operations was needed. However, each function used the law of constant differences, which is why the machine was called the Difference Engine. The following description shows how this law can be used to calculate values for the function $y = x^2$. Consider:

First Difference	Second Difference
$2^2 - 1^2 = 3$	
	$5 - 3 = 2$
$3^2 - 2^2 = 5$	
	$7 - 5 = 2$
$4^2 - 3^2 = 7$	

At each stage, the result of the 'second difference' is 2. In general, for any x

$$(x^2 - (x - 1)^2) - (\,(x - 1)^2 - (x - 2)^2) = 2$$

This can be rearranged:

$$x^2 = (x - 1)^2 + (x - 1)^2 - (x - 2)^2 + 2$$

Thus, given the values for 0^2 and 1^2, 2^2 can be calculated using the simple operations of additions and a subtraction. Then 1^2 and 2^2 can be used to calculate 3^2, and so on. Thus a simple strategy can be used to calculate the values of the function, and a machine, the Difference Engine, was designed to obey that strategy. In computer terms, the strategy is called an *algorithm*. A slightly more complex algorithm is needed for calculating the cubic function, an even more complex algorithm calculates the quartic function, and so on.

Babbage received a government grant to build the machine, but although small trial systems were made, he did not succeed in making a working full scale system, and eventually the grant was terminated. The reasons for failure are thought to be bad project management, technological problems, government interference and withdrawal of government finance. Some things never change. Babbage commented after the end of the grant that if anyone said they had a design for a potato peeler, people would say it would never work; if someone then built a potato peeler that did work, then people would say that it was no use as it could not peel an apple. Recently the Science Museum in London built a working version of the engine showing that Babbage's concept was valid.

The Difference Engine is the first idea of an automatic calculating machine, but it can solve problems in a relatively restricted domain. Therefore, Babbage went one stage further and proposed a general purpose processing machine, which he called the *Analytical Engine*. This had at its heart a mill which processed data, a store in which numbers could be stored, an input channel through which instructions could be fed, and a printer onto which the results could be printed. This is very like the form of a modern computer. The input was achieved using cards with holes in appropriate positions to indicate the instructions; this idea was invented in the previous century by Jacquard for his weaving looms, and the concept was used in computer systems up until the 1980s. Other ideas of the time which were used later include Babbage's fast parallel carry to speed the calculations (an electronic version was invented in the 1950s), and the appreciation that such a device needs a program so that it can perform the correct task. As Babbage's friend and Byron's daughter, Ada Lovelace, said of the analytical engine, 'before it can weave algebraic patterns, just as the Jacquard loom weaves flowers and leaves, it needs a program and control process'. The Analytical Engine was never built, but it did establish the basic concepts of computers. A recent work of fiction, called *The Difference Engine*, describes a world in which Babbage's machines succeeded and Faraday's work on electricity did not; this is worth reading.

It was not until 1944 that Babbage's ideas were converted to an actual machine, the Automatic Sequence Controlled Calculator, designed by Aiken and built by IBM. This had no conceptual advance on Babbage's work.

However, in the 1930s some advances were made concerning the solution of problems by machine. In order that a problem should be solved, the appropriate algorithm is required. The mathematician David Hilbert had said that any mathematical problem could be solved by a fixed and definite process, and Alan Turing interpreted this to mean that a machine could solve the problem. Turing then proposed an abstract machine, the Turing machine, and showed that it could solve many problems by being given the appropriate instructions, but there were some problems that neither it nor any other machine could solve. Thus a computer cannot solve all problems. It is interesting to note that theories on the computability of problems were investigated before computers existed.

Turing and others worked on various computer systems in the period 1939-45, but these did not advance the concepts of Babbage. These computers were mechanical devices, but then in 1946 an electronic system was built, called ENIAC. This had 18000 valves, but these were unreliable, so the machine rarely worked for more than an hour at a time. Other than the fact that they were non-mechanical, they followed Babbage's engine, and like his machines, they processed decimal numbers.

However, in 1946, John Von Neumann took the next step forward. He proposed a structure for a computer which has been used in many computers since. The system is shown in figure 1.1. The central processing unit contains the circuitry for processing data (like Babbage's mill) and coordinating the action of the machine, the memory is used to contain both data and the program (Babbage's store contained only data), and the system communicated with the outside world using the input and output channels. In addition to storing data and the program in memory, the other radical change was that computers should process binary data, rather than decimal.

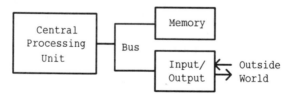

Figure 1.1. Von Neumann structure of a computer

The advantage of using binary data is that simple circuits can be produced which process such data, performing logical operations. Many such circuits can then be connected together to perform more complex operations, for example, arithmetic. Logic circuits can also be used as memory elements, and allow the different parts of a computer system to be connected together. In fact, a modern electronic computer consists of a large number of logic circuits.

Since then, many electronic computer systems have been built, many developed in the UK by Manchester University and Ferranti. The early machines used valves. Then in 1948 the transistor was invented, and this replaced the valve, being a much more reliable and smaller device. (A contemporary reviewer in *Wireless World* commented that a transistor was an interesting device, but did not think it had much applicability.) Transistors can be used for various purposes, one of which is to implement logic operations.

Subsequently, integrated circuits were developed in which many transistors and other components were built on one piece of material, so that circuits became even smaller, and this process has continued, until now it is possible to put a complete computer on one piece of silicon.

Systems which differ from the Von Neumann concept include those where there are many central processing units. Usually each has its own memory, and each unit communicates with others. However, it is often the case that each sub-system has a structure similar to that proposed by Von Neumann.

The instructions, that is the program, for the machines in the 1950s were binary values, so the user of the computer had to write programs in binary, that is, in the language of the machine (called *machine code*). This, as shall be explained later, is a tedious process, so it was suggested that it should be possible to program the computer in a language more readily understood by humans. This lead to the invention of FORTRAN, or formula translation, a high level programming language; a name, incidentally, which does nothing to change the view that computers are calculators. Since then better languages have been invented, although many people still use FORTRAN. (A discussion of various programming languages is given in chapter 2.)

In the early 1970s, integrated circuits had become complex. One use of these was in calculators, which contained dedicated circuitry for performing calculations. In fact these were electronic versions of the mechanical calculators first produced in the 17th century. Then Hoff, who had to design a calculator, suggested that the calculator should contain a general purpose processing machine, not a specific calculator. This was the first microprocessor, a computer on a chip.

Since then techniques have been developed which allow more and more circuitry to be put on a chip. Thus microprocessors and their associated devices have become more and more complex and much more powerful; even the early microprocessors were more powerful than the electronic computers of the 1940s which filled a room, but modern systems have still greater power (though they never seem to be powerful enough). Similarly, the increased density of circuits has allowed for a great increase in memory. In 1980, 16 thousand locations of memory was considered a lot in a microprocessor system, by 1990 16 million locations was more appropriate. Also, the cost of these devices has reduced rapidly, so microprocessors can be found in very many applications.

The interested reader is referred to Randall's collection of papers which contains some descriptions of the original ideas described above. Contributions to the above include papers by Babbage, Aiken and Von Neumann.

It is interesting to note, however, that the first machine, the Difference Engine, was developed to produce arithmetic tables, the first high level language was for formula translation and the first microprocessor was developed to be put in a calculator. No wonder that most people believe that a computer is a number cruncher. However, during the time since 1820, the concepts of the modern microprocessor system have developed so that the microprocessor is an invaluable tool to be used in a great variety of systems, and not just for performing arithmetical functions.

1.3   Computer applications

A general definition of a computer is that it is an information processor, a device which obeys instructions which tell it to perform logical operations on binary data. In this section some possible applications of computers are given which illustrate their versatility. In later chapters, some of these applications will be considered in more detail, thereby demonstrating the facilities required.

A computer could be a dedicated controller. Microprocessors are found in many household appliances, including washing machines, video players and CD players. In an industrial environment, computers could be controlling robots or numerically controlled machines like milling machines and drills. A microprocessor system which is programmed for one particular task, such as one used in a washing machine, is often called a *microcontroller*; often the microprocessor chip contains its own memory and input/output devices.

Computers can also be used as data logging devices, recording various data, for example a measurement system like a seismometer; when an earthquake occurs, the force of the quake and its after shocks need to be recorded and analysed subsequently. Logging is also required when testing a device; the device is left operating over a long period and its outputs measured and stored.

Computers can be used for both purposes; good control of a system requires its outputs to be measured and compared with their set values, and differences between the actual and desired values should be corrected by the computer. Also, when testing a device, measurements should be made at various operating conditions; the computer sets these conditions and takes the measurements.

In a less technical environment, computers can be used for secretarial work, such as word processing, storing and processing data on clients and orders and maintaining a diary. It is possible to buy machines which are marketed as word processors, implying that they can only be used as such. In fact, such word processors are general purpose computers which are provided with a program for word processing. It is usually better to buy a general purpose computer and the appropriate programs for the various tasks which are required. Such computers are usually connected to printers which allow the word processed data, or the stored data, to be printed on to paper. Such printers themselves usually contain a computer which receives the data to be printed and controls the actual print mechanism. The computers can also be connected to fax machines, allowing them to receive and transmit messages. Fax machines also contain a dedicated computer.

Computers can also be used for running computer aided design programs (CAD). Simple CAD applications allow the user to enter drawings of circuits, components or buildings. Others allow the connections of a printed circuit board to be placed suitably; the user defines the circuit, perhaps suggests appropriate positions of components, and then the program works out the placing of the wires joining the components. For mechanical systems, the program can calculate the stresses and strains of components; for electrical systems, the program can calculate the values of signals in the system; for control systems, the CAD program could allow the user to design a suitable controller so as to meet a required specification.

In addition to running programs like word processors, computers also allow users to write their own programs to solve particular problems. This requires various support programs to allow the entering, processing, running and 'debugging' of the user programs. A microprocessor system which can be used for various tasks, such as one on which the user can write programs, is often termed a *microcomputer*.

One area where various programs are written is the field of artificial intelligence. Here the attempt is made to make computers 'think', a problem which is more difficult than early programmers believed. Currently computers can do some intelligent tasks, but no computer is as powerful as HAL, the super computer predicted by Arthur C Clarke in *2001 - a Space Odyssey*. Incidentally, Clarke claims that it is a fluke that the letters in the alphabet after HAL are IBM, the name of the giant computer firm.

Computers can be stand-alone machines, perhaps connected to a printer, or many computers may be connected together, thereby allowing certain resources to be shared, and for information to be transferred between the machines. Electronic mail is a system which allows computers throughout the world to be connected. In universities this is invaluable; it allows a researcher in the UK, say, to communicate with someone working in a similar field in the USA, exchange ideas and send useful information. Also, public domain software, that is, programs available to any one, can be transferred across such links.

Most of the above are achieved on simple computer systems with a dedicated microprocessor. There are larger computers, called main frames, which typically are used by many people at one time. These can be used for solving large problems which take a long time to process. An example problem for such a machine is weather forecasting. Here very complicated mathematical models are used to represent the behaviour of the weather, and calculations are performed on these models so as to attempt to predict the weather.

Simple microprocessor systems contain one unit which is capable of performing one task at a time. Some modern systems contain many processing units each of which is allocated a given task. This operation is termed *parallel processing*, as many tasks are solved at one time, in parallel. Note, in this book, only simpler systems involving one microprocessor are described.

Thus computers can be used in a great variety of applications. All they require is the appropriate facilities, the machine (the hardware) and the program (the software). The hardware and the software for computers vary considerably depending on the application, but the fundamental principles do not. Thus, these principles are described in this book. However, to ensure that the concepts can be tested practically, two different microprocessors are also described; the 68020, an advanced processor from Motorola; and the 8051, a relatively simple single-chip processor. These two processors were chosen as they are very different, being appropriate to different applications, and having been produced by two manufacturers. (It is notable that when two manufacturers design computer products, and have the opportunity to design machines with contradictory facilities, the results are invariably incompatible.)

1.4   Introduction to the rest of the book

This chapter has introduced microprocessor systems, showing that a computer is an information processor; under instruction the computer performs logical operations on binary data. Some applications of computers are given, showing the flexibility of these machines. The next stage is to describe the parts of a computer in more detail.

Such descriptions are difficult to organise; the subject of computers is notoriously circular, where any explanatory statement presupposes the knowledge of some other aspect of the subject. For example, when describing the internal structure of a computer, it is important to consider how a computer processes data, and that has a bearing on the components of a computer.

However, when trying to handle a complex problem, the best approach is to try to divide that problem into smaller parts, and then tackle each part separately, dividing each part into smaller parts. Thus the overall system, say, consists of parts A, B and C, and A consists of parts A1, A2, A3 and A4, and so on. An initial understanding of the system requires an acceptance that parts A, B and C exist, and a general understanding of their actions and how they fit together. Then, further understanding can be achieved by considering parts A1, A2, A3 and A4 ignoring, to some extent, parts B and C. Thus the complete picture can be developed gradually, becoming more detailed, but in such a manner that the reader can see how the detail fits into the complete picture.

Therefore this book is organised in such a *top down* manner. This first chapter has given an overview; the next three chapters give an overview of the three important aspects of a computer. These are the software, that is, the program; the hardware, that is, the actual machine; and logic, the functions and circuits which allow computers to process data and for connecting the components of microprocessor systems. These chapters are followed by more detailed analysis of logic, hardware and software. In this way, it is hoped that the circular descriptions will be avoided, and the reader is able to follow how the computer operates and how the various parts of the computer fit together. Figure 1.2 below shows the structure of the book, outlining the chapter topics and their chapter numbers.

The three themes of the book, logic, hardware and software, are introduced in chapters 2, 3 and 4. The logic section (chapters 5, 6 and 7) describes simple logic circuits, circuits with memory and how logic operations can be used to process various types of data. The hardware section (chapters 8, 9, 10 and 11) considers microprocessor structure and operation, interfacing, hardware

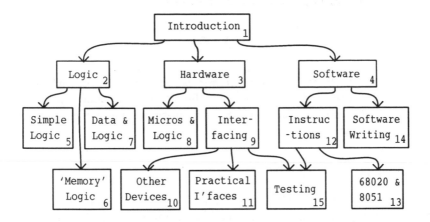

Figure 1.2 Structure of the book

development and details about specific hardware, and these use logic circuits and specific details about the two microprocessors. The software section (chapters 12, 13 and 14) considers how information is processed, with sub chapters on the actual instruction types and those employed on the two microprocessors, and software development. The final chapter (15) describes methods of testing both hardware and software. Exercises are given at the end of most chapters, answer to some of which can be found in an appendix. Other appendices give other relevant information.

Exercise

Derive the algorithm which allows the Difference Engine to calculate the values for the function $y = x^3$.

References

S.H. Hollingdale & G.C. Tootill *Electronic Computers* Penguin, 1970.

B. Randall (ed) *The Origins of Digital Computers: selected papers* Springer Verlag, 1973.

P. & E. Morrison, *Charles Babbage and his Calculating Engines* Dover Publications.

William Gibson and Bruce Sterling *The Difference Engine* VGSF, 1992.

Alan Turing *On Computable Numbers with an Application to the Entscheidungs problem* Proc. London Mathematical Society, Vol 42, pp 230-265, 1937.

Arthur C Clarke *2001 - a Space Odyssey* Arrow, 1968.

2   Computer Software

A computer system has two major components, the software, that is the program which tells the computer what to do, and the hardware, which is the actual machine obeying the program. This chapter discusses the software, describing the concepts, considering how programs are written and giving example programs.

2.1   Computer programs

A program is the list of instructions which the computer obeys in order to solve the task that it has been assigned. There are many tasks which computers can solve, so there are many different programs. However, there are some common aspects of programs. The following example illustrates these.

Suppose a robot is to be programmed to make coffee. This is a complicated problem which should be broken down into parts and then each part solved. As a first approximation the program is as follows:

```
PROGRAM Make Coffee;
   Put Coffee In Cup;
   IF Sugar Is Required THEN Add Sugar;
   IF Milk Is Required THEN Add Milk;
   Boil Water;
   Pour Boiling Water Into Cup;
END.
```

These tasks have been identified. Next, each task can be considered in more detail, independently of the others. A part program, or *procedure*, to boil the water is as follows:

```
PROCEDURE Boil Water;
   Put Water In Kettle;
   Switch Kettle On;
   Wait Until Water Has Boiled;
   Switch Kettle Off;
END.
```

Similarly, the Add Sugar procedure could be:

```
PROCEDURE Add Sugar;
   REPEAT
     Put Sugar Lump In Cup
   UNTIL Enough Lumps Have Been Added
END.
```

10

The parts of each procedure can then be considered; for example, to put the water in the kettle the procedure is:

```
PROCEDURE Put Water In Kettle;
   Remove Kettle Lid;
   Put Kettle Under Tap;
   Turn Tap On;
   Wait Until Kettle Sufficiently Full;
   Turn Tap Off;
   Replace Kettle Lid;
END.
```

This process of dividing the problem continues until each part becomes sufficiently simple to be solved. The above procedures illustrate some basic principles required in programming. These are now expounded in more detail.

Initially the appropriate algorithm is required. This defines the actions which should be followed if the computer is to solve the given task. Once this has been produced, the algorithm should be turned into a program, which contains the actual instructions that the computer obeys. It should be possible to use the following facilities in a program.

* First, it should be possible to divide a task into smaller tasks. Thus the program consists of smaller part programs, called *procedures* or *subroutines*, and the main program operates by obeying specific instructions and calling the other procedures. Similarly, a procedure obeys its specific instructions and calls other subroutines.
* Second, the program should be able to do certain actions many times. For example, procedure Add Sugar requires a sugar lump to be added many times.
* Third, the program should allow conditional operation. For example, the Add Sugar procedure is obeyed only if sugar is required.

Thus the features of programs have been demonstrated. The next section considers the ways in which programs can be produced.

2.2   Program development

Programs are written to solve problems. When a new problem is to be solved, the appropriate program must be produced. This section considers how a program is developed.

First, the specification for the program must be determined. Next, this specification is turned into a description of how a computer could achieve the task; essentially this is the appropriate algorithm. Then the algorithm is converted into the instructions which the computer can 'understand'. Then the program can be run. At this stage it is often discovered that the program does not achieve the task, in which case errors must be found and corrected. These errors could be due to an incorrect algorithm, or to incorrect coding of the algorithm into the instructions. Thus the programmer identifies the error, makes the changes and then tests the new program, and continues this process until the program is correct. The above is a somewhat simple view of program development, in practice it is not that easy; more details can be found in books on software engineering, for example that by Somerville.

The program must contain instructions that the computer can 'understand'. What does this mean? The next sections describe the different ways in which the instructions can be written, namely in machine code, assembly language or a high level language.

Machine code

A computer is a device which, under instruction, performs logical operations on binary data. The data being processed are binary, so are the instructions. Thus each instruction consists of many binary values. If each binary value is represented by '0' or '1', then for a hypothetical computer an instruction to add two numbers might be 10001000, and one to perform the logical OR function on two numbers could be 10000110.

Thus, binary is the language that the computer 'understands'; it is the language of the machine, so it is called *machine code*. Ultimately all programs must be in machine code if the computer is to obey them. However, it is not necessary, nor is it desirable, to program in machine code, for various reasons.

First, a machine code program is long and tedious, containing many strings of binary digits. It is very difficult to spot errors in these digits. The computer understands the binary strings, humans do not, the binary means nothing or very little to the human. Modifications to programs can be tedious; inserting an extra instruction can require other instructions to change. Another problem is that the machine code for each type of microprocessor is different, thus a program written for one microprocessor will not, in general, work on another; the program is not portable. A more fundamental problem is that programs are written in order to solve tasks, and when programming in machine code, the programmer has to write a program in terms of the facilities of the machine, not in terms of the task being solved.

Thus it is not desirable to program in machine code. It is, however, a useful discipline to have programmed in binary at some time. It demonstrates that a computer is a device performing logical operations, and it proves that you do not want to do it again!

Assembly language

The next level up from machine code is assembly language. As, for example, in our hypothetical computer, the binary string 10001000 is the instruction ADD and the string 10000110 is OR, it is more convenient for the human to be able to write ADD if two numbers are to be added, or OR if the logical 'or' function is to be performed on two numbers. This is *assembly language*, where simple names, usually consisting of between two and five letters are used to represent instructions; these names are called *mnemonics*, from the Greek word for memory, and they should be easy to remember. In addition to writing the instructions using names instead of binary, it is also possible to use names to represent procedures and to write numbers in decimal; these are all converted to their equivalent binary. Thus if two is to be added, the assembly language instruction would be ADD 2, rather than the binary strings for ADD and 2. It is also possible to write comments in the program, which help the programmer, or anyone else using the program, to understand its action.

There are clear advantages to using assembly language over machine code, not the least that it is easier to understand, as the mnemonics are meaningful and explanatory comments are allowed. However, there are disadvantages.

First, in order to write a program in assembly language, at least two other programs are needed; an editor is needed to allow the user to type in the program (this is called the *source code*); and another program, called an assembler, is needed which converts the program into machine code (the *object code*). Also, many of the disadvantages of machine code programming also apply: the program is still long as there is a 1:1 correspondence between assembly language and machine code instructions; it is not portable, as the assembly languages of different microprocessors vary; and the program must be written in terms of the computer and not the task being solved.

High level languages

The alternative is to write programs using *high level* languages. These languages consist of English-like statements. The following is a legal statement in a program playing chess:

```
IF KingIsInCheck THEN MoveTheKing;
```

Here, *KingIsInCheck* might be a procedure which determines whether the king is in check, and which returns TRUE or FALSE. *MoveTheKing* is another procedure; it moves the king. Thus the king will be moved only if the king is in check. Clearly, such a program has been written in terms of the task being solved and not in terms of the machine.

Another advantage of using high level languages is portability. A program written on one computer can often work on another computer, provided that both computers have the appropriate programs to convert the source code into the object code. Two types of program are used for the conversion process, *compilers* and *interpreters*.

A compiler is presented with the complete program. It then analyses the whole program, converts it to binary, and the binary can then be executed.

An interpreter takes one part of the program at a time, converts that to machine code, executes it, and then moves to the next part, converts it, and so on. Effectively the interpreter is running the high level language.

One advantage of an interpreter is that it quickly informs the programmer of syntactical errors, as soon as they are found, whereas compilation is a slower process (although some compilers are very fast). The main advantage of an interpreter is that it often allows a program to be typed in and then analysed and executed, needing no other program; nor does it need separate memory for the source program and its object code. Some small systems exist, therefore, with a built-in interpreter, often a BASIC interpreter.

However, the compiled program will run more quickly, as the computer is just executing the machine code, not converting and executing code.

In summary, to demonstrate by analogy how programs could be written, consider the problem of understanding a foreigner. One could:
- Learn his language   equivalent to programming in machine code
- Get a translator   like using a compiler
- Teach him your language   like using an interpreter

The only problem with this analogy is that a person who translates foreign languages is not called a compiler.

A program written in a high level language consists of a number of instructions which are converted to machine code instructions by a compiler or interpreter. In fact, several machine code instructions are usually required to implement each statement in a high level language. Thus, when writing in a high level language, the program entered by the user will probably be much shorter than if the program was written in assembly language or machine code. However, the machine code produced by the conversion program is likely to be longer than if the program had been written in machine code. This is because the assembly language programmer can often spot short cuts which the compiler cannot. Modern compilers, however, often have an optimisation process which does help make efficient code. Note, some compilers convert from high level to assembly language and then an assembler converts this to machine code.

Thus a program written in a high level language is likely to be slower and larger than if the program had been written in machine code or assembly language. However, it is likely that the program will be written more quickly and have fewer errors if it is written in a high level language. Also, with modern fast microprocessors which have much memory, it is not so important for programs to be fast and compact.

Sometimes, one part of a program needs be very fast, or it may require code which accesses a specific part of the computer for which there are no appropriate instructions in the high level language. In such cases the program should be written mainly in the high level language, but with the relevant part of the program written in assembly language. Both parts are then converted to machine code, and then put together to form the complete program.

This is one reason why it is useful to learn assembly language programming. Another, perhaps more important one, is that programming in assembly language teaches the programmer more about the operation of computers. In this way the programmer can appreciate what can be done efficiently with a computer, and so program in such a manner.

There are many high level languages; in fact a few years ago the US military were concerned that over 170 languages were used in their sponsored projects. They decided that all contractors should use one language, so that, they believed, people would be able to understand the code written by other programmers. They felt that no language was suitable, so they arranged for yet another language to be defined; this is ADA, named after Lady Ada Lovelace (see chapter 1). However, this language has not proved very popular, and since the end of the cold war, its use has declined.

In fact, there is no single language suitable for all tasks. FORTRAN is quite good for numerical processing especially because of the availability of suitable library software; PASCAL and MODULA-2 are good for teaching as they encourage the writing of well structured programs; BASIC is a simple language, often the first one learnt; C is available on many different machines, so it is an appropriate language to use if the program is to run on many different types of computer; C++ is an increasingly popular language; LISP and PROLOG are very popular amongst some workers in the artificial intelligence field; COBOL is recommended by some for the writing of 'business' software.

An obvious question, since no computer language seems suitable for all tasks, is why not write programs in English, not in pseudo-English. There are many reasons why this is not done. Understanding English is very complicated as it is a large language; it is much easier to understand the simpler languages. Also, consider the phrase 'white green sheep sleep furiously' which is grammatically correct, but which is meaningless; a computer must be quite advanced to detect this. Also, English can be ambiguous; the phrase 'fruit flies like a banana' could mean that the insects are partial to bananas, or that fruit goes through the air in the same way as a banana. Other problems include the use in English of metaphors; the phrase 'gather ye rosebuds while you may' does not mean that you should pick flowers.

High level language programming, like assembly language programming, requires other support programs, including editors, compilers or interpreters, and possibly assemblers and linkers. Linkers are used to connect together the various parts of a program, such as the high level language and the assembly language parts. Also, it is often desirable to write the program in separate parts, perhaps these parts being written by different people, so they must be linked together. Other reasons for having a program in parts are as follows: solving a large problem is best achieved by dividing it into parts as it is not possible to think about the whole program at a time; also, a part program written for one problem may be appropriate in another, thus if it is written separately, as a useful 'library' facility, it can be incorporated in those programs which need it.

2.3 Example programs

The fundamental principles of various programs and the means whereby programs can be written have now been identified. The next section gives some examples of the typical programs which are used on two types of computer, a microcomputer and a washing machine microcontroller. These descriptions demonstrate the hardware facilities required by these computers.

Microcomputer

A microcomputer is a general purpose microprocessor system which can be used for many tasks. These include word processing, desk top publishing, storing and processing data in a database or a spreadsheet, drawing diagrams and writing programs. All of these are achieved by allowing the computer to execute programs specific to the particular application.

A *word processor* allows the user to write documents, whether they be simple letters, memoranda, reports, lecture notes or even books (where would the author be without a word processor?). This requires a keyboard with which the user enters characters and a display where these characters are displayed. The word processor must also allow the user to search through the words, checking for errors, allowing some text to be removed, added or changed. This requires cursor keys or a mouse device which allow the user to move up, down, left or right in the document. In addition, the system should allow the document to be saved and others to be reloaded for subsequent examination or modification. Often the documents are saved on and retrieved from a disk (either a hard disk or a floppy disk), and this disk may be part of the computer, or it may be on another computer which is connected via a communications link. Also, the word processor should allow the user to print the document. Therefore the computer should be connected to a printer. Again there may be a printer connected directly, or the document may be sent down a link to a printer which is connected to another computer. Modern systems increasingly include facilities to check spelling, grammar and even style.

A *drawing package* is another utility program. It allows the user to draw a diagram, by placing graphical items like lines, circles and text. The drawing could, for example, be a simple circuit diagram, a three-dimensional representation of a mechanical component, or a graph. This requires keyboard, mouse and display, with disk storage and printing facilities.

A *desk top publisher* is more advanced than a word processor. It is a program which allows the text produced by a word processor to be arranged neatly on a page. Multiple columns of text can be specified, and different character fonts. In addition, it is also possible to include in the text diagrams which may have been produced by the drawing package. Thus the desk top publisher requires a keyboard, a display, a mouse, a disk for storing documents and drawings and a printer for obtaining hardcopy of the final document. Note, this book was produced using a desk top publisher.

A *data base* program allows the storage and processing of data. A typical application would be to complete an inventory of equipment in a company. For each item, the name, type, serial number, order number, cost, location, date of purchase and the person responsible for the item could be stored. The data base should thus allow the user to enter the data about a new item, and to examine or modify data about existing stored items. Then the program should allow searches of the data to find, for example, all items bought in a particular year, or to list all computers which have been bought. This requires the same hardware facilities as a word processor program.

A *spreadsheet* also allows data to be stored and processed. However, in a spreadsheet some of the values associated with an item are calculated by the program by processing other values. For example, a spreadsheet could be used to process examination marks. Suppose each student sat three examination papers, did practical work and a project; and the average examination and practical/project marks were required, and the final mark was weighted 60% for the examination and 40% for the rest. The user would enter for each student the marks obtained for each examination, the practical and the project, and the system would calculate the other data. An example data set is given below.

ExamA	ExamB	ExamC	Av. Exam	Practical	Project	Av P/P	Total
65%	75%	40%	60%	80%	60%	70%	64%

A spreadsheet also requires the same hardware facilities as a word processor.

The above application programs can be obtained for a computer. The user, however, might also wish to develop his or her own programs. This requires an *editor* program to enter the program (an editor is like a word processor), and a compiler, interpreter or assembler to convert the program into the binary which the computer understands. Once the program has been written, it must be tested. In an ideal world, programs would work first time, but often they have errors or bugs. Thus special programs are needed to help identify such errors. These *debuggers* allow the user to run parts of the program, and then determine the state of the machine, so as to verify that the program is working correctly. If there is no error, the next part of the program is obeyed and the machine tested. In this way errors can be found.

Thus a microcomputer requires a keyboard, display, mouse, disk storage and printers, as well as suitable application programs such as those described above. In addition, the computer requires another program, usually called an *operating system*, which allows these application programs to be run themselves and which handles the actual hardware.

When the computer is switched on, it runs the operating system which first initialises the hardware. Then the operating system allows the user to enter a command, to list for example the data on a disk, or perhaps to run another program. The operating system thus contains the instructions to read from the keyboard or mouse, to write to the display, to handle the communication ports and the disks. Other programs also require such code, so it is usual for these other programs to be able to call these routines (which are often called traps).

Much of the work of the operating system is stored on and is concerned with the handling of disks; hence the term disk operating system or DOS is used. The typical DOS functions are to list the files on the disk, giving such information as the name, size and date of creation of the file; to erase files; to rename files; to transfer a file to another disk or part of the disk, or down a communications link to a printer or other computer; to display the contents of a file; or to load a file into the memory and to execute it.

A standard microcomputer has a single-user operating system, that is, one person uses the machine at any time. More complex machines have multi-user/multi-tasking operating systems where, apparently, the computer is doing many tasks at once for one or more users. In fact, the computer does parts of each task in turn, first obeying one task for a short time, then obeying another, and so on. As such a machine operates very quickly, more quickly than a human user can respond, each user believes that the computer is continually obeying his or her task. One function of the operating system is to allocate the time slots for each task. More details on operating systems can be found in Lister and Eager.

Washing machine controller

A washing machine controller is a small microprocessor system which allows the user to specify the type of wash required (like the temperature, duration, and whether to pause before the final rinse), and then performs the actual wash. This requires control of valves allowing water, washing powder and conditioner to be fed into the tub, control of motors for spinning the tub, control of the water temperature (which requires measurement of the temperature and control of the water heater) and means whereby the control panel settings can be read.

Only one piece of software is required for the controller, and this is stored in the computer memory. The program waits for the user to request that the program should start, then reads the control panel to determine the precise details of the wash (like the required temperature), and then starts the actual washing process. This consists of opening valves to let the water in, heating the water to the correct temperature, loading in the washing powder, spinning the drum, and so on. When the washing is complete, the program returns to the state where it is waiting for the next load to be washed.

Summary

This chapter has given an overview of computer software, describing the fundamental requirements of software, describing how software can be produced, and giving examples of the software required on a personal computer and a simple controller. The next chapter considers the other part of a computer, the hardware.

Exercise

Outline the program obeyed by a microprocessor controlling a CD player, in the manner described for the washing machine controller.

References

Ian Somerville *Software Engineering* Addison-Wesley, 4th Edition, 1992.
A.M. Lister and R.D. Eager *Fundamentals of Operating Systems* Macmillan Press, 5th Edition, 1993.

3 Computer Hardware

One part of a computer system has been considered, the software. In this chapter the other part is considered, the hardware. The structure of a computer is given in more detail, and the general principles by which information is transferred between the components of the computer are described. Some examples of the parts of three computer systems are also outlined.

3.1 Computer structure

A block diagram of the Von Neumann structure of a computer is shown in figure 3.1. This consists of the *central processing unit* (the CPU), *memory* and *input/output* devices, all connected by a *bus*. The central processing unit coordinates the action, obtaining, decoding and executing each instruction. The memory is used to store both the program which the computer obeys, and its associated data. The input/output units allow the system to communicate with the outside world; sometimes only data are input, but at other times an actual program is fed into the system via a suitable input device. These devices are connected together by a series of wires, called a bus, along which information is passed; the information consists of binary electrical signals. The CPU, memory, input/output devices and buses will now be described in more detail.

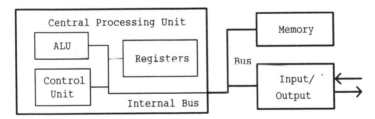

Figure 3.1 Block diagram of a computer

3.2 Memory devices

Memories are devices which allow the storage and retrieval of information. This information could be the program being obeyed, or it could be data being processed, or the results of the processing operations.

There are different types of memory; some memory is fast and can be accessed directly by the central processing unit, whereas other slower memory is normally used for storing larger amounts of data.

The fast memory comes in two types, ROM and RAM. ROM (or read only memory) maintains its contents even when the power is removed (that is, it is non-volatile memory), and this is often used for storing the program which the computer runs when it is first switched on. Note, microprocessor systems often contain EPROM (erasable programmable read only memory) or EEPROM (electrically erasable programmable read only memory); these memory can have there contents specified (they are programmable), but their contents can be changed by erasing them and then reprogramming. RAM (or random access memory), however, is usually a volatile store, it loses its contents when the power is removed; this is used for storing temporary data, although programs can also be loaded into RAM.

The slower memory is provided by such devices as floppy and hard disks, and sometimes tape or (for modern systems) CD-ROM. These are often used for storing large amounts of more permanent data, like a database or a word processor document, for storing programs, or for keeping a backup of important material in case the original is corrupted. Programs stored on a disk are read into RAM memory where they are then executed.

ROM and RAM memory contain many locations in which data can be stored. It must be possible to identify uniquely each location, so a number or *address* is associated with each location. When the central processing unit requires to write data into a location, it must specify the address of the location, the data to be written there, and an indication that data are to be written. Similarly, when the contents of a location are to be read, the central processing unit specifies the address of that location and an indication that data are to be read, and the memory then returns the data at that address.

Computers process many binary digits, or bits; a group of eight bits is termed a byte. The capacity of memory is usually measured in terms of the number of bytes of data which can be stored there. ROM devices containing 64K bytes (actually 2^{16} or 65536 bytes) are common. RAM modules containing up to 4M bytes (4×2^{20} bytes) are also available. Floppy disks capable of storing 1.4M byte are in wide use and hard disks with 200M byte are common, and some with many G bytes are available ($1G = 2^{30}$).

3.3 Input/Output devices

There are many different input/output devices or *peripherals*, some examples of which are given below. These allow the computer to communicate with a variety of different systems. The first few allow a human to communicate with a computer, the others allow the computer to interface with other machines.

A keyboard allows the user to enter data into the computer; it could be a full keyboard with keys for the complete alphabet, the numerical digits, punctuation, function and arrow keys; or it could be a simpler keypad with, perhaps, just the digits 0 to 9 and two control keys. For either type, the device can indicate whether a key has been pressed and, if so, output the value of that key.

A display is used to output information to the user. This could be a cathode ray tube display, like a television, or perhaps a liquid crystal display (LCD) or plasma screen, all of which allow many lines of text and sometimes graphics to be shown. Alternatively simpler displays, like seven-segment light emitting diodes (LEDs), can be used. A seven-segment display has seven segments arranged in the shape of an 8, and different segments are illuminated depending upon the number being displayed. To output to any display, data are written in the appropriate form to the device.

Communications devices allow information to be transferred between two or more computers, or from a computer to a printer or similar device. The communications may be in parallel, where many bits of data are sent at the same time, or in serial, where each bit of data is sent separately. A single link may be used, or the various devices may be connected by a network which allows many computers to communicate with each other and to share devices like printers. Special circuitry is provided which allows such communications; in use, the CPU just outputs to, or inputs from, these circuits.

Disk and tape storage are also sometimes considered to be input/output devices. They are also controlled by special logic circuits which allow data to be read from or written to the storage device. The CPU communicates directly with the controller circuits.

Other peripherals include simple ports which contain various logic signals which could be output or input. Each logic signal on an output port can be set to '0' or '1' by the microprocessor, and thus used to open or close a valve, say, or a relay. Each logic signal on an input port can be set to '0' or '1' by some external component, say a switch or a thermostat indicating that a temperature has reached a set value. The CPU can then read the values of the signals on the input port.

If, however, the computer is processing analog signals (that is, signals which are not restricted to '0' or '1'), suitable circuitry is required which converts between these analog signals and the digital numbers which represent them. An analog-to-digital converter processes an analog voltage and generates its equivalent digital number, whereas a digital-to-analog converter is passed a digital number and generates the equivalent analog voltage. Like other peripherals, these conversion devices are read from or written to by the central processing unit.

Thus there are many types of input/output device and each computer system is provided with those devices which are appropriate. In a given system it must be possible to identify each device so, as for memories, each device has a unique address. Thus, to write to an output port, the address of the device, the data to be written and a 'write' signal are required. Similarly, when reading from an input device, the address of the device and a 'read' signal are required and the data from that port are returned to the central processing unit.

3.4 Central processing unit

In most microprocessor systems, the central processing unit or CPU is the microprocessor, although some microprocessors also contain the memory and peripherals. The CPU contains the circuitry which coordinates the actions of the system, and the specific circuitry for processing the data. This processing is achieved by a complex logic circuit which can perform various arithmetic and logical operations; this is called the *arithmetic and logic unit*, or ALU. The coordination is achieved by the *control unit* which ensures the computer gets its next instruction and obeys it. The microprocessor often has some memory called *registers* which are used for storing temporary data values and other values needed for the operation of the machine. The components of the CPU are shown in figure 3.2.

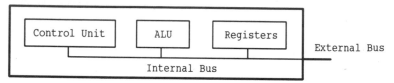

Figure 3.2 Components of a CPU

Microprocessors come in various forms, with different features. The early systems, for example, did not have circuitry to perform multiplication and division; many modern ones do. The number and size of the registers also varies between different microprocessors.

There are three types of registers, though they are given different names by different microprocessor manufacturers. Data registers are used for storing data, and a typical operation is to take the contents of a register, process them with some other data, and to put the result back in that register; for example, the instruction ADD D0, 2 will add 2 to register D0. Address registers are often used to store addresses, that is, they specify where in the memory some data may be found; the instruction ADD D0, @A0 will cause the data in the memory at the address found in the A0 register to be added to the D0 register. Microprocessors usually have two special address registers, the *program counter* and the *stack pointer*. The program counter contains the address in memory of the next instruction; more will be said about this in chapter 8 where the fetching and executing of instructions is considered. The stack pointer points to the stack, which is a mechanism used for temporary storage of information; again, more will be said of this in chapter 8. The final type of register is the *status* register. This contains information about the machine; for example, it can indicate if the result of the last operation was zero, or if an error occurred.

Some microprocessors, often called single chip microcomputers, contain a complete system, the central processing unit, memory and input/output devices. However, in general a system contains these devices separately.

3.5 Buses

Data can be read from a memory or input device, or written to a memory or output device. This is achieved by transferring signals between the central processing unit and the memory or peripheral. The medium by which the information is transferred is the bus.

The bus is the series of connections which allow the various devices in the computer system to intercommunicate. Physically, the bus corresponds to a number of wires in parallel. Figure 3.3a shows a 4-bit bus connecting a CPU and memory, there are 4 wires between the CPU and memory; figure 3.3b shows one way such a bus is drawn, being one line with a bar through it above which is a number indicating the number of wires.

a) *4-bit bus*   b) *bus symbol*

Figure 3.3 4-bit bus connecting CPU and memory

The different types of microprocessor use different signals on the bus, and hence the ways in which devices are connected to the bus will vary. However, these tend to follow certain rules or protocols, which are discussed in detail later, but the fundamental principles are considered here.

As stated earlier, a memory or peripheral is identified by its address and another signal indicates whether data are read or written. Thus address, data and read/write signals must be transferred along the bus. In fact, the bus can be divided into three parts, the address bus, the data bus and the control bus. These are described in more detail below.

Address bus

The address bus is the series of wires which contain the address of the device being accessed. When reading from or writing to a memory or peripheral, the CPU puts the address of the desired location on to the address bus.

The size of the address bus varies between different microprocessors; early microprocessors had only 16 address lines (a 16-bit address bus), many modern processors have 32. The size of the address bus determines the number of memory locations: a 16-bit address bus can address 2^{16} or 65536 locations, a 32-bit address bus can address 2^{32} or 4294967296 locations.

Data bus

The data bus is the series of wires along which data are transferred. When the CPU is writing to a memory or peripheral, the data are output from the CPU on to the bus, whereas in a read operation, the addressed memory or peripheral outputs the data on to the data bus for the CPU to read.

Microprocessors are classified as being 8-bit, 16-bit or 32-bit. This indicates the width of its data bus, and so is a measure of the number of bits of data which the microprocessor processes at a time. In general, a 32-bit processor will be faster than an 8-bit device as it can transfer more data at a time. The early microprocessors were 8-bit devices, the more advanced ones are 32-bit.

Some systems have a multiplexed address/data bus. At the beginning of a data transfer operation, the CPU puts the address on this bus, and some other device remembers that address. Subsequently the bus contains actual data.

Control bus

The control bus contains the other signals used for transferring information between components of the computer. There are various signals used here, depending upon the microprocessor.

There is often a signal indicating if data are to be read or written; this is a logic '1' if data are being read from a memory and '0' if data are being written. In addition there is often a *strobe* signal which is '0' when the other signals on the bus are stable and hence data can be transferred. On some systems two signals are used in a different manner to indicate that a read or write operation can occur; there is a read strobe, which is '0' if the other signals are stable and a read operation is to occur, and a write strobe, which is '0' if a write operation can occur.

The strobe signals are needed to inform the memory or peripheral that the other signals on the bus contain valid information. Another signal is sometimes required by which the device being accessed informs the CPU that the data have been transferred correctly. These signals are part of the control bus.

On some systems, input/output devices are treated as if they were memory locations, but with different addresses; if data are written to a 'peripheral' address, then the data are written to the associated output device; but if a read operation occurs, then data from the associated input device are read. The peripherals are said to be *memory mapped*. On other systems, memory and peripherals are treated separately, and the control bus contains a signal which, for example, is a '1' if memory are to be accessed, and '0' if the peripheral is to be accessed.

Thus a system contains a CPU, memory and input/output devices all connected together by a bus, which has three components, an address bus, a data bus and a control bus. Figure 3.4 shows such a system, with a 16-bit address bus, an 8-bit data bus and a 4-bit control bus.

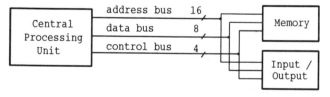

Figure 3.4 Microprocessor system

The parts of the computer have now been described. The next stage is to consider how information is passed between these parts. This occurs in three ways; *data transfer cycles*, *interrupts* and *direct memory access*.

Data transfer cycles

The normal operation of the computer is for the CPU to instigate a data transfer between the CPU and a memory or peripheral. The CPU is the master device and the memory or peripheral is the slave responding to the master. The CPU either reads from a slave or writes to a slave, such actions being determined by the program that the CPU is executing.

Interrupts

Sometimes, however, a peripheral can inform the CPU that a transfer should occur. For example, consider a system with a keyboard on which the user can press keys; when a key is pressed, the CPU reads the value of the key and, perhaps, shows it on a display. The computer could operate by continually checking to see if a key has been pressed, and if so reading the value. Alternatively, if there were some other task the CPU could do, the keyboard device could tell the CPU when a key has been pressed. Then the CPU would temporarily stop its current task, read the key and display it, and then return to the other task. The keyboard would cause the CPU to be interrupted. The actions performed by the CPU in response to the interrupt, in this case the reading of the keyboard, are encoded in an *interrupt service routine*.

Thus another signal on the control bus is an interrupt request line, and this is asserted when a memory or peripheral wants to stop the CPU during its current task. Other signals are used by the CPU to indicate that it is responding to the interrupt, and hence that the interrupt request should be removed. Each microprocessor has its own ways of achieving these actions, with one or many interrupt lines and means whereby the CPU responds to the interrupt.

Direct memory access

If the computer is being sent data from another computer along a suitable communications link, each data item received down the link is often stored in memory for subsequent processing. This requires the data to be read from the link into the CPU and then written from the CPU to the memory. If, however, the data are sent more quickly than the CPU can respond, then a better method is for each data item to be written directly from the link to the memory.

This requires that the peripheral controlling the link should itself cause data to be transferred along the bus to the memory; this device should output the address, data and appropriate control signals.

One problem is that the CPU and the peripheral cannot both output signals to the bus at the same time. Thus the peripheral should first request that it be given control of the bus, the CPU then issues an acknowledge and, as a result of this, the peripheral is able to use the bus. At the end of the data transfer, the request signal and then the acknowledge are removed; the CPU can then use the bus.

The control bus thus contains signals for the device to request control of the bus and for the CPU to acknowledge the request. In this scenario, the peripheral accesses the memory directly, hence the process is described as direct memory access or DMA.

Bus systems

Figure 3.5 shows another way of representing a computer, as a number of modules connected to a common bus. This is a bus system, and has the advantage of all modular systems namely that only those modules which are required for a given application are included in the system. In such a system, the appropriate modules not only include the memory and input/output devices, but also the microprocessor. The choice of microprocessor may be determined by the speed at which the system needs to operate: normally a 32-bit microprocessor will run more quickly than an 8-bit device. Other factors which may be considered are the facilities available for programming the microprocessor and for testing the system to verify that it works.

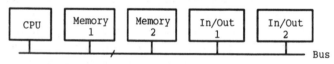

Figure 3.5 A bus system

As the various microprocessors have different ways of using a bus, some bus standards have been proposed defining the signals required for the bus. Thus each microprocessor module needs circuitry to convert the signals from the microprocessor into those required for the bus. Similarly, all memory and peripheral devices must use these signals. The great advantage of such systems is that the same memory and peripheral modules can be used with a great variety of microprocessors. Examples of such bus standards include VME, STE and Futurebus; these are described in Mitchell (1989).

3.6 Some computer systems

In this section the structure of three microprocessor systems is given, that of a general purpose microcomputer, a washing machine controller, and a simple system which will be used as an example throughout the book.

Microcomputer

In chapter 2, the software run on a microcomputer (a general purpose microprocessor system) was described, thereby demonstrating the facilities required by the system. These are listed below and shown in figure 3.6.

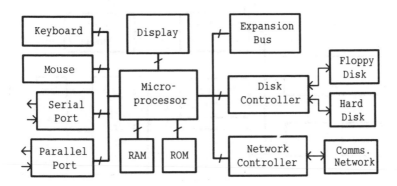

Figure 3.6 Block diagram of a microcomputer

- A *central processing unit*, the main microprocessor. A 32-bit micro-processor is preferable here.
- *Memory*. Large amounts of memory are needed in order to run various software. A modern microcomputer requires at least 4M of RAM, as well as some ROM containing the initial program.
- A full *keyboard*. This has the complete alphabet, numbers, punctuation, function and arrow keys.
- A *display*. This is capable of showing text and graphics.
- A *mouse*. This allows input of graphical data, and for selection from lists.
- A *floppy disk*. For storing data and for loading information.
- A *hard disk*. For storing larger amounts of data. Modern software is large and extensive; a 100M disk will fill up quickly. Some modern systems also have a CD ROM for reading large amounts of information.
- *Communication ports*. A parallel printer link and a serial communications link are both useful. In addition, a connection to a local area network can be invaluable.
- *An expansion bus*. This is a number of connectors, which are provided with the appropriate bus signals, and into which extra peripherals and memory can be plugged. These extra devices include such devices as analog-digital converters, or extra faster graphics cards and extra communications ports.

Washing machine controller

The computer controlling a washing machine requires a different set of facilities. Again an overview of the facilities required was given in chapter 2. Here they are listed and shown in figure 3.7.
- A *microprocessor*. As little processing is required an 8-bit microprocessor is adequate.
- *Memory*. Some ROM for the program and RAM for storing data. 64K of memory is probably more than adequate.

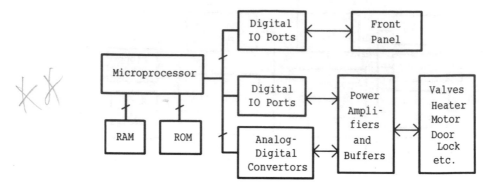

Figure 3.7 Block diagram of washing machine controller

- *Interfaces for the front panel.* These allow the program and various options to be selected, and these will be various binary values. Some machines have a rotary switch for selecting the program, and during operation this switch is turned by the machine as the program progresses; a port for a motor to drive this switch is needed.
- *Interfaces for the control* of the water, heater, valves and lock for the door (to prevent it opening when full of water). Some of these will be ports containing various binary values, others will contain analog-digital convertors.

Simple system

In this book the following system will be used as an example of a simple microprocessor system. In the course of the book more details will be given on the programs needed to operate the system, and how the various devices are interfaced to the microprocessor. The system is shown in figure 3.8, and contains a microprocessor, a ROM and a RAM, and the peripherals are some seven-segment displays, a simple keypad, an analog-to-digital converter (ADC) and a digital-to-analog converter (DAC).

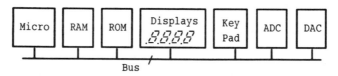

Figure 3.8 Block diagram of example system

The various devices in the system come in many forms, so typical devices will be used in the book. More details are given of these devices when they are required, but here an introduction to each device is given so as to illustrate the basic concepts involved.

- *The microprocessor.* A simple processor.
- *The ROM and RAM.* Standard memory devices which can contain programs and/or data.
- *Seven-segment displays.* A seven segment display is a device as shown in figure 3.8 in which there are typically 8 lights! Seven of these form segments which may be illuminated appropriately so as to produce patterns of numbers, the eighth is a dot which is often to the left of the number. The device has 8 binary inputs, one for each light, and (for many such devices) an input should be a logic 0 for its associated segment to be lit.
- *A keypad.* This has 16 keys on it, and 5 output signals which indicate the state of the keypad. One signal indicates whether the user is pressing a key, and if so, the other four signals indicate which key has been pressed. It is possible to arrange that an interrupt is generated when the user presses a key on the keypad.
- *A digital-to-analog converter.* The DAC is a device which converts the 8-bit data presented at its inputs into the equivalent analog voltage.
- *An analog-to-digital converter.* The ADC has a binary input called StartConvert, which when asserted causes the analog input signal to be ·converted to the equivalent digital number. While the conversion is occurring the Busy output of the ADC is asserted. When Busy is released, the converted data may be read from the 8 data outputs of the ADC.

As the book progresses descriptions will be given of the appropriate programs for using these devices, and the ways in which the devices may be connected together.

Summary

This chapter has given an overview of the hardware of a computer, so now the hardware and software of computer systems have been described. The next chapter, the final 'overview' chapter, considers the fundamental operation of microprocessors, that is, the performing of logical operations on binary data.

Exercise

Define the hardware components of a microprocessor system controlling a CD player, in the manner used above to describe the washing machine controller.

Reference

R.J.Mitchell *Microcomputer Systems Using the STE Bus* Macmillan Press, 1989.

4 Logic and Binary Data

A computer system consists of the actual machine, the hardware, and the programs which instruct the machine as to what it should do, the software. When the computer executes these instructions, it processes various data which are input to or stored in the machine. One of the innovations suggested by Von Neumann was that the data should consist of various binary values rather than decimal values. Binary data can have one of two values and the processing of such data is achieved by operations known as logic functions, and simple logic circuits exist which perform these functions.

Logic circuits are to be found in all parts of a modern microprocessor system. First they are used for manipulating data; for example, adding two numbers together is achieved by a number of simple logic circuits connected together. Second they are used for storing data; two simple logic circuits can be connected as a memory device. Third, logic circuits are needed for connecting together the various components of a microprocessor system. In addition, logical operations are also required in various programs.

In this chapter, binary data and logic are introduced. More details are then given in the following three chapters, where the topics covered are, respectively, simple (so-called *combinational*) logic circuits and their design, *sequential* logic circuits (which can be used to provide memory), and data representation and processing using logic functions. In addition, applications of logic circuits are given in the later chapters on interfacing the components of a microprocessor system.

4.1 Introduction

Computers process binary data. These data are called binary digits, or *bits*, and they can take one of two values, which are described as being on and off, or '1' and '0', or TRUE and FALSE. Note, it is because the computer processes binary digits that it is known as a digital computer.

Inside a microprocessor system, these bits are implemented by signals which have one of two voltage levels, usually considered to be 0 V for a logic '0' and 5 V for a logic '1', but in practice, for many of the common devices, logic '0' is indicated by a voltage less than 0.8 V and logic '1' is a voltage greater than 2.0 V. The computer does not 'think' of these data as being '1' or '0', it just processes signals which have a suitable voltage.

One reason why binary data are used is that very simple circuits are required to process such data, and these can be manufactured easily. The circuits which process binary data consist of logic circuits which perform such operations as AND, OR and NOT; these circuits are called *gates*, and they are often represented by the symbols shown in figure 4.1.

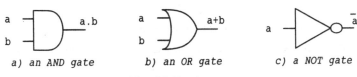

Fig 4.1 Logic gates

There are also the ANSI/IEEE standard symbols for logic gates. These, however, have not been universally accepted in industry, as many people do not like them. Therefore, the symbols in figure 4.1 are used throughout the book; however, details about the standard are given in appendix 4.

AND gates and OR gates can have many inputs, although only two are shown in figures 4.1a and 4.1b. The output of an AND gate is a 1 only if all its inputs are 1; and the output of an OR gate is a 1 if at least one of its inputs is a 1. A NOT gate has one input and its output has the inverse value of the input. These definitions can be shown in truth tables; a truth table shows the output(s) of a circuit for all possible combinations of its input(s). The truth tables shown below are for two input AND and OR gates and for a NOT gate.

a	b	a AND b
0	0	0
0	1	0
1	0	0
1	1	1

a	b	a OR b
0	0	0
0	1	1
1	0	1
1	1	1

a	NOT a
0	1
1	0

The following description shows how these simple circuits can be used to perform addition, and thus demonstrates that although the computer may be thought of as performing an arithmetic operation, it is in fact just performing simple logic operations on binary data.

Suppose two bits are to be added together, and these are designated a and b. Each bit can have one of two values, '0' or '1', which represent the numbers 0 or 1; therefore there are four possible combinations of the two bits, for which the results can be described by the following truth table.

a	b	Sum	Carry
0	0	0	0
0	1	1	0
1	0	1	0
1	1	0	1

If both inputs are '0', then their sum is 0; if one input only is a '1', then the sum is 1; but if both inputs are '1', the answer is 2 which cannot be represented by values that can only be 0 or 1. Thus, in this case the sum is 0, but there is a carry, just as when in decimal arithmetic 5 and 5 are added, the answer in the unit's column is 0, and there is a carry to the ten's column.

Clearly, the Carry signal should be a '1' if both a and b are '1', that is:

•   Carry is '1' IF a is '1' AND b is '1'

In practice, the *is '1'* is usually omitted, so in algebraic terms, this condition can be written as an equation:

Carry = a . b

where the . represents the AND operation. Similarly,

* Sum is '1' IF (a is '0' AND b is '1') OR (a is '1' AND b is '0')

that is,

* Sum is '1' IF (NOT (a is '1') AND b is '1')
             OR (a is '1' AND NOT (b is '1'))

The equation for this is

Sum = $\bar{a} . b + a . \bar{b}$

where the line over a value means NOT and the operator + means OR. Note, the function which generates Sum is also called exclusive-or.

The functions for Carry and Sum can be implemented by circuits made out of the AND, OR and NOT gates suitably interconnected, as shown in figure 4.2. The Carry circuit is just an AND gate, whereas the Sum circuit requires AND, OR and NOT gates. Such a circuit is called a *half adder*.

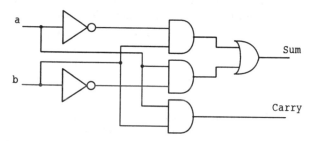

Figure 4.2 Logic circuit to add two bits

The description above gave equations for Sum and Carry. These equations represent the functions using boolean algebra, and rules are available for manipulating such algebraic equations, just as there are algebraic rules for 'normal' equations. Boolean algebra is a branch of mathematics much of which was developed by George Boole in the 19th century.

The above is one example of a logic circuit, but computers contain many different logic circuits, and anyone designing circuitry to interface to a microprocessor needs to know about logic circuits. Thus more details about such circuits, methods for their design and applications for them in computers are described in subsequent chapters.

4.2 Multi-bit data

The above describes how binary data can be used to represent one of two values, and how they may be added. Some problems can be solved with just such data, but for many other problems two-valued data are limiting. Therefore, just as humans use many decimal digits to represent numbers, so inside a computer many bits are combined together to represent different types of data.

One bit can take two possible values. Two bits can each take two values, so there are four possible values for them both: 0 0, 0 1, 1 0 and 1 1. Three bits can take 8 different values, four bits can take 16 different values, and so on. In general n bits can take 2^n different values.

Names are given to groupings of specific numbers of bits. A *byte* is 8 bits, which can take 2^8, that is 256, different values. Sometimes a group of 4 bits (half a byte) is referred to as a *nibble* (or sometimes a *nibl*). 16 bits are also often grouped, and can represent 2^{16} or 65536 different values, similarly 32 bits can represent 2^{32} or 4294967296 values. In the following, the processing of bytes is considered, but the ideas can be extended easily to handle 16 or 32 bit groups.

A byte can represent 256 different values and often these values are chosen to be the numbers 0 to 255. The least significant bit (LSB) of a byte is called bit 0, whereas the most significant bit (MSB) is bit 7, and, in this case, bit r of the byte is a 1 if the number contains a component 2^r. Consider the following examples:

$00000000 = 0$
$00000101 = 2^2 + 2^0 = 5$
$10000000 = 2^7 = 128$
$11111111 = 2^7 + 2^6 + 2^5 + 2^4 + 2^3 + 2^2 + 2^1 + 2^0 = 255$

The next stage is to consider how two such bytes can be added; the answer is based on the way that humans perform addition. If the decimal numbers 125 and 369 are to be added, the 5 and 9 are added giving 4 with a carry, then 2, 6 and that carry are added, giving 9 and no carry, and then 1 and 3 are added, so that the answer is 494. Here each decimal digit in the first number is added to its corresponding digit in the second number, together with any carry from the previous sum. In binary, the same process is used; bit r of one byte is added to bit r of the second byte together with any carry resulting from the addition of bits $r - 1$ of the bytes. Thus a logic circuit is needed which adds three bits, one from the first byte, one from the second byte, and one from the carry of the previous stage; and the circuit produces the sum digit and a carry to the next stage. Such a circuit, a block diagram of which is shown in figure 4.3, is called a *full adder*. Eight such circuits can be used to add two 8-bit numbers.

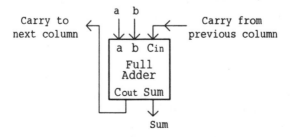

Figure 4.3 Block diagram of a full adder

The design of such a circuit requires a truth table for the problem and the generation of suitable boolean expressions, as given above, from which suitable circuits can be generated. However, further analysis of these expressions produces simpler circuits; such analysis is considered in the next chapter.

Note, a computer does not 'think' that a byte represents the numbers 0 to 255, it just processes 8 binary signals. It is only our interpretation of a byte that it takes these values. In fact, different interpretations of these values are used, for example, it is also common for a byte to be used to represent all the integers from −128 to 127. More details about the different uses of such data, and the ways in which they may be processed, are given in chapter 7.

In the system described above, three bits could be used to represent the numbers 0 to 7. The decimal numbers and their equivalent binary are shown in the left hand table below.

Decimal	Binary		Decimal	Gray Code
0	000		0	000
1	001		1	001
2	010		2	011
3	011		3	010
4	100		4	110
5	101		5	111
6	110		6	110
7	111		7	100

Another way in which three bits are sometimes used to encode numbers is shown in the right hand table above. This is called *Gray code* and it has the property that each number in the sequence differs from the previous one by only one bit; for example, the codes for the numbers 3 and 4 differ only in bit 2 and the codes for the numbers 5 and 6 differ only in bit 0. The code is cyclic; only one bit is different between the first and last codes.

Although Gray code is not usually used inside microprocessors, it can be used in peripherals. Consider, controlling the position of some device requires that the current position of that device be measured. This can be achieved by having a plate with various black areas encoded photographically on it. The position of the plate is detected by pairs of infra-red emitters and detectors: an infra-red signal is emitted towards the plate, on the other side of which is the detector; if at that position the plate is black, the detector does not receive the signal, so the output of the detector is logic '0'; however, if the plate is blank at that point, the detector receives a signal, so its output is logic '1'.

Figure 4.4a shows a plate with a 'normal' 3-bit binary pattern encoded; associated with this there will be three emitters and detectors; the outputs from the detectors will give a number in the range 0..7, indicating the position of the plate. Although this should work, in practice, because of imperfections in the plate and the detectors, the bits will not change simultaneously. Thus, as the plate moves from position 3 to 4, the binary values from the sensors might be 011 010 000 100, so that the actual position appears to change from 3 to 2 to 0 to 4. If, however, a Gray code pattern is encoded on the plate, as shown in figure 4.4b, there is no problem as only one bit changes between each position.

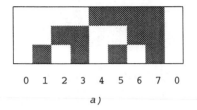

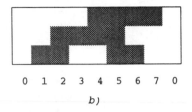

	0	1	2	3	4	5	6	7	0

a)

	0	1	2	3	4	5	6	7	0

b)

Figure 4 Natural and Gray code plates

4.3 Characters

One of the many uses of a computer is as a word processor. Thus the computer must be able to process characters as well as numbers, where a character is a letter (A..Z or a..z), a number (0..9), punctuation, or a 'control' character which is used for a special purpose. In this section, therefore, a means of representing characters is given. Two main codes have been suggested, EBCDIC and ASCII. EBCDIC was proposed by IBM, but for once the computer industry largely ignored this and chose the ASCII code instead.

Originally ASCII code was developed for processing data entered at a terminal which was then sent down a communications line to a computer. As it is possible for data to be corrupted in such cases, it is a good idea to include in the data some means of detecting errors. Thus the ASCII code was originally a 7-bit code, and the 8th bit of a byte, the so called parity bit, was chosen so that the number of 1s in the byte is odd (say). Then if the received byte had an even number of 1s, this indicated an error in transmission. A logic circuit can be used to detect such an error.

More recently the ASCII code has been extended to an 8-bit code, for which the top 128 values contain some graphics symbols, diphthongs, etc. Here, however the original code is given.

Table 4.1 shows the 7-bit ASCII code; at each position in the table is the character, like '0' or 'A', or the name of a control character, like 'CR' or 'TAB'. The code for each character is found as follows. The code at the top of the column of the character gives the value for bits 6 to 4, and that at the start of the row gives the value for bits 3 to 0.

Referring to the table, the binary code for 'A' is 1000001, that for '3' is 0110011, and that for a is 1100001; the difference in code between a lower case letter and its corresponding upper case letter is that bit 6 is '1' for the lower case and '0' for the upper case letter. The first two columns contain the control characters where, for example, SOH is control-A, STX is control-B. The names given here for these control characters are those used in some communication systems; some of these names are used more than others, for example, CR or control-M is 'return', LF or control-J is 'line feed', TAB or control-I is the tab key. Whenever the user presses a key on the keyboard, the key is read and the associated value in the ASCII code is generated.

b3..b0 \ b6..b4	000	001	010	011	100	101	110	111
0000	NUL	DLE	SP	0	@	P	'	p
0001	SOH	DC1	!	1	A	Q	a	q
0010	STX	DC2	"	2	B	R	b	r
0011	ETX	DC3	#	3	C	S	c	s
0100	EOT	DC4	$	4	D	T	d	t
0101	ENQ	NAK	%	5	E	U	e	u
0110	ACK	SYN	&	6	F	V	f	v
0111	BEL	ETB	'	7	G	W	g	w
1000	BS	CAN	(	8	H	X	h	x
1001	TAB	EM	)	9	I	Y	i	y
1010	LF	SUB	*	:	J	Z	j	z
1011	VT	ESC	+	;	K	[	k	{
1100	FF	FS	,	<	L	\	l	|
1101	CR	GS	-	=	M	]	m	}
1110	SO	RS	.	>	N	^	n	~
1111	SI	VS	/	?	O	_	o	DEL

Table 4.1 ASCII character code

4.4   Octal and hexadecimal notation

In the above sections, numbers were written out in binary. This is tedious and it is very easy to type errors. Thus two notations have been used to make writing numbers easier, *octal* and *hexadecimal* or *hex*.

In octal notation, bits are grouped together in threes, starting with the least significant bit, and each three bit group is represented by a digit in the range 0 to 7, as shown in table 4.2; the last group may not have three bits, so leading 0s are assumed. Below the table are some bytes written in binary and octal.

Binary	Decimal	Octal
000	0	0
001	1	1
010	2	2
011	3	3
100	4	4
101	5	5
110	6	6
111	7	7

Table 4.2 Binary data and their octal values

01110100 is grouped as 01 110 100 and represented by $(164)_8$
10011111 is grouped as 10 011 111 and represented by $(237)_8$
11101000 is grouped as 11 101 000 and represented by $(350)_8$

In hexadecimal (or hex) notation, bits are grouped in fours, and each four bit number represented by a digit in the range 0..9 or A..F, as shown in table 4.3. Below this are some bytes written in binary and hex, the H after the final number indicating that it is in hexadecimal not decimal.

Binary	Decimal	Hex
0000	0	0
0001	1	1
0010	2	2
0011	3	3
0100	4	4
0101	5	5
0110	6	6
0111	7	7
1000	8	8
1001	9	9
1010	10	A
1011	11	B
1100	12	C
1101	13	D
1110	14	E
1111	15	F

Table 4.3 Binary data and their hexadecimal values

01110100 is grouped as 0111 0100 and represented by 74H
10011111 is grouped as 1001 1111 and represented by 9FH
11101000 is grouped as 1110 1000 and represented by E8H

Note, these notations are used to help humans represent numbers, the computer only 'understands' binary signals. However, it is much easier to read octal or hex digits than strings of binary 0s and 1s.

Summary

This chapter has introduced the concepts of binary data and logic functions, and it has shown how many binary data can be grouped together to represent numbers and characters. More details about logic circuits and their applications are given in the following chapters.

Exercises

1) Write down the binary, octal and hexadecimal values representing the following numbers and characters:
  a) 59   b) 137   c) 253   d) 'Z'   e) '4'   f) '#'

2) Write down a truth table for a full adder (section 4.2), produce boolean expressions for the sum and carry outputs and draw a logic circuit implementing these equations (like that in figure 4.2).

3) Write down a 4-bit Gray code sequence.

5 Combinational Logic

A microprocessor system is full of logic circuits, including circuitry to perform the arithmetic functions, to determine how to obey an instruction, and to allow other devices to be interfaced to the microprocessor. Therefore it is important to understand logic circuits and to be able to design them. It should be noted, however, that computer systems are not the only systems which contain logic circuits. Indeed, the pioneering work on logic was done by the mathematician George Boole in the 19th century, before the invention of computers. Boolean algebra, one method of analysing simple logic circuits, is named after him.

Logic systems can be built using a great many different devices, for example mechanical, electrical and pneumatic, but microprocessor systems are built using electronic circuits. However, the techniques described here can be appreciated independently of the method of implementation.

In this chapter, simple logic circuits and methods for their design are introduced. These circuits are called *combinational* logic circuits. Chapter 6 describes some examples of another type of logic circuit, *sequential* logic.

5.1 Logic elements

Logic elements are circuits which process binary signals, and these signals can have one of two values which are here referred to as '0' and '1'. These can be implemented using various technologies, though microprocessor systems use electronic circuits; even then, there are many electronic technologies with which logic can be implemented. Most microprocessor systems use two such 'families', TTL and CMOS. Within the families there are various members, and the different types used affect such factors as the power consumed by the device, the speed of operation, the voltages used to supply the device and the logic levels, that is, the voltages which are considered to be '1' and those which are '0'.

Microprocessors use logic devices which are compatible with TTL logic circuits, that is, microprocessors can be connected directly to TTL circuits. Therefore, the following discussion refers to TTL devices. More details on the different logic families, their characteristics and operation are summarised in appendix 5 and are described in more detail in the books by Lewin and Protheroe, by Stonham, by Mano and by Bannister and Whitehead.

In microprocessor systems, nominally a signal is '1' if the voltage of that signal is 5 V, and the signal is '0' if its voltage is 0 V. In practice, to ensure real circuits operate unambiguously and in the presence of noise, for most TTL devices, if the signal voltage exceeds 2.0 V it is considered to be '1', and if the signal is below 0.8 V it is '0'. The speed of operation of a simple TTL logic gate is about 10 ns, and its supply voltages are 5 V and 0 V.

These binary signals are processed by logic elements called gates. These gates represent various processing operations, the main operations being AND, OR and NOT, and all logic functions can be made using a combination of AND, OR and NOT gates. However, other functions are also provided which can be used to advantage, these being NAND, NOR and EXOR, being respectively, NOT AND, NOT OR and exclusive-or. Figure 5.1 shows the symbols used to represent these gates, and truth tables showing the output of each gate for all possible combinations of its inputs. Note, apart from the NOT gate which can have only one input, the exclusive-or gate which has two inputs, the others can have many inputs, although two inputs only are shown here. An alternative set of symbols for these gates, specified in an ANSI/IEEE standard, but not in common use, is given in appendix 4.

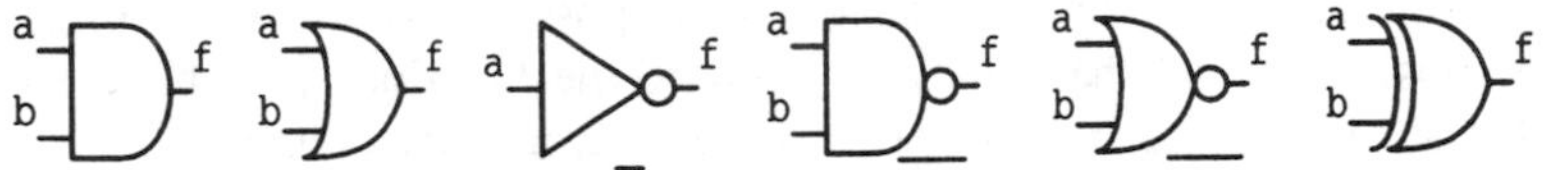

a b	f		a b	f		a	f		a b	f		a b	f		a b	f
$f = a.b$			$f = a+b$			$f = \bar{a}$			$f = \overline{a.b}$			$f = \overline{a+b}$			$f = a \oplus b$		
0 0	0		0 0	0		0	1		0 0	1		0 0	1		0 0	0	
0 1	0		0 1	1		1	0		0 1	1		0 1	0		0 1	1	
1 0	0		1 0	1					1 0	1		1 0	0		1 0	1	
1 1	1		1 1	1					1 1	0		1 1	0		1 1	0	
a) AND			*b) OR*			*c) NOT*			*d) NAND*			*e) NOR*			*f) XOR*		

Figure 5.1 Logic gates and their operation

If a logic signal is called a, then *a is '1'* is represented by a, and *a is '0'* is NOT (a), which can be written $\bar{a}$. The + operator is used to designate OR, and a dot, or sometimes no symbol at all, is used to represent AND. Note the + operator should not be confused with addition: 1 + 1 means true once, not twice! A + symbol inside a circle represents exclusive-or: $a \oplus b = \bar{a}.b + a.\bar{b}$

The output of an AND gate is '1' if all its inputs are '1'; the output of an OR gate is '1', if at least one of its inputs is '1'; the output of a NAND is '0' if all its inputs are '1', and so on.

It is also true to say that the output of an AND gate is '0' if at least one of its inputs is '0', and the output of an OR gate is '0' if all its inputs are '0'. From these observations De Morgan's laws can be deduced:

- NOT (a AND b) = NOT (a) OR NOT (b), that is $\overline{a.b} = \bar{a} + \bar{b}$
- NOT (a OR b) = NOT (a) AND NOT (b), that is $\overline{a + b} = \bar{a}.\bar{b}$

5.2 Boolean algebra

De Morgan's laws are examples of some theorems of boolean algebra, some more are listed below. In these a, b and c represent logic signals, and '0' and '1' are the logic values 0 and 1.

1) $0 + a = a$ $1.a = a$
2) $1 + a = 1$ $0.a = 0$
3) $a + a = a$ $a.a = a$
4) $a + \bar{a} = 1$ $a.\bar{a} = 0$
5) $a + b = b + a$ $a.b = b.a$
6) $a + b + c = (a + b) + c = a + (b + c)$ $a.b.c = (a.b).c = a.(b.c)$
7) $(a + \bar{b}).(a + b) = a$ $a.\bar{b} + a.b = a$
8) $a.(a + b) = a$ $a + a.b = a$
9) $\bar{a}.(a + b) = a.b$ $a + \bar{a}.b = a + b$
10) $\overline{a + b} = \bar{a}.\bar{b}$ $\overline{a.b} = \bar{a} + \bar{b}$
11) $(a + b).(a + c) = a + b.c$ $(a.b) + (a.c) = a.(b + c)$

Some of these are obvious, others require some comment; they can be demonstrated to be true using truth tables or by boolean algebra. For example, to demonstrate rule 11 by truth table, all the possible combinations of a, b and c are considered, and the values for each of the functions $(a + b).(a + c)$ and $a + b.c$ are written down, thus (with some intermediary columns):

a b c	a+b	a+c	(a+b).(a+c)	b.c	a+b.c
0 0 0	0	0	0	0	0
0 0 1	0	1	0	0	0
0 1 0	1	0	0	0	0
0 1 1	1	1	1	1	1
1 0 0	1	1	1	0	1
1 0 1	1	1	1	0	1
1 1 0	1	1	1	0	1
1 1 1	1	1	1	1	1

The columns marked *(a + b).(a + c)* and *a + b.c* are equal; clearly, therefore, $(a + b).(a + c) = a + b.c$

Alternatively, boolean algebra can be used to demonstrate such equality:
$(a + b).(a + c)$
     $= a.a + a.c + b.a + b.c$
     $= a + a.c + a.b + b.c$ by rules 3 and 5
     $= a + b.c$ by rule 8 $(a + a.b = a)$

Similarly,
$(a + \bar{b}).(a + b)$
     $= a.a + a.b + \bar{b}.a + \bar{b}.b$
     $= a + a.b + a.\bar{b} + 0$ by rules 3, 4 and 5
     $= a$ by rules 1 and 8

Another example, to show that $(a + c).(\bar{a} + b) = a.b + \bar{a}.c$
$(a + c).(\bar{a} + b)$
     $= a.\bar{a} + a.b + c.\bar{a} + c.b$
     $= 0 + a.b + \bar{a}.c + b.c$
     $= a.b + \bar{a}.c + b.c.a + b.c.\bar{a}$ (as $b.c = b.c.(a + \bar{a}) = b.c.a + b.c.\bar{a}$)
     $= a.b + a.b.c + \bar{a}.c + \bar{a}.c.b$
     $= a.b + \bar{a}.c$

Note the expression a.b + $\bar{a}$.c is in the so-called *sum of products* form, being the sum (really the or) of various product terms (that is bits anded together). The expression (a + c).($\bar{a}$ + b), however, is in the *product of sums* form. Each sum of products expression has its equivalent product of sums form.

Next consider the full adder circuit which was introduced in chapter 4. This is the circuit which is used to add two bits from two multiple bit numbers; the two bits and the carry from the previous stage are added together to form the sum digit and the carry to be passed on to the next stage. The full adder calculates the carry and sum given three inputs a, b and c (a and b are data to be added, c is the carry from the previous stage). Its truth table is as follows:

a b c	Sum	Carry
0 0 0	0	0
0 0 1	1	0
0 1 0	1	0
0 1 1	0	1
1 0 0	1	0
1 0 1	0	1
1 1 0	0	1
1 1 1	1	1

The function for carry is thus:

Carry = $\bar{a}$.b.c + a.$\bar{b}$.c + a.b.$\bar{c}$ + a.b.c

= $\bar{a}$.b.c + a.b.c + a.$\bar{b}$.c + a.b.c + a.b.$\bar{c}$ + a.b.c

= b.c + a.c + a.b

Some expressions cannot be simplified, for example, the sum function of a full adder:

Sum = $\bar{a}$.$\bar{b}$.c + $\bar{a}$.b.$\bar{c}$ + a.$\bar{b}$.$\bar{c}$ + a.b.c

The above illustrate the use of boolean algebra to manipulate expressions of boolean functions; more details on the subject can be found in Lewin and Protheroe. The next stage is to convert these into actual circuits.

5.3 Logic circuits

Logic circuits can be built by connecting logic gates together in a suitable manner. Figure 5.2 shows some examples of logic circuits to implement the functions a.b + c, (a + c).($\bar{a}$ + b), a.b + $\bar{a}$.c, as well as the Sum and Carry functions of a full adder.

In practice, logic circuits can be built in this manner. However, there are some limitations: the output from one gate cannot be connected to the inputs of too many other gates as one gate cannot provide enough power to drive too many other gates. This limitation if termed the '*fan-out*' of a gate; refer to data sheets to find more details of fan-out and other practicalities.

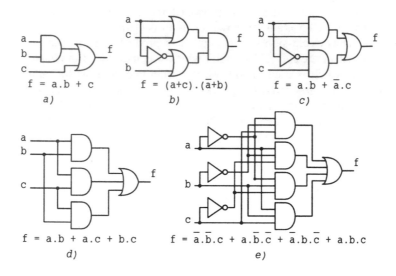

$$f = a.b + c$$
a)

$$f = (a+c).(\bar{a}+b)$$
b)

$$f = a.b + \bar{a}.c$$
c)

$$f = a.b + a.c + b.c$$
d)

$$f = \bar{a}.\bar{b}.c + a.\bar{b}.\bar{c} + \bar{a}.b.\bar{c} + a.b.c$$
e)

Figure 5.2 Logic circuit examples

5.4 Universal functions

It was stated earlier that all logic functions can be implemented using AND, OR and NOT gates suitably interconnected. Why then are the functions NAND and NOR provided? The answer is that all logic circuits can be implemented using just NAND gates, and similarly all logic circuits can be implemented using just NOR gates. NAND and NOR are said to be the *universal functions*. The universality of NAND can be demonstrated by showing that all other functions can be formed using just NAND gates. It is left to the reader as an exercise to do the same for NOR. NAND, remember, is NOT AND.

- As $\overline{a.1} = \bar{a}$, if a signal is connected to one input of a NAND gate, and 1 is connected to the other, then the gate has been configured as a NOT gate. Note, the above could be implemented by connecting the signal to both inputs of the gate, but because of fanout limitations it is best to connect one input to a 1.
- AND is NOT AND, thus a NAND gate followed by a NAND configured as a NOT gate will provide the AND function.
- De Morgan's law can be used to provide a NAND only version of the OR function: $\bar{a} + \bar{b} = \overline{a.b}$. Thus a OR b can be implemented by generating $\bar{a}$ and $\bar{b}$ (using NAND gates configured as NOT gates) and connecting these to a NAND gate.
- The above followed by a NOT gate provides NOT OR, or NOR.

Circuits implementing these concepts are shown diagramatically in figure 5.3.

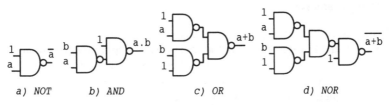

a) NOT   b) AND   c) OR   d) NOR

Figure 5.3 NAND universality

At first sight this does not seem much use: 3 NAND gates being used instead of one OR gate. However, it is often the case that four gates of the same type are provided on one integrated circuit, so to use AND and OR gates requires at least two circuits. Also, some simplification is possible. Any logic function in the sum of products form, that is, like

a.b + b.c + c.d

can be implemented using AND and OR gates, or NAND gates only. See figure 5.4. First, the AND and OR version is given (5.4a). Then these are replaced by NAND gates (5.4b), which results in two NAND gates connected as NOT gates in series. These can be removed, leaving the simplified version (5.4c).

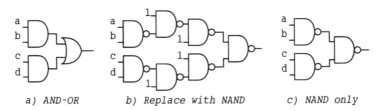

a) AND-OR   b) Replace with NAND   c) NAND only

Figure 5.4 NAND implementations

Implementation of the exclusive-or function is also interesting. Figure 5.5 shows the AND-OR-NOT version, the NAND only implementation of that circuit, and then an improved version using only four gates. The output of the third circuit is (by recognising the output as being the NAND only implementation of a sum of products expression):

$$\overline{a.\overline{a.b}} + \overline{b.\overline{a.b}} = a.(\overline{a} + \overline{b}) + b.(\overline{a} + \overline{b}) = a.\overline{a} + a.\overline{b} + b.\overline{a} + b.\overline{b} = a.\overline{b} + \overline{a}.b$$

which is the correct answer.

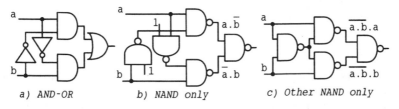

a) AND-OR   b) NAND only   c) Other NAND only

Figure 5.5 Exclusive-or implementations

5.5 Design example

Designing a circuit to implement a logic problem consists of three stages; deriving a suitable logic function (or functions), simplifying the function, and then connecting suitable logic gates together. Consider the following example:

Design a logic circuit to determine if a four bit number is a member of the Fibonacci sequence, that is, if it is 0, 1, 2, 3, 5, 8 or 13.

These numbers can be represented by four bits (numbered bits 0 to 3) using the scheme introduced in chapter 4 where bit r is '1' if the number has a component 2^r. Here, for example, 5 is $2^2 + 2^0$, so bits 2 and 0 should be '1', the others should be '0'.

In the design of any problem an initial stage is to assign suitable names to the inputs and outputs. Let a b c d be the four bit number, a being the most significant bit (bit 3), d being bit 0, and f the output which is true if the number is in the sequence. Next a truth table for the problem is constructed, thus:

```
a b c d | f |  explanation
0 0 0 0 | 1 |  number is 0
0 0 0 1 | 1 |  number is 1
0 0 1 0 | 1 |  number is 2
0 0 1 1 | 1 |  number is 3
0 1 0 0 | 0 |
0 1 0 1 | 1 |  number is 5
0 1 1 0 | 0 |
0 1 1 1 | 0 |
1 0 0 0 | 1 |  number is 8
1 0 0 1 | 0 |
1 0 1 0 | 0 |
1 0 1 1 | 0 |
1 1 0 0 | 0 |
1 1 0 1 | 1 |  number is 13
1 1 1 0 | 0 |
1 1 1 1 | 0 |
```

The next stage is to derive the boolean expression for f from the above. This is achieved by writing down all the combinations of a b c d for which f is 1. Thus:

$$f = \bar{a}.\bar{b}.\bar{c}.\bar{d} + \bar{a}.\bar{b}.\bar{c}.d + \bar{a}.\bar{b}.c.\bar{d} + \bar{a}.\bar{b}.c.d + \bar{a}.b.\bar{c}.d + \bar{a}.\bar{b}.\bar{c}.\bar{d} + a.b.\bar{c}.d$$

The next stage is to see if the above can be simplified. In this case it can, the following being produced using the rules of boolean algebra (the reader might like to verify this, as an exercise). The first four terms form a.b, the second and fifth reduce to $\bar{a}.\bar{c}.d$, the first and sixth give $\bar{b}.\bar{c}.\bar{d}$ and the fifth and seventh give $b.\bar{c}.d$. So:

$$f = \bar{a}.\bar{b} + \bar{a}.\bar{c}.d + \bar{b}.\bar{c}.\bar{d} + b.\bar{c}.d$$

Note, it appears that the $\bar{a}.\bar{c}.d$ term is unnecessary, as it is made from the second and fifth terms in the original expression $\bar{a}.\bar{b}.\bar{c}.d$ and $\bar{a}.b.\bar{c}.d$, and the second term is included in the $\bar{a}.\bar{b}$ term and the fifth in the $b.\bar{c}.d$ term. Thus the simplest expression is:

$$f = \overline{a}.\overline{b} + \overline{b}.\overline{c}.\overline{d} + b.\overline{c}.d$$

There are reasons why the $\overline{a}.\overline{c}.d$ term may sometimes be needed, as is explained later. A circuit implementing the above is shown in figure 5.6.

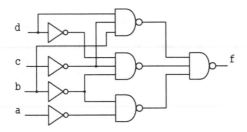

Figure 5.6 Logic circuit for design problem

5.6 Karnaugh maps

Boolean algebra can be used to simplify boolean expressions. However, many people do not like algebra, and so an alternative graphical method is presented here. This method was derived by Veitch and improved by Karnaugh, but originates from set theory and Venn diagrams (see Karnaugh, 1953).

Indeed, there is a relationship between boolean algebra and set theory. For example, in the symbolic logic notation for representing logic expressions, the symbol for AND is $\wedge$, that for OR is $\vee$, and that for NOT is $\neg$. So $a.\overline{b}+c$ can be written using symbolic logic notation as $(a \wedge \neg b) \vee c$. In set theory the symbol $\cap$ is used to represent intersection, which is like AND, and the symbol $\cup$ means union, which is like OR. Thus the set theory symbols are 'rounded' versions of those used in symbolic logic.

Figure 5.7 shows some Venn diagrams. 5.7a shows one set in a universe; inside that set represents the logic function a, outside is $\overline{a}$. Figure 5.7b shows two sets, a and b, and the areas a.b, a.$\overline{b}$, $\overline{a}$.b and $\overline{a}.\overline{b}$ are marked. This provides a graphical demonstration of one of De Morgan's laws. Anywhere inside either the a or b sets is the area a + b (as shown in 5.7c). Outside that area is $\overline{a+b}$, which is $\overline{a}.\overline{b}$ as shown in 5.7b. This concept can be extended to handle 3 sets or more, but it becomes more difficult to draw, so a different method is used.

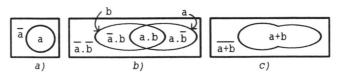

Figure 5.7 Venn diagrams for logic

Instead of dividing the area by drawing circles, it is possible to produce a rectangular version. Figure 5.8 shows such maps for 1, 2 and 3 variables. Here each column and row is labelled, and the values of each square are written inside. These are called *Karnaugh maps*, or *K-maps* for short.

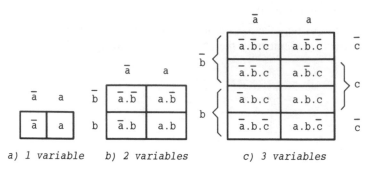

a) 1 variable   b) 2 variables   c) 3 variables

Figure 5.8 Rectangular 'maps'

One point to note is that for any two adjacent squares, only one variable changes (for the three variable map the square at the top of a column is considered to be adjacent to the square at the bottom of that column).

It is possible to take any logic expression in the sum of products form and represent it on a k-map, by writing a 1 in each square which is represented by a term in the expression. For example, the map in figure 5.9a is for the function a.b + $\bar{a}$.b, in 5.9b is a map for the function $\bar{a}$.b.c + a.$\bar{b}$.c + a$\bar{b}$.$\bar{c}$ + a.b.c (the carry for a full adder), and in 5.9c is the map for the sum digit of a full adder.

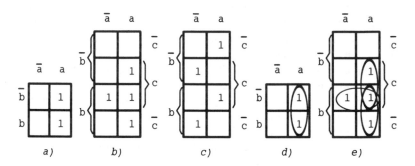

a)   b)   c)   d)   e)

Figure 5.9 Some Karnaugh maps

The function a.b + a.$\bar{b}$ simplifies to a. This simplification can be done on the k-map because the two marked squares are adjacent and so can be combined: see figure 5.9d. In fact, the simplification of expressions is achieved using a k-map by combining pairs (or fours, or eights) of mutually adjacent squares. The process is shown in 5.9e for the full adder carry; there are three pairs of adjacent squares representing the simplified expression: a.b + b.c + a.c. As regards the sum digit of a full adder, there are no adjacent squares in 5.9c, so no simplification is possible.

Sometimes each term in the original expression represents more than one square; for example, consider the expression

a.$\bar{b}$.$\bar{c}$ + a.b + $\bar{a}$.b.$\bar{c}$ + $\bar{a}$.c here a.b represents the squares a.b.c and a.b.$\bar{c}$. Thus when filling in the K-map, both squares must be considered. Figure 5.10a shows the K-map for this expression, and 5.10b shows the groupings. Note the grouping of the top of the 'a' column with the bottom of that column, and the grouping of four squares at the bottom of the map. The expression simplifies to

$b + \bar{a}.c + a.\bar{c}$

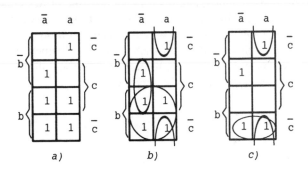

Figure 5.10 More K-maps

Consider the k-map of 5.10c for the expression

$\bar{a}.\bar{b}.c + \bar{a}.b.\bar{c} + a.b.\bar{c} + a.\bar{b}.c$

Here three of the squares can be combined with another square, the fourth cannot. The expression thus simplifies only to

$\bar{a}.\bar{b}.c + b.\bar{c} + a.\bar{c}$

Figure 5.11 shows the four variable K-map for the example design exercise given above. With the four variable map, the first square in a row is considered to be adjacent to the last one in that row. The seven squares are those products found from the truth table and given in the expression:

$f = \bar{a}.\bar{b}.\bar{c}.\bar{d} + \bar{a}.\bar{b}.\bar{c}.d + \bar{a}.b.c.\bar{d} + \bar{a}.b.c.d + a.b.\bar{c}.d + a.\bar{b}.\bar{c}.\bar{d} + a.b.\bar{c}.d$

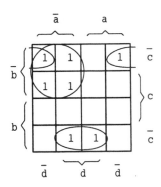

Figure 5.11 K-map for the design example

Examining the map, there are the three groupings which cover all the squares, leading to the same reduced expression as was derived before:

$$f = \bar{a}.\bar{b} + \bar{b}.\bar{c}.\bar{d} + b.\bar{c}.d$$

5.7 Don't care conditions

In the design of many practical circuits it is not possible or desirable to specify the output(s) for all possible combinations of input. This can happen because in practice particular input conditions may not occur, so it does not matter what the output of the circuit should be. In such a case, the value for the output is called don't care, and this is denoted by x. Consider the following truth table for the function with inputs a, b and c, and output f.

a	b	c	f
0	0	0	1
0	0	1	1
0	1	0	0
0	1	1	x
1	0	0	0
1	0	1	1
1	1	0	x
1	1	1	1

The k-map for the above is shown in figure 5.12a, where a 0, 1 or x is placed in each square. The simplification process continues as normal, with groupings of suitable adjacent squares, except that an x can be treated as being '0' or '1', whichever is more convenient. In this case, the $\bar{a}.b.c$ square is best considered as '1', so that the four middle squares can be grouped together as the term c, and the $a.b.\bar{c}$ square is best considered as '0'. The simplified function is thus $c + \bar{a}.\bar{b}$.

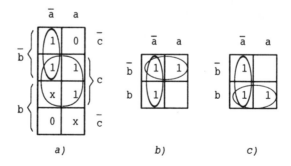

a)   b)   c)

Figure 5.12 Don't care examples

Also, if one input is, say, '0', this may determine the output irrespective of the values of the other inputs. In such a case, the values of the other inputs need not be considered; they can also be marked as don't care. Consider the following truth table for inputs a and b and outputs f and g.

a	b	f	g
0	x	1	1
1	0	1	0
1	1	0	1

If a is '0', then irrespective of the value of b, both f and g are '1'. If, a is '1', however, then b determines whether g or f is '1'. The first line of the table is therefore the condition a is '0'. Hence, the boolean expressions for the table are as shown below, together with their simplified versions as derived from their K-maps shown in figures 5.12b and 5.12.c respectively.

$$f = \bar{a} + a.\bar{b} = \bar{a} + \bar{b}$$
$$g = \bar{a} + a.b = \bar{a} + b$$

5.8   Hazards and other practicalities

One limitation of gates, fan-out, has been mentioned earlier. In this section some other points are raised which the logic designer needs to consider. When an input to a gate changes, this may result in a change at the output, but there will be a delay before the change occurs (no delay implies that signals travel at infinite speeds). This delay is termed the *propagation delay*. Also, it takes time for the output of a gate to change, the so-called *transition time*. The transition time for a signal to change from '0' to '1' can differ from the time to change from '1' to '0' in many practical circuits.

These practicalities lead to an interesting problem, hazards. One of the rules of boolean algebra states that

$$\bar{a} + a = 1$$

However, a practical realisation of this may not always be true: consider the circuit shown in figure 5.13a, and the effect on the circuit when the signal a changes from '1' to '0'. The variation of the parts of the circuit with time is shown in figure 5.13b: for a short period of time both inputs to the OR gate are '0', so the output will be '0' for a short time; such a signal is sometimes called a *glitch*. This problem is termed a *static hazard*.

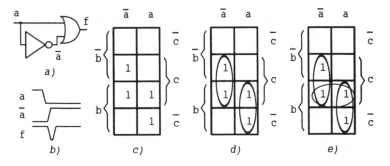

Figure 5.13 Hazard examples

Consider the expression given earlier, a.b + $\bar{a}$.c. When b and c are both 1, this reduces to a + $\bar{a}$. Thus, when b and c are both 1, and a changes from 1 to 0, there will be a hazard, the output of the function will be 0 for a short time. When this expression was introduced, boolean algebra was used to show that

(a + c).($\bar{a}$ + b) = a.b + $\bar{a}$.c

and an intermediate stage showed that these expressions also equalled

a.b + b.c + $\bar{a}$.c

If a.b + b.c + $\bar{a}$.c was used instead of a.b + $\bar{a}$.c, then there would be no hazard problem, because the hazard, when the output is 0 for a short time, occurs only when b and c are both 1, and then the function a.b + b.c + $\bar{a}$.c is

a + 1 + $\bar{a}$ = 1

Thus, the term b.c, the *hazard term*, is needed to avoid hazards.

To ensure that hazards do not occur, hazard terms must be included in expressions, but how can they be found? Again K-maps can be used. Consider the K-map for the function a.b + $\bar{a}$.c, as shown in figure 5.13c. Adjacent squares can be combined, as in 5.13d, for the two terms a.b and $\bar{a}$.c. Here all marked squares have been circled, but another pairing is possible, as shown in 5.13e: the third pairing is that for the hazard term b.c.

Remember the design example given earlier, whose K-map is redrawn in figure 5.14a. Here there are three groupings which include all the squares. However, there is another pair of sqaures which can be grouped, as shown in figure 5.14b; this is the the hazard term, $\bar{a}$.c.d. Thus the hazard-free expression for the problem is:

f = $\bar{a}.\bar{b}$ + $\bar{b}.\bar{c}.\bar{d}$ + b.$\bar{c}$.d + $\bar{a}.\bar{c}$.d.

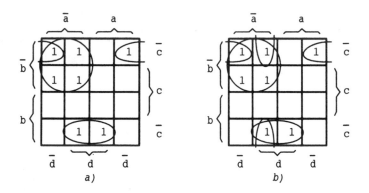

Figure 5.14 K-map showing hazard term for the design problem

In general, to avoid hazards, all adjacent pairings of a K-map must be considered. Sometimes a designer does not need to worry about hazards, for example in the design of some sequential logic circuits, but on other occasions the designer has to be more careful.

Sometimes the above are called race hazards; the glitch occurs because some signals in the circuit change before others (they win the race). Races can also occur when two signals change at the same time, but the change due to the first signal reaches the output before that due to the second signal. More details on races can be found in Lewin and Protheroe.

Alternative methods for minimising logic expressions and finding hazard terms include the Quine-McCluskey and Sharp function methods. These provide a formal algorithm for processing boolean expressions, and hence can be automated on a computer. More details of the methods can be found in Lewin and Protheroe.

5.9 More complex devices

The circuits described above consist of various logic gates suitably interconnected. These are available to the logic designer for inclusion in logic circuits. However, combinations of gates are also available readily packaged producing some useful circuitry. The purpose of this section is to describe some typical combinational logic devices. Some other devices, which provide sequential logic circuits, are described in chapter 6.

Multiplexers

Consider the circuit shown in figure 5.15a. The boolean expression describing the output Y is:

$$Y = a.s + b.\bar{s}$$

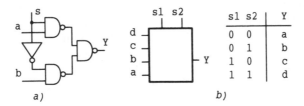

Figure 5.15 Multiplexer circuits

If s = 0 then Y = b, but if s = 1 then Y = a. Thus Y takes the value of a or of b depending on s, that is, s selects a or b. Such a device is termed a multiplexer. The example in figure 5.15a is a 2-1 multiplexer, which uses one select input to select one value out of a choice of two. A 4-1 multiplexer has two select inputs and the output is chosen out of a choice of four: a block diagram and truth table for such a device is shown in figure 5.15b. 8-1 multiplexers are also available. Sometimes these devices have an enable signal as well; if this is 1 say, then the appropriate input is selected, but if the enable is 0, the output is 0 irrespective of all other signals.

Decoders

Consider the circuit shown in figure 5.16a. This has an enable input G, a select input a, and two outputs $\overline{Y}_1$ and $\overline{Y}_0$. If G is 0, both outputs are 1, but if G is 1, then signal a selects which of the outputs is 0; if a is 0, $\overline{Y}_0$ is 0, if a is 1, $\overline{Y}_1$ is 0. This is a 1 to 2 decoder. A block diagram of a 2 to 4 decoder is shown with its truth table in figure 5.16b. If G is 0, all outputs are 1, but if G is 1, the device is enabled, and one of the four outputs is 0, which one being determined by the inputs a and b. a and b can be considered to form a 2-bit number in the range 0 to 3 (00 = 0, 01 = 1, 10 = 2 and 11 = 3); if this number is called n, then output $\overline{Y}_n$ will be 0 and all the other outputs will be 1. Similarly 3 to 8 and 4 to 16 decoders are available. These devices are often used in interface circuits; they select the particular device which is to be accessed by the microprocessor.

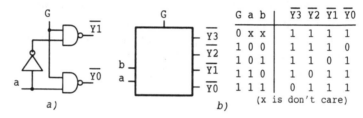

G a b	$\overline{Y3}$ $\overline{Y2}$ $\overline{Y1}$ $\overline{Y0}$
0 x x	1 1 1 1
1 0 0	1 1 1 0
1 0 1	1 1 0 1
1 1 0	1 0 1 1
1 1 1	0 1 1 1

(x is don't care)

Figure 5.16 Decoders

Encoders

An encoder is the opposite of a decoder. A block diagram and truth table for a 4 to 2 line encoder is shown in figure 5.17. Essentially the device has 4 inputs, $\overline{Y3}..\overline{Y0}$, an output $\overline{S}$ which reports if any of the inputs is 0, and two outputs, b and a, which give a 2-bit number indicating the highest numbered input which is a 0; for example, if $\overline{Y3}$ is 1 and $\overline{Y2}$ is 0, then it is input number 2 which is 0, so b and a indicate the number 2. As more than one input could be a 0, the outputs b and a only report the highest numbered such input; therefore these devices are sometimes termed *priority encoders*. 8 to 3 line decoders also exist. In microprocessor systems these devices are sometimes used to determine which of many interrupting devices should be processed first.

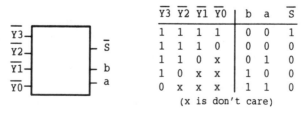

$\overline{Y3}$ $\overline{Y2}$ $\overline{Y1}$ $\overline{Y0}$	b	a	$\overline{S}$
1 1 1 1	0	0	1
1 1 1 0	0	0	0
1 1 0 x	0	1	0
1 0 x x	1	0	0
0 x x x	1	1	0

(x is don't care)

Figure 5.17 Priority encoder

Adders

Circuits are provided which allow data to be added together. A typical device consists of four full adders, each full adder being a circuit which adds two bits and a carry from the previous stage, generating a sum and a carry output (as described in section 5.2). Such a 4-bit adder will have as input 4 pairs of data inputs and a carry input and it will generate 4 sum outputs and a carry output. If 8-bit numbers are to be added, two such circuits are used, with the carry output from the first circuit being connected to the carry input of the second.

Comparators

These circuits compare two n-bit numbers, with an output indicating if the two numbers are equal. Some devices also have outputs indicating if the first number is less than or greater than the second.

Monostables

A monostable is a device which when triggered outputs a pulse which lasts for a given length of time, as determined by a resistor and a capacitor which are connected suitably to the device as shown in figure 5.18. The device is usually triggered by an input changing state suitably; in the circuit of figure 5.18, when the Trig input changes from '0' to '1' the Q output goes to '1' and stays there for the time t, after which Q returns to '0'; the time t is determined by the values of the resitor and capacitor.

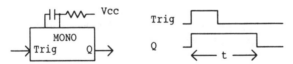

Figure 5.18 Monostable circuit and operation

Logic arrays

A programmable logic array, or PLA, is a device which allows the direct implementation of a number of sum of products expressions. Associated with each output is an OR gate whose inputs are the outputs of several AND gates, and the inputs to the AND gates are any combinations of the inputs to the PLA and their inverses. The connections of these inputs to the appropriate AND gates are achieved by suitable programming of the device. Figure 5.19 shows the arrangement with the programming connections shown by blobs. The circuit is that to provide the Carry and Sum for a full adder, for which the expressions for Carry and Sum are:

Carry = a.b + a.c + b.a
Sum = a.$\bar{b}$.$\bar{c}$ + $\bar{a}$.$\bar{b}$.c + $\bar{a}$.b.$\bar{c}$ + a.b.c

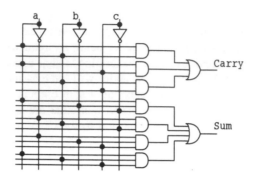

Figure 5.19 PLA implemention of a full adder

These devices are very appropriate for implementing boolean expressions in the sum of product form. Devices come in various forms, with different numbers of inputs, outputs and internal gates; some can be programmed once only, others can be erased and reprogrammed. Suitable software packages are available for programming the devices. These also come in various forms, some just allow the logic expressions to be entered, some will take each expression and simplify it as well, others allow the circuit to be specified schematically, that is, the logic circuit itself is entered.

These devices have a fixed architecture, allowing easy implementation of sum-of-product expressions. Another type of device, a gate array, is more flexible. This also has various elements which can be suitably interconnected, but the architecture is not restricted to the AND-OR arrangement; it can have multiplexer circuits or other more complex devices, and these can be configured in any appropriate arrangement. Again suitable software is needed to help design and program these devices.

Devices with Schmitt trigger inputs

Many logic devices used in microprocessor systems have Schmitt trigger inputs. Figure 5.20a shows a NOT gate with such inputs; the *hysteresis* symbol in the gate indicates the input type. The important property of these inputs is that they have two threshold or trigger points; the circuit will only respond to such an input when it increases passed its upper threshold point (UTP) or it decreases passed the lower thrshold point (LTP). For the inverter, the output will change to '0' when the input goes up passed the UTP and it will change to '1' when the input goes down passed the LTP. These changes are shown in figure 5.20b. A 'normal' gate has only one threshold point.

The major advantage of two threshold points is that the system becomes more tolerant of noise. If the input to a gate with such inputs changes by a small amount around a threshold point, without exceeding the other threshold point, that gate changes state only once. This is also shown in figure 5.20b.

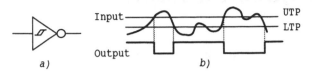

Figure 5.20 Schmitt trigger inputs

Summary

This chapter has described simple logic gates and the basic means by which they can be connected to produce useful logic circuits. Also outlined are more complex elements which consist of a number of these simpler gates. More details, including the precise configurations (such as the number of inputs and polarity of enable signals) can be found by consulting the appropriate data books. All of these circuits are combinational logic elements: the next chapter describes another useful family of circuits, sequential logic elements.

Exercises

1. Show that NOR is a universal function.

2. Show, using boolean algebra, that the expression

$$f = \overline{a}.\overline{b}.\overline{c}.\overline{d} + \overline{a}.\overline{b}.\overline{c}.d + \overline{a}.\overline{b}.c.\overline{d} + \overline{a}.\overline{b}.c.d + \overline{a}.b.\overline{c}.d + a.\overline{b}.\overline{c}.\overline{d} + a.\overline{b}.\overline{c}.d$$

can be simplified to

$$f = \overline{a}.\overline{b} + \overline{b}.\overline{c}.\overline{d} + b.\overline{c}.d$$

3. Design circuits to implement a 4-1 multiplexer, a 2 to 4 decoder circuit and a 4 to 2 line encoder circuit.

4. Design a circuit which compares two 2-bit numbers having three outputs reporting respectively whether the first number is greater than, equal to, or less than the second.

5. Design a circuit which converts a three bit number represented in natural binary into its equivalent three bit Gray code number.

References

B.R.Bannister & D.G.Whitehead *Fundamentals of Modern Digital Systems* 2nd Edn, Macmillan Press, 1987.

D.Lewin & D Protheroe *Design of Logic Systems* Chapman and Hall, 1992.

M.Morris Mano *Digital Design* Prentice-Hall, 2nd Edn, 1990.

T.J.Stonham *Digital Logic Techniques* Chapman & Hall, 1987

M.Karnaugh 1953 *The map for synthesis of combinational logic circuits* AIEE Trans. 72, Pt1, pp593-599.

Texas Instruments *TTL Data book*.

6 Sequential Logic

The circuits described so far are combinational logic circuits which process some inputs and generate a suitable output (or outputs) whose value depends only upon those inputs. Another form of logic circuit is termed sequential logic, and here some of the outputs are fed back as inputs to the circuit, so the outputs now depend upon both the current and the previous inputs. One use of such circuits is to provide memory elements, sometimes called latches or flip flops. These are described here as they are used extensively in microprocessor systems.

6.1 Memory elements

Consider figure 6.1a in which two NAND gates are connected together with feedback. This is redrawn in its normal form in 6.1b. Figure 6.1c contains a truth table for the circuit. If a is '0', then Q1 is '1', similarly if b is '0', Q2 is '1'. But what if a and b are both '1'? If Q1 was '1', then Q2 will be '0', which confirms that Q1 is a '1'. Similarly, if Q2 was '1', then Q1 will be '0' and so confirm that Q2 is '1'. Thus the state of the system before a and b both became '1' is retained when a and b are '1'; in the truth table, Q1 and Q2 are given the value u meaning unchanged. Thus if a and b were '0' and '1' respectively, Q1 would be '1', and would remain so when a and b then both became '1'. Thus the circuit is a memory or latch; in fact it is termed an *ISR* latch, or *inverse set reset* latch, inverse because an input has to be 0 to make the corresponding output '1'.

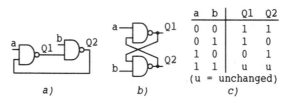

a	b	Q1	Q2
0	0	1	1
0	1	1	0
1	0	0	1
1	1	u	u

(u = unchanged)

a) b) c)

Figure 6.1 Feedback NAND elements: ISR latch

Next consider the circuit of figure 6.2a, whose actions are defined in the associated truth table. If c is '1', then a and b determine the outputs Q1 and Q2 as in figure 6.1, except that this is a SR latch not an ISR latch. However, if c is '0', the outputs of the first two NAND gates are '1' irrespective of a and b, which means that the outputs Q1 and Q2 cannot change. Thus a and b determine the outputs while c is '1', but the outputs cannot be changed when c is '0'.

56

An extension to this is shown in 6.2b, where the b input is now the inverse of a; this is a D-type latch (D for data). When c is '1', the input determines the output Q, but if c is '0' the output is latched. This is called a *transparent* latch, as the input can be effectively 'seen' from the output when c is '1'.

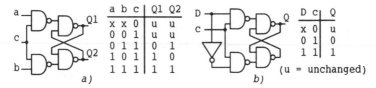

a	b	c	Q1	Q2
x	x	0	u	u
0	0	1	u	u
0	1	1	0	1
1	0	1	1	0
1	1	1	1	1

a)

D	c	Q
x	0	u
0	1	0
1	1	1

(u = unchanged)

b)

Figure 6.2 Transparent latches

This is a useful form of circuit, but it can be extended. Consider figure 6.3, which consists of two such D-type latches concatenated, in which c is passed to the second latch, and c inverted is passed to the first. This is termed a *master–slave* flip flop; the first part of the circuit is the master, the second is the slave. When c is '0', the input D determines the value of Q', but the output Q is unaffected as the slave part of the circuit is latched. However, when c becomes '1', Q' is latched, and Q can change. But the value of Q is determined by Q', which now cannot change. Thus the value of Q is determined by the value of D when c changed from '0' to '1'; in the truth table, such a change to c is shown by an arrow, $\uparrow$. This is a very useful circuit and can be used to store information in a microprocessor system. Note, in some latches, the output changes when c changes from '1' to '0'.

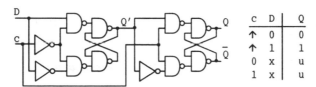

c	D	Q
$\uparrow$	0	0
$\uparrow$	1	1
0	x	u
1	x	u

Figure 6.3 D-type master-slave flip flop

Another useful type of flip flop is called the JK flip flop, whose circuit and truth table are shown in figure 6.4. The outputs of the latch are Q and $\overline{Q}$; the second output from the ISR latch is the inverse of the first, hence the labels Q and $\overline{Q}$ are appropriate. The circuit is another master–slave device, whose output changes when the c signal changes from '0' to '1'. At such times the outputs are determined by the inputs J and K and the previous values of the outputs. Thus the truth table to determine the outputs requires both the inputs and the previous outputs; hence the truth table in figure 6.4 has Q_t meaning the output before c changes from '1' to '0', and Q_{t+1} being the output after these changes.

Thus, if J = K = '0', the outputs are unchanged on the rising transition of c; if J = '0' and K = '1', then Q is set to '0'; if J = '1' and K = '0', then Q is set to '1'; and if J = K = '1', then Q and $\overline{Q}$ are inverted.

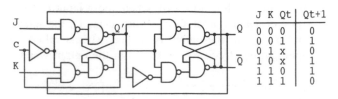

J	K	Qt	Qt+1
0	0	0	0
0	0	1	1
0	1	x	0
1	0	x	1
1	1	0	1
1	1	1	0

Figure 6.4 JK flip flop

The master–slave D-type and JK flip flops described above change state when the c signal changes from '0' to '1'. A circuit whose outputs change on the transition of a signal is termed an *edge-triggered* device. Master–slave circuits can be used for this purpose, but many practical circuits use a different configuration, such as that shown in figure 6.5. This circuit is a positive edge-triggered D-type flip flop, that is, its output Q is determined by the value on its D input on the positive going edge of the signal c. In addition, the circuit has two extra inputs, clear ($\overline{\text{clr}}$) and preset ($\overline{\text{pr}}$). If $\overline{\text{pr}}$ = '0', then Q is '1', so the output Q is set; if $\overline{\text{clr}}$ = '0', then $\overline{\text{Q}}$ is '1' which, if $\overline{\text{pr}}$ = '1', means that Q is '0', so Q is cleared; both clear and preset override the c signal.

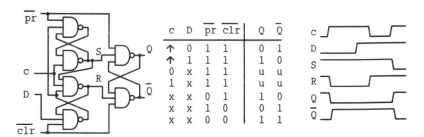

c	D	$\overline{\text{pr}}$	$\overline{\text{clr}}$	Q	$\overline{\text{Q}}$
↑	0	1	1	0	1
↑	1	1	1	1	0
0	x	1	1	u	u
1	x	1	1	u	u
x	x	0	1	1	0
x	x	1	0	0	1
x	x	0	0	1	1

Figure 6.5 D-type bistable with preset and clear

Assuming that $\overline{\text{pr}}$ and $\overline{\text{clr}}$ are '1', the circuit operates as follows (as shown in figure 6.5. When c is '0', the signals S and R are both '1', so the output ISR latch is latched. When c changes to '1', either S or R will change to the '0' state, and so determine the output Q. If D is 0 when c changes to '1', then R is '0', so Q will become '0'; but if D is '1', then S will be '0', so Q will become '1'.

If $\overline{\text{pr}}$ is '0', the output Q is forced to the value '1'; also S is given the value '0', so when $\overline{\text{pr}}$ becomes '1' again Q will remain '1' until the next positive edge of c or $\overline{\text{clr}}$ is set to '0'. When $\overline{\text{clr}}$ is '0', Q is forced to the value '0', as can be shown by a similar argument. Note, $\overline{\text{pr}}$ and $\overline{\text{clr}}$ affect the output immediately (ignoring propagation delays through circuits), whereas the value of D only affects the output on the next positive edge of c.

Note, for the D-type flip flop, the value of D determines the Q output when the c signal changes from '0' to '1'. Strictly this is not quite true, as the value for Q is determined by the values S and R, and these are determined by the D value a short time before because of the propagation delay through the circuit. Therefore it should be arranged that the D input is at a stable level a short time before the control signal changes. It is also a good idea to keep the D signal stable from then until after the edge of the control signal.

The circuits given above are positive edge-triggered devices, but negative edge-triggered devices and other master–slave devices are also available. More details can be found in such books as Lewin and Protheroe.

A latch is a useful device for storing one bit of data. However, often many bits of data are required, in which case a circuit with many single bit latches is needed. Many such devices are available: some are edge-triggered, some are transparent. These circuits, made up of the basic logic elements, can be used to provide simple memory elements or registers in the CPU. However, they can also be used to produce more complex circuits, as is described below.

6.2 Counter circuits

The following circuits use edge-triggered D-type flip flops, although JK flip flops could be used in their place with suitable modifications. Figure 6.6a shows the symbol which is used here to represent the D-type flip flop and figure 6.6b shows that which is used for JK flip flops. For these, the signal on whose edge the outputs may change is called the clock signal.

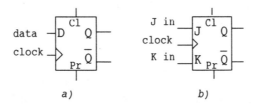

Figure 6.6 Symbols for D-type and JK flip flops

Asynchronous counters

Consider the circuit of figure 6.7a), in which the $\overline{Q}$ output of each flip flop is connected to its D input and to the clock of the next flip flop. Thus on every rising edge of the clock of that flip flop, the Q output will take the value $\overline{Q}$ had before, that is, Q will be inverted. The variation of outputs of that circuit when the input to the first flip flop is passed a square wave clock signal is shown in figure 6.7b: when the clock changes from '0' to '1', Q_0 inverts, when $\overline{Q}_0$ changes from '0' to '1', Q_1 is inverted, and similarly for Q_2 and Q_3.

The values of each output after the rising edge of the input clock are listed in figure 6.7c. These show that the outputs represent the binary number 0000 = 0 initially, then 0001 = 1 after the first change, then 0010 = 2, etc. Thus the circuit is a counter, counting from 0 to 15, and then back to 0 again.

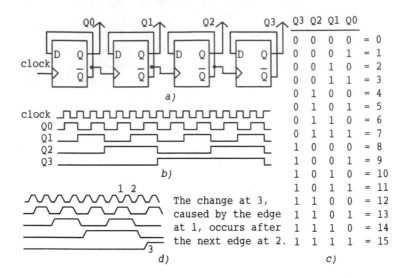

Figure 6.7 Asynchronous 4-bit counter

If the input is a clock signal with a given frequency, Q_0 is a clock signal with half that frequency, Q_1 is a clock signal with a quarter of the frequency, and so on (see figure 6.7c). Such a device is also called a divide by n counter.

The above device is a *ripple through* or *asynchronous* 4-bit counter, and is so called because the change in clock input may cause the output of the first flip flop to change, which may cause the second flip flop to change, and so on; the changes ripple through. Thus there is a delay between the change in the input and any change in the last flip flop, and the more flip flops in the circuit, the longer the delay. This can cause a problem. Consider a counter which is passed a very fast clock: the variation in outputs may be as shown in figure 6.7d; here the change to the last flip flop has not occurred before the next change of input. This problem can be overcome using synchronous counters.

Synchronous counters

A synchronous circuit is one whose outputs all change at the same time (or as nearly as possible), typically on the edge of some clock signal. This can be achieved by a series of D-type flip flops whose c inputs are connected to a common clock signal. Then, when the clock changes from '0' to '1' (say), all the Q outputs change together to the values determined by the corresponding D inputs. Thus a synchronous 4-bit counter can be made in the form shown in figure 6.8, where the D inputs contain the value that the Q outputs should have next time. This requires a circuit to generate the correct values for the D inputs.

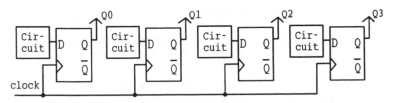

Figure 6.8 Block diagram of a synchronous counter

The D inputs are the values that the Q outputs should have after the next change in the clock signal. So, if the outputs $Q3..Q0$ are 0000, the outputs should be 0001 next time, so the inputs $D3..D0$ should be 0001, and if the Q outputs are 0001, the D inputs should be 0010, and so on. The following truth table defines what the D inputs should be in terms of the current Q outputs:

Q_3	Q_2	Q_1	Q_0	D_3	D_2	D_1	D_0
0	0	0	0	0	0	0	1
0	0	0	1	0	0	1	0
0	0	1	0	0	0	1	1
0	0	1	1	0	1	0	0
0	1	0	0	0	1	0	1
0	1	0	1	0	1	1	0
0	1	1	0	0	1	1	1
0	1	1	1	1	0	0	0
1	0	0	0	1	0	0	1
1	0	0	1	1	0	1	0
1	0	1	0	1	0	1	1
1	0	1	1	1	1	0	0
1	1	0	0	1	1	0	1
1	1	0	1	1	1	1	0
1	1	1	0	1	1	1	1
1	1	1	1	0	0	0	0

K-maps or boolean algebra can be used to analyse these to determine the circuits for the D inputs; this is left to the reader to do as an exercise. The results, though, can be expressed as follows:

$D_0 = \overline{Q}0$
$D_1 = Q_1 \oplus Q_0$
$D_2 = Q_2 \oplus Q_1.Q_0$
$D_3 = Q_3 \oplus Q_2.Q_1.Q_0$

Such a counter will count from 0 to 15, and then back to 0, each change in the outputs occurring after the clock signal changes from '0' to '1' (say). The same idea could be used to produce a decimal counter, that is, a circuit which counts from 0 to 9, and then starts again from '0'. Similarly, a Gray code counter could also be generated.

Note that the counter will work well provided that the propagation delay through the circuit generating the D signals is less than the period of the clock signal, that is, the new value for D has been produced in time for the next rising clock edge. Thus this propagation delay determines the maximum speed clock signal which the counter can process successfully. In such cases the combinational logic circuit need not be hazard free, as any unwanted glitch will have disappeared before the D input is sampled on the clock edge.

Practical counters often have a clear input, for setting all outputs to '0'. Some of these have an asynchronous clear, that is, the outputs are set to '0' as soon as the 'clear' signal is asserted. This can be achieved easily by connecting the clear signal to the $\overline{clr}$ inputs of all flip flops.

Other counters have a synchronous clear, where the outputs change to '0' when the clear signal is asserted but only when the clock changes from '1' to '0'. This requires a change to the circuits for generating the D signals. If the 'clear' signal is '0' to clear the outputs (it is active low), then the above expressions for the D inputs should be changed to:

$D_0 = clear.\overline{Q}0$
$D_1 = clear.(Q_1 \oplus Q_0)$
$D_2 = clear.(Q_2 \oplus Q_1.Q_0)$
$D_3 = clear.(Q_3 \oplus Q_2.Q_1.Q_0)$

Thus if clear is '0', all the D inputs are '0', so the Q outputs will be '0' next time. If clear is '1', it has no effect upon the circuit.

A counter might also (or instead) have a load capability in which the outputs are set to a specified pattern. Again this could be asynchronous, in which case the $\overline{pr}$ and $\overline{clr}$ inputs of the D types would be used, or synchronous, when suitable values for the D inputs should be determined.

Now consider a JK version of the above. If $J = K = $ '0', then the Q output of the flip flop will not change, but if $J = K = $ '1', then the output will invert. Thus a simple method of implementing a counter is to connect each J to its corresponding K, and set these to '1' if the output is to change. Observations of the above truth table indicate that Q_0 needs to change each time, Q_1 should change when Q_0 is '1', Q_2 should change when Q_1 and Q_0 are both '1', and Q_3 should change when Q_2, Q_1 and Q_0 are all '1'. Thus

$J_0 = K_0 = $ '1'
$J_1 = K_1 = Q_0$
$J_2 = K_2 = Q_1.Q_0$
$J_3 = K_3 = Q_2.Q_1.Q_0$

The circuits described above can count up, but circuits are also available which can count down (or do either).

6.3 Shift registers

Another synchronous circuit is a shift register, as shown in figure 6.9, where the D of each flip flop is connected to the Q of the previous flip flop. On each rising edge of the clock signal, the Q outputs are thus shifted to the right, with the value of the serial input being passed to Q_0.

There are various forms of shift register. The above is a serial in parallel out (SIPO) device, that is, data are loaded in one bit at a time (serially), and

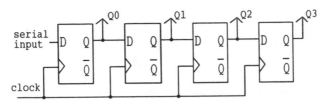

Figure 6.9 4-bit shift register

all four outputs can be accessed together (in parallel). With some shift registers it is also possible to load each flip flop directly (either asynchronously by setting pr and clr, or synchronously by setting the D input), so parallel in shift registers are possible. Also available are shift registers where the only available output is the Q of the last flip flop, that is, the output is serial. Thus there are SIPO, SISO, PISO and PIPO devices. Shift registers with synchronous and asynchronous clear signals are also available. Some devices can be shifted left or right, or even both (though not at the same time).

These are obviously useful circuits with various applications. Sometimes computers communicate with printers or other computers by sending data serially, that is, one bit at a time. As in general the computer sends data in parallel internally, the data must be converted from parallel to serial if the data are to be sent serially. A PISO device will achieve this. As regards receiving the data, a serial stream must be converted to parallel; a SIPO shift register will provide this. Peripheral devices are available which contain such shift registers. More is said about these devices in chapter 10.

Another use of shift registers is to provide pseudo random numbers. Many applications require random data, that is, one value is generated, then another, and so on, with no immediately obvious correlation between the numbers. One method of achieving this is to use a *feedback shift register*; the circuit for a 4-bit device is shown in figure 6.10. This is a shift register with certain of its outputs fed back, that is, exclusively-orred together and fed into the serial input. Assuming that the outputs are initially 0001, say, the outputs will change after each clock in a pseudo-random sequence, as follows: 0001 1000 1100 1110 1111 0111 1011 0101 1010 1101 0110 0011 1001 0100 0010 and then it repeats. Thus the first time the register has 1, then it has 8, then 12, and so on. In fact all the numbers from 1 to 15 are generated by the circuit, but not zero. An 8-bit shift register can generate all the numbers from 1 to 255 if suitable bits are fed back, and a 16-bit register can generate all numbers in the range 1 to 65535. If a large shift register is used, then many operations are required before the sequence repeats, which makes the system useful for generating random numbers. Selecting which bits to feed back is important, as is explained in Peterson. These circuits are sometimes called *chain code* generators.

Another use of shift registers is to delay a signal. If the signal is fed into the serial input of a shift register, it will appear at the Q outputs some time later: at Q_0 after the next rising clock edge, at Q_1 one clock cycle later. An application of this is given in the chapters on interfacing.

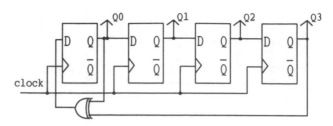

Figure 6.10 Feedback shift register

6.4 Synchronous sequential logic circuits

Shift registers and synchronous counters are specific examples of synchronous sequential logic circuits: they are devices whose outputs can change on the edge of a clock signal, and these outputs are determined by the input to the circuit and the values of the outputs before (outputs which have been fed back). A general block diagram of such circuits is shown in figure 6.11. The inputs and fed back outputs are processed by a combinational logic circuit, whose outputs are passed to the D inputs of an edge-triggered latch, and on the appropriate edge of the clock, each D input is passed to its corresponding output. Some PLAs contain latches as well as the normal combinational logic elements, so a complete circuit can be put into a PLA.

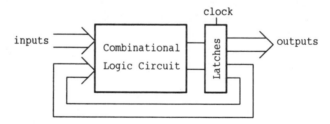

Fgure 6.11 General synchronous sequential logic circuit

In general, to design such a circuit, a suitable combinational logic circuit is required. If the appropriate truth table and boolean expressions can be formed, this is straightforward. However, producing these may not be easy, so in general, more complex techniques are needed, which are beyond the scope of this book. More details can be found in Lewin and Protheroe and in Mitchell.

In microprocessor systems, one application of this type of circuit is in the arithmetic and logic unit. This is passed, say, two sets of data to be processed (added or anded, for example), suitable logic operations are performed on the data by a combinational logic circuit, and the result is then stored in a latch.

Summary

This chapter has demonstrated how logic gates can be connected to produce memory elements, including transparent, master–slave and edge-triggered devices and D-type and JK flip flops. It is then shown how such devices can be used to produce more complex circuits, including various forms of counters and shift registers.

Exercises

1. Design a synchronous up/down 3-bit counter with D-type flip flops; an extra input should determine whether the counter will count up or down.

2. Modify the counter so that it has a synchronous clear.

3. Modify the circuit so that it can load data synchronously. This requires 4 data inputs, one for each flip flop, and a load signal: when the load input is low, each data input sets the corresponding Q output on the next falling clock edge. The synchronous clear signal should override this.

4. Design a 3-bit synchronous Gray code counter.

References

B.R. Bannister & D.G. Whitehead *Fundamentals of Modern Digital Systems* 2nd Edn, Macmillan Press 1987.

D. Lewin & D. Protheroe *Design of Logic Systems* Chapman & Hall, 1992.

R.J. Mitchell *Microcomputer Systems Using the STE Bus* Macmillan Press, 1989.

W.W. Peterson *Error Correcting Codes* Wiley, 1961.

7 How Computers Process Data

Computers process information by performing logical operations on binary data. Such operations are performed by logic circuits, as described in the last two chapters. This chapter considers how such circuits can be used in the processing of various arithmetic and logical functions, functions which are performed in the arithmetic and logic unit inside the central processing unit.

7.1 Multi-bit addition

One bit can represent one of two values, say the numbers 0 and 1; many bits can be combined to represent many more numbers, for example, one byte, that is 8-bits, can represent 256 values, say the numbers 0 to 255, where bit r is '1' if the number contains a component 2^r. This was explained in detail in section 4.2. The next stage is to consider how two bytes are added.

When two decimal numbers are added, the two values in the unit's column are added and a result for that column produced with a possible carry to the ten's column. The two digits in the ten's column are then added with the carry from the unit's column if there was one, and so on. That is, the two digits from each column are added with any carry from the previous column producing the sum for that column and a carry to be passed to the next stage. The same concept is used for adding binary digits.

A circuit is thus required which adds two binary digits and any carry from the previous stage, producing a sum value and a carry. Such a circuit is called a full adder and a circuit implementing a full adder was given in section 5.3.

Figure 7.1 shows how eight such full adder circuits are used to add two bytes; each full adder adds bit r of byte a, a_r, bit r of byte b, b_r, and the carry from the previous stage; the result is bit r of the byte sum, sum_r, together with a carry to the next stage. Note that the carry to the first stage is given the value '0'. The eight full adder circuit takes two bytes and a carry input and generates a byte containing the sum of the inputs and a carry output.

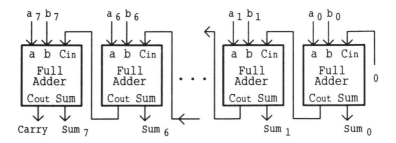

Figure 7.1 Circuit to add two bytes

One point to note in the circuit adding two bytes is the carry from the last stage. This will be '1' if the sum of the two numbers being added is too large. For example, if a and b are both 128, the answer should be 256, but a byte can only represent the numbers 0 to 255. In this case, the sum byte is 0, and there is a carry from the full adder from bit 7 which indicates that there is an error. If, however, 64 and 128 were added, the answer is 192, which is correct, and there is no such carry.

The above states there is an error when 128 and 128 are added. This perhaps is the wrong word as it does not mean that the calculation is performed incorrectly; the logic circuit operates correctly. The problem occurs in our interpretation of the operation; we require the answer to be 256, not 0. A check can be made if there is such an error, by testing to see if there is a carry from the full adder from bit 7; most microprocessors have a carry flag which stores this value, and this can be tested by a program.

In the descriptions of other arithmetic operations below, the word error is used in this context, not meaning that the logic circuits are wrong, just meaning that our interpretation of the result implies that the answer is wrong.

The above shows how two bytes are added. The process can be extended easily if 16-bit or 32-bit numbers are added; more full adders are required. If, however, a machine has the circuitry to add only 8-bit numbers and two 16-bit numbers are to be added, then the least significant bytes of both numbers are added, and then the most significant bytes of both numbers are added together with any carry from the addition of the least significant two bytes. Note, the least significant bytes are added in one operation, the most significant bytes are added in a subsequent operation.

This is illustrated in figure 7.2 where the two binary numbers 0111001111000110 and 0100110110011101 are added; the right hand side of the figure shows the addition of the least significant bytes (11000110 and 10011101), with the generation of the result (01100011) and a carry which is stored in the carry flag; the right hand side of the figure shows the addition of the most significant bytes (01110011 and 01001101) and the carry from the previous addition, generating the result (11000000) and (in this case) no carry, so the carry flag is cleared. If the carry flag was set after the addition of the most significant bytes, then the result of the calculation would be in error.

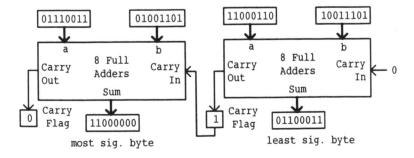

Figure 7.2 Addition of 16-bit numbers

7.2 Two's complement numbers

Although many problems require only positive numbers, frequently numbers which can be positive or negative are needed. The two's complement notation is usually used to represent these signed numbers, although other methods are possible (see Bartee). In two's complement notation, a byte represents integers in the range −128 to 127, 16 bits represent the numbers −32768 to 32767 and 32-bits the numbers −2147483648 to 2147483647. In general n bits can take values in the range -2^{n-1} to 2^{n-1}-1. Again, the processing of bytes only will be described here, but the concepts can be extended easily for other sizes.

The positive range, 0 to 127, is achieved by the same patterns used for positive only numbers, that is bit 7 is '0', and each of the other r bits is set if the number has the component 2^r. However, if bit 7 is '1', the byte represents a negative number. One process by which a positive number is converted to its equivalent negative number (and also for converting from negative to positive) is to invert all the bits (the so-called *one's complement*), and to then add 1 (hence *two's complement*!). For example, consider the following which shows the stages of conversion:

1	=	00000001	->	11111110	->	11111111	=	−1
−1	=	11111111	->	00000000	->	00000001	=	1
49	=	00110001	->	11001110	->	11001111	=	−49
127	=	01111111	->	10000000	->	10000001	=	−127

As regards adding such numbers, the process used for adding positive only numbers is still used; the corresponding bits from each byte and the carry from the previous stage are all added together. Consider adding −1 and + 1:

11111111	: −1
00000001	: 1
00000000	: 0

The answer is 0, as is required. Note, however, that there is a carry from the addition of the most significant bits. In the case of adding positive only numbers, this would indicate an error, as 255 + 1 = 256 which is out of the range for 8-bit numbers. Here −1 + 1 = 0, which is correct. Thus the presence of a carry does not indicate an error when adding signed numbers. To find an indicator of an error more examples are needed. First, consider adding 3 to 126:

01111110	: 126
00000011	: 3
10000001	: −127

If positive only numbers are added then the answer is 129, but if the binary values represent two's complement numbers the answer is −127, which is clearly wrong. Here, there is no carry from the most significant bit. Next consider adding −3 to −126:

11111101	: −3
10000010	: −126
01111111	: 127

The answer is 127, which is wrong, and in this case there is a carry from the most significant bit. Finally, consider adding −2 to +1:

11111110	: −2
00000001	: 1
11111111	: −1

Here the answer is −1, and there is no carry. These four examples illustrate the conditions where an error occurs and where there is no error. Careful scrutiny of these examples shows the following:

The sum	Carry from bit 6	Carry from bit 7
-1 + 1	1	1
3 + 126	1	0
-3 + -126	0	1
-2 + 1	0	0

Thus an error occurs when the carries from the most significant bit and the second most significant bit are different. This is often called an overflow.

Most computers have a carry flag and an overflow flag, the first being determined by the carry from the most significant bit, the second by whether there was an overflow. The user of the computer tests the carry flag to detect an error if positive only numbers are being summed, and the overflow flag if two's complement numbers are added. Thus the computer hardware does not 'know' whether it is processing positive only numbers or signed numbers, the interpretation of the data and the results is done by the user of the computer.

Note, if −128 is inverted (or negated):

−128 = 10000000   -> 01111111   -> 10000000   = −128

The answer is incorrect, as − −128 should not be −128. However, in this process, there is an overflow, as the carry from bit 7 is '0', but that from bit 6 is '1', and so the error is detectable.

7.3 Offset binary coding

An alternative method of handling signed numbers is to use offset binary codes. For a byte, the lowest value in the range is the binary value 00000000, and the highest value is 11111111. Thus if bytes are to represent numbers in the range −128 to 127, 00000000 is used to represent −128, and 11111111 represents 127: 10000000 represents 0.

Although this method is not normally used for representing numbers, possibly because it is more logical for 00000000 to be 0, the code is often used by analog-to-digital converters and digital-to-analog converters: the lowest analog voltage (say −5 V) is encoded as 00000000, the middle voltage (0 V) is 10000000 and the highest voltage (4.96 V) is 11111111. The reason that the highest voltage is 4.96 V not 5 V is that there are 128 combinations of bits representing voltages less than 0 V, but only 127 combinations for voltages greater than 0 V; 4.96 is (5 × 127) / 128.

7.4 Subtraction

Subtraction can be achieved by full subtracter blocks, derived in much the same way as the full adders used for addition. This requires extra circuitry, so many computers use the adder circuit with only a slight extension.

Subtracting byte b from byte a can be achieved by adding –b to a. The negative of a number is achieved by inverting all its bits and adding 1. Thus, to subtract b from a, each bit in b should be inverted and passed to the adder with each bit from a, and the extra 1 is added by setting the carry bit of the first stage, whereas the carry into the first stage is a 0 when adding data. A circuit to perform subtraction is shown in figure 7.3.

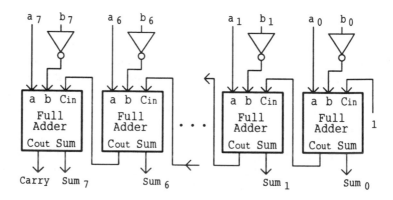

Figure 7.3 Circuit to subtract one byte from another

As an example, consider subtracting 1 from 4. 1 = 00000001; the one's complement of 1 is thus 11111110; 4 is 00000100. Thus 4 – 1 is achieved by:

$$
\begin{array}{lll}
 & 00000100 & = 4 \\
 & 11111110 & = \text{One's complement of 1} \\
+ & 00000001 & = \text{the carry} \\
\hline
 & 00000011 & = 3
\end{array}
$$

7.5 Logical operations

The microprocessor can also perform the logical operations on two data bytes. The functions provided are AND, OR and XOR (exclusive-or). Each of these operations processes each bit of one byte and the corresponding bit in the other byte. The examples below show the three functions (AND, OR and XOR respectively) processing two bytes.

$$
\begin{array}{ccc}
\ 10110001 & \ 10110001 & \ 10110001 \\
.\ 01101101 & +\ 01101101 & \oplus\ 01101101 \\
\hline
\ 00100001 & \ 11111101 & \ 11011100
\end{array}
$$

7.6   Shifting

Another operation provided in most microprocessors is to shift data, that is, to move all the bits in a byte to the left or to the right. These represent the operations of multiplying or dividing by two. Consider shifting left; the following examples show the original number, its binary representation, this binary number shifted and its equivalent decimal number.

3	=	00000011	->	00000110	= 6
64	=	01000000	->	10000000	= 128 (or −128 if signed)
128	=	10000000	->	00000000	= 0
−5	=	11111011	->	11110110	= −10

Clearly shifting left has resulted in values being multiplied by 2. As regards the detection of errors, if the value being shifted from each bit is thought of as the carry from that bit, then the carry flag will have been set when 128 is shifted, and the overflow flag set when 64 was shifted. Again, if positive only numbers are processed, the carry flag should be checked, otherwise the overflow flag indicates if there is an error. Shift left is shown in figure 7.4.

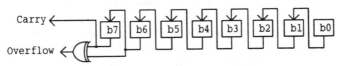

Figure 7.4 Shift left

In the figure, each box represents one bit of a byte, the line going into the box is the new value to be loaded there, the line coming out is the value of that byte. In practice, each box could be an edge-triggered D-type flip flop, the output from one flip flop being the D input to the next. Note, the output from bit 7 would be stored into the carry flag, the outputs of bits 6 and 7 are exclusive-orred and stored in the overflow flag.

The following examples show shift right:

3	=	00000011	->	00000001	= 1
64	=	01000000	->	00100000	= 32
128	=	10000000	->	01000000	= 64
−5	=	11111011	->	01111101	= 125

In general, shifting right has divided the numbers by 2 given the constraints of being able to represent integers only (so 3 becomes 1, although the carry flag contains the 'lost' half). The process is shown in figure 7.5. Note that the carry flag is set by the value from bit 0, not from bit 7.

Figure 7.5 Logical shift right

There is a problem, though, when negative numbers are shifted, as shown by the last example, where −5 divided by 2 is 125! Therefore, many computers provide two forms of shift right, logical shift, as shown above where '0' is shifted into the most significant bit, and arithmetic shift right, where the value of the top bit is unchanged and the other bits are shifted as normal, as shown in figure 7.6.

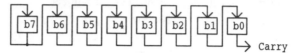

Figure 7.6 Arithmetic shift right

The following are examples of arithmetic shift right:

$$
\begin{array}{rcllcl}
-128 &=& 10000000 &\rightarrow& 11000000 &= -64 \\
-3 &=& 11111101 &\rightarrow& 11111110 &= -2 \\
3 &=& 00000011 &\rightarrow& 00000001 &= 1
\end{array}
$$

Thus, if the number being processed is positive only, then the logical shift right should be used, but if a two's complement number is processed, then the arithmetic shift right should be used.

The last two examples pose an interesting point. −3 shifted right = −2, whereas 3 shifted right = 1. This shows an imbalance of the two's complement notation. Similarly, 1 shifted right = 0, whereas −1 shifted right is −1. This last example presented a problem to the author who implemented an algorithm which continually divided a number by 2 until it reached 0, and used the shift right operation for the purpose; when the number was negative, the program did not terminate.

The solution to this imbalance, which is not provided for by any micro-processor known to the author, is to add 1 to the number if it is negative, before doing the shift right. For example

$$
\begin{array}{rcllcllcl}
-3 &=& 11111101 &\rightarrow& 11111110 &\rightarrow& 11111111 &= -1 \\
-1 &=& 11111111 &\rightarrow& 00000000 &\rightarrow& 00000000 &= 0 \\
3 &=& 00000011 &\rightarrow& 00000001 & & &= 1
\end{array}
$$

This technique is justified in Mitchell and Minchinton (1989).

7.7 Multiplication

Multiplication can be achieved in a manner analogous to long multiplication of decimal numbers. For example, if 125 and 25 are multiplied, the answer is the sum of 5 × 125 and 2 × (125 shifted left). For binary numbers, the multiplier contains 0's and 1's by which the multiplicand is to be multiplied, and multiplying by 0 or 1 is easy. Thus the answer consists of the sum of various instances of the multiplicand shifted and being multiplied by 0 or 1; when multiplied by 0, of course, the answer is 0, otherwise the answer is the shifted multiplicand. This process is best illustrated by the following example:

```
 25 = 00011001    the multiplicand
  5 = 00000101    the multiplier
      00011001    1 * multiplicand
 +    00000000    0 * multiplicand shifted left
 +    01100100    1 * multiplicand shifted left twice
 +    00000000    0 * multiplicand shifted left three times,
 +    00000000    0 * multiplicand shifted left four times,
etc.  _____
 =    01111101      = 125
```

Thus multiplication can be achieved by the following algorithm:

```
Set Answer to 0
REPEAT
   IF least significant bit of Multiplier is 1 THEN
      Add Multiplicand to Answer
   Shift Multiplicand to the Left
   Logical Shift Multiplier to the Right
UNTIL Multiplier is 0
```

The above algorithm works if the numbers being added are positive. To process signed numbers, both numbers should be converted first to their positive equivalent, they should then be multiplied using the above method, and then the result should be negated if only one of the original numbers was negative. Other algorithms for multiplying signed numbers are possible, notably Booth's algorithm; the interested reader should consult Booth.

One point to note is that if two bytes are being multiplied together, then the answer is in the range 0 to 65025, that is, the answer should be stored as a 16-bit value. In the course of operation of the above algorithm, the multiplicand should also occupy 16 bits.

7.8 Division

Division of binary integers can also be achieved by a process analogous to that used for handling decimal numbers. Consider the following in which 126 is divided by 25:

```
                101
         _____
11001 ) 1111110
        -11001          11001 will go, put 1 in total
         _____
         01101
        -00000          11001 wont go, put 0 in total
         _____
         11010
        -11001          11001 will go, put 1 in total
         _____
         00001
```

In this case the answer is 5, and the remainder is 1.

The following algorithm can be used to divide two positive numbers.

```
Set Counter to 1
WHILE most significant bit of Divisor is 0 DO
   Shift Divisor to Left
   Increment Counter
Set Answer to 0
WHILE Counter > 0 DO
   Shift Answer to Left
   IF Divisor <= Dividend THEN
      Subtract Divisor from Dividend
      Increment Answer
   Shift Divisor to Right
   Decrement Counter
The result is in Answer, the remainder is in Dividend
```

As with multiplication, the above works for positive only numbers, so signed numbers are converted to their positive equivalent first, the above used, and the answer negated if one of the divisor or dividend only was negative. Also, before the above is used, a check is made to see if the divisor is zero.

Thus multiplication and division can be achieved using shifts, adds and subtracts, all of which require many simple logic operations. However, more complex hardware is required to perform multiplication and division than for addition and subtraction. Thus it is likely that a computer will take longer to multiply than to add. Although most modern systems provide multiplication and division, many early systems did not, so these operations were achieved by the computer obeying many shift, add and subtract instructions.

7.9 Binary coded decimal

Humans use decimal numbers, computers use binary. Thus decimal numbers must be converted to binary for the computer to process them, and then the results converted back to decimal for the benefit of the human. An alternative is to use Binary Coded Decimal or BCD. Different BCD codes are used, the following describes 8-4-2-1 BCD in which each digit is stored in a 4-bit nibble.

A nibble can represent 16 different values, in the range 0 to 15, but in BCD, only the values 0 to 9 are allowed, that is the decimal values. Thus a byte can represent two BCD digits, and hence the numbers 0 to 99. Such bytes can be processed using extensions to the above techniques. Consider addition: if 32 and 47 were added using the circuitry described in section 7.1:

32	=	00110010
47	=	01000111
79	=	01111101

This is correct, but if 33 and 47 were added, the result would be:

```
33   = 00110011
47   = 01000111
7?   = 01111010
```

In this case, the least significant nibble contains a non-BCD digit. This is corrected by a post process, here adding 6 to the least significant nibble, thus

```
7?   = 01111010
06   = 00000110
80   = 10000000
```

Similarly, if 32 and 86 were added, the most significant nibble would be non-BCD, so 6 would have to be added to the most significant nibble:

```
32   = 00110010
86   = 10000110
?8   = 10111000
60   = 01100000
18   = 00011000
```

The answer should be 118, but as a byte can only represent BCD numbers from 0 to 99, the answer is 18, but the carry flag would indicate an error.

Note, the addition of BCD numbers with suitable post processing works only if the original data being added are correct BCD.

7.10 Scaled numbers

In the above it is stated that a byte can be used to represent the positive integers in the range 0 to 255. However, the user could also interpret the same byte as being every 10th integer from 0 to 2550, so that 00000101 represents 50. The computer will still process the data in the same way; it is up to the user to interpret the data in the appropriate manner.

Thus it is also possible for the user to interpret a byte as being every 256th fraction from 0 to 255/256. Thus bit r of the byte is a 1 if the number contains a component $2^r/256$. For example, 01110010 = 114/256, and 11111111 = 255/256 = 0.99609375. Similarly, a byte could be used to represent every 16th fraction from 0 to 255/16, that is 15.9375.

Such numbers can be processed by much the same techniques as those described above. For addition, subtraction and shifting the answers are correct, but some minor changes are needed for multiplication and division. For example, consider the case when 01000000 and 00100000 are multiplied, for which the 16-bit result is the binary number 0000010000000000.

If the bytes are representing the integers in the range 0 to 255, then the above is the product of 64 and 32, that is 2048. Thus the 16-bit result is correct. If, however, the bytes represent each 16th fraction of an integer, then the product is 64/16 × 32/16 = 8. Thus the answer 2048/16, that is, 128, is wrong. The correct answer can be found by dividing the result by 16. If the bytes represent each 256th, the product is 64/256 × 32/256 = 8/256. Thus the answer, 2048/256, that is, 8, is wrong. However, dividing the result by 256 produces the correct answer. Therefore, when scaled numbers are multiplied, the result must be scaled suitably to achieve the correct result. Scaling is also required when dividing scaled numbers.

The above numbers are termed fixed point, because for all such data the position of the 'binary' point is fixed (binary point is the term used here for binary numbers, being the equivalent of decimal point used for decimal numbers). For integers, the binary point is at the end of the data, after bit 0. For the scaled numbers above, the point is put at one particular position; for example, when a byte represents so many 16ths, the binary point is (notionally) between bits 4 and 3. Another type of number used allows the decimal point to move depending on the data; these are called floating point numbers and are described in the next section.

It should be noted, of course, that the computer knows nothing about binary points; the human interprets the data so that there is a binary point in the appropriate place.

7.11 Floating point numbers

Although integers, and occasionally fractions, can be used in many applications, for some problems a mixture of integers and fractions is required, or numbers containing values in a much greater range are needed than is provided by even 32-bit integers. For these floating point numbers are used.

A floating point number consists of three parts, the sign, the mantissa and the exponent. The sign, which can be one bit, indicates if the number is positive or negative. The rest of the number is of the form:

mantissa $\times 2^{exponent}$

where the exponent is often a two's complement signed integer; and the mantissa is a fraction, defined by the range 0.5 <= mantissa < 1, which is often a fractional integer for which the most significant bit is always '1'. The exception to this is when the mantissa is 0 which occurs only when the number 0 is represented.

It should be noted that there are various recognised standard formats for floating point numbers; in the following a simple format is used. The following examples illustrate some floating point numbers using this format for which an 8-bit mantissa and an 8-bit exponent are assumed:

sign	mantissa	exponent	number	explanation
0	10100000	00000100	10	$16 \times 5/8$
0	11100000	00000010	3.5	$4 \times 7/8$
1	11000000	00000000	−0.75	− 3/4
0	10000011	00000001	1.0234375	
1	10000000	11111100	0.03125	-0.5×2^{-4}
0	10000000	00001010	512	$1024 \times 1/2$

Now consider the representation of 513; this is $1024 \times (1/2 + 1/1024)$. Thus the mantissa should be $1/2 + 1/1024$, but this cannot be achieved by an 8-bit value. Therefore the best attempt at representing 513 is 512! Thus, for an 8-bit exponent, although the range of numbers which can be represented is $+/-10^{-38}$ to $+/-10^{37}$, not all the numbers in that range can be uniquely specified. Thus it is normal for the mantissa to have more bits than the exponent. For example, a typical implementation may use 48 bits to store a floating point number, 1 bit for the sign, 8 for the exponent and 39 for the mantissa.

Note, as the top bit of the mantissa is always '1' and hence this is redundant information, in some implementations the top bit is omitted, so that all the bits of the mantissa contain useful data.

Processing of floating point numbers is more complicated than for handling integers, but can be achieved using combinations of the techniques used for processing integers, and thus can be implemented as a series of logical operations on binary data.

First consider adding two positive floating point numbers. $a \times 2^b + c \times 2^d$ is not directly evaluable, but $a \times 2^b + c \times 2^b$ is $(a + c) \times 2^b$. Therefore, to add two floating point numbers together, their exponents must be made the same. This is achieved by incrementing the smaller exponent (which multiplies the number by 2) and shifting its mantissa right (thus dividing the number by 2, and hence balancing the increment of the exponent) until both exponents are the same; then they can be added. For example, consider adding 5 and 56:

$56 = 11100000 \times 2^6$
$5 = 10100000 \times 2^3 = 00010100 \times 2^6$
So $5 + 56$ is $(11100000 + 00010100) \times 2^6 = 11110100 \times 2^6 = 61$.

In this case, the processing is quite straightforward, but sometimes the mantissa needs to be *normalised* after operation, to ensure that bit 7 of the mantissa is '1', or to deal with a carry. Consider the following, $61 + 5$:

$61 = 11110100 \times 2^6$
$5 = 10100000 \times 2^3 = 00010100 \times 2^6$
So $61 + 5 = (11110100 + 00010100) \times 2^6$

When 11110100 and 00010100 are added, the result is 00001000 and the carry flag is set. The carry is an important part of the result, it can be considered to be bit 8, and should be moved back into bit 7. Thus after the addition has occurred the mantissa should be shifted left and the state of the carry flag moved into bit 7. This division of the mantissa by 2 should be balanced by incrementing the exponent, so the result is $10000100 \times 2^7 = 66$.

Subtraction of two positive numbers is achieved in a similar manner to addition, except that the mantissa of the second is subtracted from, not added to, the first. Consider subtracting 27 from 49:

$49 = 11000100 \times 2^6$
$27 = 11011000 \times 2^5 = 01101100 \times 2^6$
So $49 - 27 = (11001000 - 01101100) \times 2^6 = 01011000 \times 2^6$

In this case, the top bit of the mantissa is not '1', thus normalisation is required and this is achieved by shifting the mantissa left and decrementing the exponent until the top bit of the mantissa is a '1'; thus the answer to the above becomes $10110000 \times 2^5 = 22$.

The above examples show how positive floating point numbers are added or subtracted. In general, the sign of the numbers must be taken into account, and so, for example, if a positive number is added to a negative number, the mantissa of the negative number should be subtracted from that of the positive number, or if a negative number is to be subtracted from a positive number, then their mantissae should be added.

As regards multiplication, $(a \times 2^b) \times (c \times 2^d) = (a \times c) \times 2^{c+d}$, so this is achieved by multiplying the mantissae, adding the exponents and then normalising; the sign of the result is the exclusive-or of the signs of the original data. Note, as both mantissae have values between 0.5 and 1.0, their product is in the range 0.25 to 1.0; thus in the normalisation process at maximum the mantissa will have to be shifted and the exponent decremented once only.

Division is also straightforward: $(a \times 2^b) / (c \times 2^d) = (a / c) \times 2^{c-d}$, so this is achieved by dividing the mantissa and subtracting one exponent from the other; the sign is also set by the exclusive-or of the signs of the numbers. Again, as both mantissae are in the range 0.5 to 1.0, their division is in the range 0.5 to 2, so normalisation consists of at maximum one shift of the mantissa and one increment or decrement of the exponent.

Computers also process numbers in many ways, such as returning the square root or the sine of a number. These functions can be achieved using the basic processing operations described here, provided that an appropriate algorithm is used. The techniques required, however, are beyond the scope of this book.

Thus floating point numbers can be processed using combinations of integer arithmetic and, as integers are processed using logical operations on binary data, all processing of numbers is achieved by a series of logical operations. Clearly, much more processing is required for handling floating point numbers than for handling integers; thus it is usually better to use integers if possible. Many computer systems, however, have special circuitry for performing floating point operations, which can greatly speed the operation of a program. This extra hardware is often called a floating point coprocessor.

Summary

This chapter has demonstrated that a computer just performs logical operations on binary data, and that the interpretation of the data is done by the human not the computer. The description has shown how positive only and signed integers are represented and processed, as well as floating point numbers. The operations on floating point numbers are more complicated than those on integers, hence it is best, whenever possible, to use integers.

Exercises

1. Evaluate the following integer expressions in binary:
   a) 27 + 59 b) −28 − 56   c)   65 × 7   d) 121 / 7

2. Define the algorithms for adding, subtracting, multiplying and dividing two floating point numbers, in the manner used above to describe integer division.

3. Figure 7.1 shows a circuit for adding two bytes, containing eight full adder circuits. In general, a computer needs to be able to add, subtract, and, or and exclusive-or two data items. Design a circuit, to replace the full adder, which provides these five functions as selected by the following three signals:

M2	M1	M0	Action
0	0	0	Add
0	0	1	Subtract
0	1	x	And
1	0	x	Or
1	1	x	Ex-Or

Show how eight such circuits can be connected together to process two bytes, and include circuits to report if the answer is zero, and whether there is carry or overflow when the bytes are added or subtracted.

4. Consider the following additions in BCD arithmetic:

```
     34              49
  +  57           +  38
     --              --
     8B              81
```

In both cases, the least significant nibble of the data must be adjusted, that is, 6 must be added, to get the correct answer, namely 91 and 87.

In the first case, the nibble contains a non-BCD digit, and in the second case there was a carry from bit 3 in the addition (the so called half-carry). Design a logic circuit which takes suitable signals from the circuit answering question 3 to report whether the answer should be adjusted.

References

T.C. Bartee *Digital Computer Fundamentals* McGraw-Hill, 1981.

A.D. Booth (1951) *A signed binary multiplication technique* Q.J. Mech Appl. Math, 4(2) pp236-40.

R.J. Mitchell and P.R. Minchinton (1989) *A note on dividing integers by two* The Computer Journal, 32, No 4, p380.

8 *Microprocessors and Logic*

Microprocessors process information by performing logical operations on binary data, and these data are stored in logic circuits both within the microprocessor itself and in external devices. The previous three chapters have described logic circuits and shown how logic operations are used to process data. The purpose of this chapter is to consider the structure of the microprocessor itself, its logic circuits and its operation. These basic concepts are explained using a simple imaginary microprocessor as an example, and then the 68020 and 8051 microprocessors are introduced.

8.1 System structure

First, a reminder is given of the structure of a computer, namely that a computer consists of a central processing unit (CPU), memory and input/output devices connected together along a bus. This is shown in figure 8.1.

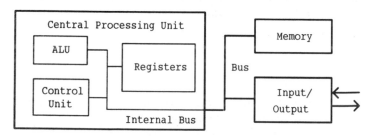

Figure 8.1 Structure of a computer system

The CPU, which is often a microprocessor, coordinates the actions of the complete system. It reads instructions from memory and executes them, often performing logical operations on binary data. Inside the CPU there are an arithmetic and logic unit (ALU) which performs the processing operations, registers which are used to store some data, and a control unit which controls the action.

There are various types of register; data registers store data, address registers usually store addresses and the status register contains information about the state of the machine. On most microprocessors the latter contains various flags indicating the state resulting from the last operation. The flags usually found are zero, which is set (it is '1') if the result of the last operation was zero; carry, indicating if there was a carry; overflow, showing if the last operation overflowed; sign, which reports if the answer was positive or negative; and half carry, which is used for BCD arithmetic. These flags are set or cleared as a result of the execution of instructions.

80

The CPU normally contains at least two special address registers, the program counter, PC, and the stack pointer, SP. The PC contains the address in memory of the next instruction, and the SP contains the address of part of the memory called the stack which is used for storing information temporarily.

Memory is used for storing both the data being processed and the program, and the input/output devices allow the computer to communicate with the outside world.

The basic operation of the computer is to transfer information between the CPU and the memory and peripherals, and to process that information. The transfers occur along the bus. One such information transfer occurs when the computer is to find out its next instruction; here the CPU arranges to read the instruction from memory. This is achieved using an instruction fetch cycle.

8.2 Instruction fetch

A microprocessor reads instructions from memory and executes them. This is achieved by the so-called fetch and execute cycle; first the instruction is fetched, then it is decoded and executed. The first stage is the fetch cycle.

A program consists of a series of instructions which are stored in order in memory, that is, the first instruction is followed by the second, and so on. It may be possible to read one complete instruction at one time, for example an 8-bit microprocessor, which can only read 8 bits of data, may have instructions which are only 8 bits long. However, it is often the case that the instruction consists of many parts, so these will have to be read by a series of read operations. For most microprocessors, the length of an instruction will vary depending on the instruction.

The address of the next instruction is stored in the program counter (PC). Therefore the process whereby an instruction is fetched is as follows:

```
REPEAT
    The CPU puts the contents of the PC onto the address bus
    The CPU specifies that data at that memory address
        are to be read
    The Memory puts the data on to the data bus
    The CPU reads the value from the data bus and stores it
        suitably within the CPU
    The CPU increments the contents of the PC
UNTIL the whole instruction has been read
```

The contents of the PC are incremented so that the PC contains the address of the next part of the instruction or, when the complete instruction has been read, the PC contains the address of the next instruction.

The control unit causes the instruction to be fetched and monitors each part of the instruction as it is fetched. An important part of this monitoring process is to determine when the complete instruction has been fetched. It is in this way that the machine knows when the whole instruction has been read.

8.3   Instruction types

The fetched instruction must now be executed, but before this is described it is necessary to consider the types of instruction provided within microprocessors. In this section, therefore, a brief overview is given of the main types of instruction; more details are given in chapter 12.

First there are the data transfer instructions, which transfer data from one part of the system to another. A typical instruction would, for example, load a register with data from a memory location, a peripheral or another register; or the contents of a register may be stored into a memory location or peripheral.

The second type are the data processing instructions, which use the arithmetic and logic unit to perform arithmetic, logical or shifting operations on data. On many microprocessors, such an instruction typically takes data from a register and often some other data, processes these, and then returns the result to the register and sets the flags in the status register appropriately. For example, the contents of a register might be added to some other data; or the logical OR function might be applied to the data in the register and the other data; or the contents of the register might be shifted left arithmetically.

The third type are the branching instructions which allow the implementation of conditional operations, a program to execute certain instructions many times and for subroutines or procedures to be executed; these will now be explained in more detail, remembering that a program consists of a series of instructions at successive locations.

Normally the next instruction to be obeyed is the one following the current one. However, a branch or jump instruction arranges that the next instruction to be obeyed is at a different location; the microprocessor 'jumps' to this other location. This can be used to allow the microprocessor to obey a series of instructions many times by following these instructions with a jump back to the first instruction; this is illustrated in figure 8.2a.

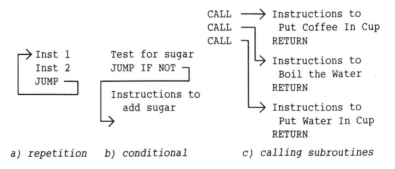

a) repetition   b) conditional   c) calling subroutines

Figure 8.2 Illustration of various branch instructions

A second type of branch instruction is the conditional branch; here the microprocessor jumps to a different location if a particular condition is true, such a condition being determined by the state of specified flags. Recalling the coffee making robot example in chapter 2, sugar is to be added only if required; thus a test is made to see if sugar is not required (using a suitable arithmetic or logic instruction) and if so the microprocessor should jump past the instructions which cause sugar to be added; this is shown in figure 8.2b.

The third type of branch instruction is one which causes a jump to a different location, but the microprocessor remembers where it jumped from so that it can subsequently return to obey the instruction following the jump; this type of instruction is often named a 'call' to a subroutine, where a subroutine is a series of instructions which are terminated by a 'return' instruction. Again recalling the robot coffee maker, three actions are required, to pour the coffee in the cup, to boil the water and then to pour the boiling water into the cup, and these actions are encoded in three separate subroutines. Thus the program should call the subroutine 'Pour coffee in cup', then call the subroutine 'Boil water' and finally call the subroutine 'Pour boiling water in cup'. This is shown in figure 8.2c.

8.4 Instruction execution

This section considers the execution of some of the different types of instructions described above using examples for an imaginary simple microprocessor. It is assumed that the microprocessor has a data register, DREG, an address register, AREG, a flag register, FREG, the program counter, PC, and the stack pointer, SP.

The first example is the instruction *LOAD DREG with 56*; this will put the number 56 into the DREG register. When the complete instruction has been fetched, the microprocessor will have read all the bytes which form the instruction and stored them internally in some temporary storage circuit; thus the instruction type (LOAD DREG with data) and the data to be loaded (56) will be in the microprocessor. Therefore the execution of the instruction is simply to move the data from the temporary store to DREG.

The second example is the instruction *LOAD DREG from address 56*; this will cause the contents of memory address 56 to be read and the value found there to be put into DREG. Again, the microprocessor will have stored the instruction type (LOAD DREG with data from an address) and the address (56). The execution of the instruction is in two stages; first the data from the address are read and then these are stored in DREG. Thus the microprocessor will instigate a data transfer from address 56, in a manner similar to that used to read an instruction, namely the address will be put on the address bus, the microprocessor will indicate that it wants to read data, and the memory will then put the data on to the bus; the received data will then be stored in DREG.

The third example is *LOAD DREG from address found in AREG*; that is, to load DREG with the data which is to be found at the address which is currently stored in AREG (if AREG contains 56, DREG will be loaded with the data at address 56). When executing this instruction, the microprocessor transfers the contents of AREG on to the address bus, specifies that it wants to read the data at that address and, when the memory has put the data at that address on to the bus, the data are stored in DREG.

The next example is *STORE DREG into address 56*, that is, to take the data in DREG and to write them into the memory at location 56. Again the instruction type and the address will have been fetched and stored in the temporary store in the microprocessor. The execution of the instruction is to put the address (56) on to the address bus, to transfer the data from DREG on to the data bus, and to specify that data are to be written; the memory will then take the data from the data bus and store them suitably.

Next consider the instruction *ADD DREG with 56*; that is, to add 56 to the contents of DREG and to store the result in DREG; the flag register will also be set appropriately. The instruction and its data will have been fetched, so the action of the instruction is to transfer the contents of DREG and the number 56 to the ALU, for the ALU to add them together and to generate the states of the flags, for the result of the addition to be transferred into DREG and for the states of the flags to be transferred into the flag register, FREG.

The sixth example is *OR DREG with data at address in AREG*; that is, to perform the logical OR function on the data in DREG and the data in memory at the address found in AREG, to store the result in DREG and to set the flags appropriately. The execution of this instruction requires the data to be read from the memory whose address is in AREG (in the manner described above) and this value and the contents of DREG to be passed to the ALU; the result of the OR operation and the states of the flags are then generated by the ALU and these are passed to DREG and FREG.

The next example is *ARITHMETIC SHIFT RIGHT DREG*; that is, to shift the data in DREG to the right, storing the result back in DREG and setting the flags accordingly. The execution of this instruction consists of the data being transferred to the ALU, the data being shifted, the result being transferred back to DREG and the values of the flags to FREG.

The eighth example is *JUMP to address 56*; that is, to arrange that the next instruction to be obeyed is at address 56. The execution of this is merely to transfer the value 56 (stored temporarily in the microprocessor) into the program counter, PC.

The ninth example is *JUMP IF ZERO to address 56*; that is, if the result of the last instruction was zero, the PC is loaded with 56, otherwise no action is taken. The execution of this requires that the zero flag in the flag register is tested to see if the result of the last instruction was zero and if so the number 56 is transferred to the PC. If the result of the last instruction was not zero, no further action is taken in the execution of this instruction, so the microprocessor will fetch and then execute the instruction at the address following the conditional jump instruction.

The next example is to *CALL to address 56*; this requires the current contents of the PC to be saved suitably and then the PC loaded with the value 56. On most microprocessors, saving the PC is achieved using the stack, which is an area of consecutive memory locations whose address is stored in the stack pointer, SP; SP contains the address of, that is, it points to, the stack. On many microprocessors, saving data on the stack is achieved by decrementing the SP and then storing the data at the address contained in the SP. Figure 8.3a and 8.3b show the stack before and after the call instruction.

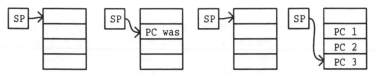

a) before call   b) after call   c) after return   d) after 3 calls

Figure 8.3 Illustration of uses of the stack

The final example is the *RETURN* instruction, which causes the microprocessor to return to the address which was saved by an earlier CALL instruction, that is, to the address which is stored in the stack. Thus the execution of the RETURN instruction is for the PC to be loaded with the data read from the address contained in the SP and then for the SP to be incremented. The state of the stack after the RETURN instruction is shown in figure 8.3c.

The reason why the SP is decremented at each CALL instruction is to allow a series of CALL instructions to be obeyed; each time the current value of the PC is stored at the next location in the stack, as shown in figure 8.3d. After each CALL, the SP points to memory containing the address of the instruction following that CALL instruction, so a RETURN instruction always causes the microprocessor to return to the instruction following the last CALL instruction.

The above examples illustrate the actions of a variety of instructions. Sometimes the complete data for the instruction will have been fetched by the fetch cycle; otherwise, a suitable data transfer is required to read or write data from memory. Sometimes the data are sent to the ALU for processing; if so the flag register may be loaded with suitable data, and the result transferred to a register. Sometimes the data fetched are transferred directly to a register.

8.5   Interrupts

Normally a microprocessor operates in the fashion described above, executing sequences of instructions and acting according to the data it processes. Sometimes, however, another device in the system can '*interrupt*' the microprocessor. Here the device issues an interrupt request, that is, it asserts a particular logic signal, when it wants to attract the attention of the microprocessor.

As an example, consider a microprocessor system with a keypad on which a user could press keys. The program on the microprocessor could continually test to see if a key had been pressed. Testing hardware in this way is called *polling*. The alternative is for the hardware to tell the computer when a key has been pressed, and this is achieved using *interrupts*.

Interrupts are straightforward, with their salient points illustrated by analogy. Suppose you are reading this book and the phone rings. You will probably finish the current sentence, mark the current position in the book and then answer the phone. At the end of the conversation, you will then return to the book and carry on reading from where you stopped.

On being interrupted, a microprocessor will finish the current instruction, remember the address of the next one (that is, it will save the program counter, usually on the stack), and then respond to the interrupt. This response is achieved by obeying a series of instructions appropriate to the interrupt; these instructions are in a small subroutine called an *interrupt service routine*. At the end of the service routine, the microprocessor returns to the program at the point where it was interrupted; this is achieved by reloading the program counter from the stack.

To continue the analogy; suppose you find this book so absorbing that you do not want to be disturbed. In this case you will ignore the phone. Similarly, a microprocessor can be set so that it ignores interrupts; they are said to be masked. Usually, in fact, interrupts are masked until they are specifically enabled. Instructions are provided to enable or disable interrupts.

However, the book will not be so absorbing that you would carry on reading in the event that your house caught on fire. Most microprocessors have a non-maskable interrupt (NMI) which is always serviced. A typical use of such is when the power supply is about to fail; it may be possible to store the contents of memory on to a disk or to some other non-volatile store.

For all these types of interrupt, the microprocessor saves the PC, loads the PC with the address of the service routine, obeys the routine and then returns to the program, by loading the PC with the value it had before the interrupt.

Interrupts can occur at any time, possibly when the microprocessor's registers contain important values. It is essential, therefore, that the service routine should not corrupt any register. Thus, at the start of the service routine, all registers used during the routine are saved, and they should be restored at the end of the routine. This is so important that some microprocessors automatically save registers when an interrupt occurs.

When an interrupt occurs, the microprocessor obeys the associated service routine; but where is the service routine? Various techniques are used by different microprocessors. These are given below.

The fixed address method; here the service routine for an interrupt is always at a given address. For example, on the 8051, the service routine for the interrupt associated with its serial port is always at address 3.

The look-up table method; here a table of addresses is used in which the address of each service routine is stored. For example, on the 68020, the service routine for the interrupt called when an attempt is made to divide by zero can be found at location 20 in the table.

The vector method; this is used when many devices are capable of issuing an interrupt, all of which assert the interrupt request signal. The problem is, which device issued the interrupt? To determine the requesting device, the microprocessor requests that the device outputs a number (called a vector), and this is used to index into a table of addresses of service routines. In this way the processor jumps to the service routine associated with the interrupting device. Again the 68020 allows vectored interrupts.

The instruction method; here the device which issues the interrupt is requested by the microprocessor to output an instruction which the processor then obeys. This can also be used when many devices are capable of issuing an interrupt. A typical instruction is to jump to a given location.

8.6 Microprocessor structure

The above descriptions allow more detailed consideration of the structure of the microprocessor. In this section, therefore, the components of an imaginary microprocessor are outlined, and the data paths are described by which data are transferred between these components. These components and the connections between them are described below, and are shown in figure 8.4.

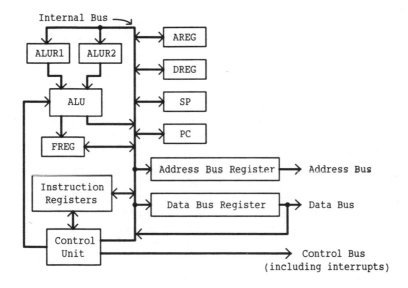

Figure 8.4 Components and data paths in a microprocessor

The connections are internal buses which allow many bits of data to be transferred between the internal components of the microprocessor, just as the main bus in a microprocessor system allows information to be transferred between the CPU, its memory and its input/output devices.

Many of the components are registers; these will often be edge-triggered devices, as were described in chapter 6. Other components, like the ALU, perform logical operations. Thus, the microprocessor contains many logic circuits.

First there are the main registers; AREG, DREG, FREG, PC and SP. These are the registers defined in the last section. Most microprocessors have at least one address register, such as AREG, and at least one data register, such as DREG, as well as a flag register, a program counter and a stack pointer. Information can be read from and written to these registers via the internal bus.

Next, there is the ALU, the arithmetic and logic unit, associated with which are two registers, ALUR1 and ALUR2; these are loaded with the data to be processed by the ALU. The outputs of the ALU are the result of the operation and the states of the flags. When the ALU is to be used to perform an arithmetic or logic operation like ADD or OR, the data to be processed are loaded via the internal bus into ALUR1 and ALUR2, then the ALU performs the appropriate operation, the result is then sent to an appropriate destination and the flag result is transferred to the flag register, FREG. For an operation like ARITHMETIC SHIFT RIGHT, only one data value is required, so the data are transferred into ALUR1 before being processed and ALUR2 is not used.

The Instruction Registers are used to store the instruction when it is fetched; this will include the instruction type as well as any address or data associated with the instruction.

The Address Bus Register and Data Bus Register are used to store information which is output on to the address and data buses. When data are to be written to memory, the appropriate address is stored in the Address Bus Latch and the data are transferred into the Data Bus Register and then on to the data bus.

Similarly, when an instruction is fetched, the contents of the PC are transferred to the Address Bus Register and so appear on the address bus; the data at that address are put by the memory on to the data bus, and so appear on the internal bus.

The Control Unit coordinates the actions of the microprocessor, causing instructions to be fetched, decoded and obeyed; in so doing it causes information to be transferred along the internal bus and to be stored in the registers. When data are to be transferred externally, the Control Unit also co-ordinates the control bus, thereby allowing data to be transferred between the microprocessor and its memory and input/output devices.

For example, the Control Unit causes the contents of the PC to be put on the address bus via the Address Bus Latch, the data at that address to be fetched and then stored in the Instruction Registers and the contents of the PC to be incremented.

When an instruction has been fetched, the Control Unit decodes the instruction and so determines suitable actions, such as those described in the previous section.

The above has described the structure and operation of a simple imaginary processor; this was chosen to illustrate the principles of operation, without getting into the details of actual microprocessors. However, one aim of this book is to describe two 'real' devices, so the next two sections introduce these microprocessors, the Intel 8051 and the Motorola 68020. Readers not interested in either of these devices can skip the appropriate sections.

8.7 Structure of the 8051

The 8051 is one of a family of microcontrollers, the MCS-51 series. Each device contains the microprocessor itself as well as some memory and peripherals. The following briefly describes the family.

The 8051 has 4K bytes of read only memory (ROM), 128 bytes of read/write memory (RAM), registers, 32 input/output lines, two 16-bit counters (also called timers), interrupt handling capability, a serial communications device and circuitry which allows the connection of extra devices. The 8052 is similar, but having 8K of ROM and 256 bytes of RAM and an extra timer. The ROM for both devices contains the program that the device obeys; this ROM can be programmed once only. The 8051 is thus suited to dedicated applications. The 8751 version has erasable programmable read only memory; that is, the contents of the ROM can be erased and new programs written there. The 8031 version does not have any on-board ROM, an external ROM is required; it is suitable for situations where the device may be used for different applications, or where a relatively large program is required.

Figure 8.5 shows a basic block diagram of the 8051, depicting its ALU, registers, ROM, RAM and control unit, all connected via an internal bus. The 32 I/O lines are four 8-bit ports, P0..P3; data are passed to these from the internal bus via suitable driver circuitry. Some of these ports, together with other control signals, are used to connect extra memory and peripherals to the 8051; for example, P0 and P2 can be used to generate the external address and data buses. The block marked registers also contains the circuitry for handling the timers, interrupts and the serial communications device.

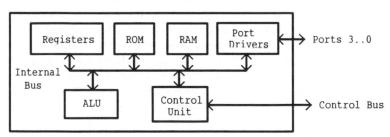

Figure 8.5 Block diagram of the 8051

The main registers are shown in figure 8.6. ACC is the 8-bit accumulator, a data register; arithmetic and logic operations typically take data from ACC and some other source, process them and store the result back in ACC. The B register is another 8-bit register which is used for storing data. The PC is the 16-bit program counter; this contains the address of the next instruction which could be in the internal ROM or external memory. SP is the 8-bit stack pointer; it contains the address of the stack within the internal RAM. As this RAM contains at most 256 locations, an 8-bit stack pointer is sufficient. DPTR is a 16-bit address register; its high and low bytes are accessible separately, being referred to as DPH and DPL.

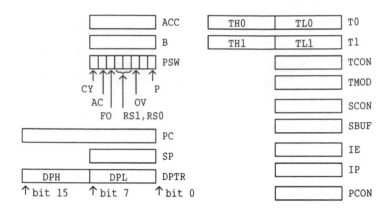

Figure 8.6 Registers in the 8051

PSW is the program status word register, namely the status or flag register. The bits in the PSW are CY, the carry flag; AC, auxiliary carry which is used in BCD arithmetic; FO, a user flag, which can be controlled and tested by the user program; OV, the overflow flag; P, the parity flag which reports if the result has an even number of logic 1's; and RS1 and RS0 select register banks (as is explained below).

In addition, the ports are also considered to be registers; programs can read from or write to each port individually. The two timers, T0 and T1, are 16-bit counters the bytes of which are accessible as registers TH0, TL0, TH1 and TL1. TCON and TMOD are two registers which control the operation of the counters. SCON and SBUF are registers associated with serial communications, IE and IP are registers used for handling interrupts, and PCON is concerned with controlling the power of the device. Full details are given in appendix 2.

The internal RAM is divided as shown in figure 8.7. The lower 32 bytes are four banks of registers; each bank being labelled R0..R7. At any time one of these banks is active, and its eight registers can be used by programs. The two bits in the PSW, RS1 and RS0, specify which bank is selected. The next 32 bytes are RAM which can be accessed as whole bytes or each bit can be accessed individually. The next 64 bytes can be used for normal storage or the stack. Thus the RAM contains 128 locations. The addresses from 128 to 255 are the locations of the registers; for example, the value of DPH can be found by reading from address 131. Many of these registers can be accessed as whole bytes or as individual bits within each byte.

Figure 8.8 shows (in a simplified form) the components and data paths within the 8051. Associated with each port are driver circuitry, which ensures that signals outside the 8051 have sufficient power, and a latch which is used to store values input or output through the port.

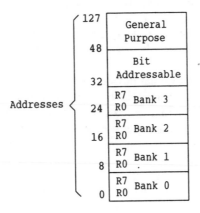

Figure 8.7 RAM in the 8051

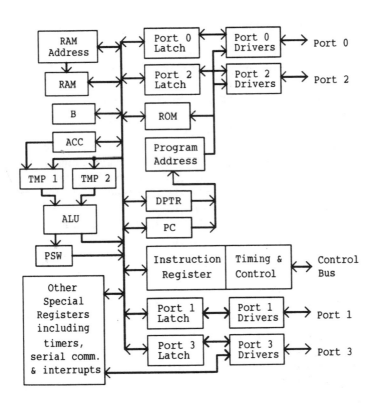

Figure 8.8 Components and data paths in the 8051

Associated with the ALU are two temporary registers which are loaded with the data to be processed by the ALU. The result is passed via the internal bus back to the ACC and the flags sent directly to the PSW.

The instruction register is used to store each instruction, and this is processed by the timing and control circuit which co-ordinates operation of the microcontroller and its external devices via the control bus and ports.

The PC and DPTR registers can be used to provide the address of locations in the ROM, either internal or external. Thus the output of one of these registers is passed to the program address register and hence to either the internal ROM or to the ports to be put on the external address bus.

Addresses for the RAM are only 8-bit, and these are passed via the internal bus to the RAM address register and hence to the address lines of the RAM. Data are passed to and from the RAM via the internal bus.

The block marked 'other special registers' contains the remaining registers and associated circuitry. These are accessible via the internal bus, but they are also directly connected to the driver circuitry of port 3, because, for example, the serial communications device uses two bits of port 3.

8.8 Structure of the 68020

The 68020 is a 32-bit general purpose microprocessor, having on-board registers but no other general purpose memory or peripherals. It is, however, a very sophisticated and powerful device. Again, the 68020 is one of a family of devices; the first being the 68000 a 16-bit microprocessor, which was followed by the 68010, then came the 68020, the 68030 and the 68040. Each successive member of the family has extra facilities.

In addition there are various coprocessors associated with these devices; for example, the floating point coprocessor provides floating point arithmetic. Also, extra peripheral devices have been designed which can be interfaced easily to these microprocessors; these can provide such functions as timing and serial communication, as are found in the 8051.

The 68020 is a sophisticated device, having a great many features. To simplify the discussion, only some of these features will be given in detail; more information is given in appendix 1. This approach is reasonable as a user of the 68020 will often be able to use only certain features.

The 68020 can operate in one of two modes, user mode and supervisor mode. Typically user mode is when the 68020 is executing an application program, such as a program written by the user or an editor, compiler, data base or wordprocessor program. However, in supervisor mode the 68020 is usually running part of the system software, such as the operating system, where the program is often utilising important parts of the computer, such as the disk or display. In supervisor mode, the 68020 can access all parts of the computer, but in user mode certain parts are inaccessible, so a user program cannot corrupt these parts. This provides some protection for the machine.

In user mode, the programming model of the 68020 is the same as for the 68000, but for supervisor mode, more registers and instructions are available. As a user will normally only operate in user mode, most will be said here of that mode and its facilities.

The 68020 is a 32-bit machine, so its registers are in general 32 bits long. Figure 8.9 shows the registers available in user mode. There are 8 general purpose 32-bit data registers, D0..D7, and 7 general purpose 32-bit address registers, A0..A6; these can be used like DREG and AREG in the imaginary microprocessor. An eighth address register, A7, is the stack pointer in user mode. In addition, the 68020 has a 32-bit program counter, PC, and an 8-bit flag register, the condition code register, CCR. In fact, the CCR is the lower half of a 16-bit status register, the SR, but the upper byte is only available in supervisor mode so it is not described here. The flags in the CCR are C, the carry flag; V the overflow flag; Z, the zero flag; N, the negative flag (it is set if the last result was negative); and X, the extend flag, which is like a carry flag. The registers available in supervisor mode are described in appendix 1.

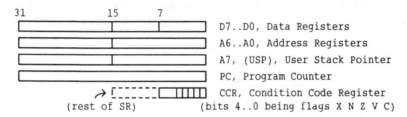

Figure 8.9 Registers in the 68020

Figure 8.10 contains a simplified block diagram of the 68020: a detailed description of the operation of the 68020 being beyond the scope of this book. This shows the components of the microprocessor and its connection to the outside world.

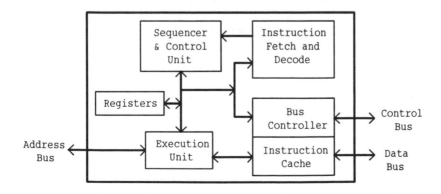

Figure 8.10 Block diagram of the 68020

The 68020 has an instruction cache which is a memory used for storing instructions. The 68020 'anticipates' the instructions that it needs and will often have fetched the next instruction some time before executing it. Thus the 68020 does not need to wait to read the instruction. More details on the cache can be found in 68020 data books. Fetching the instruction requires control of the bus, and this is provided by the 'bus control' block.

The instructions in the cache are processed by the 'instruction prefetch and decode' block which determines the instruction type and passes this information to the sequencer which coordinates the actions of the 68020.

The 'execution' unit contains three ALUs which are used to process the instruction; three are needed as some processing is often required in calculating the address of data being processed, as well as the normal arithmetic and logic operations on data in registers. The last block contains the registers.

Summary

This chapter has briefly described the components and operation of a simple microprocessor. The microprocessor has registers for storing data, and circuits, such as the ALU and the Control Unit, for performing logical operations. The basic operation of the microprocessor is to fetch instructions and to execute them. In addition, the two microprocessors described in this book, the 8051 and 68020, have been introduced, and their structure and facilities have been outlined.

Two major topics need to be considered, interfacing hardware to the microprocessors and writing software for them. The next few chapters describe the interfacing and these are followed by chapters describing software which uses this hardware.

Exercise

Describe the execution of the following instructions:

    a) STORE DREG at address whose value is found in AREG,

    b) AND DREG with data at address 65,

    c) ARITHMETIC SHIFT LEFT data at address 76,

      Note, this requires the data at the specified address to be fetched, shifted and the result then stored in the specified address.

    d) JUMP IF CARRY CLEARED to address found in AREG.

    e) JUMP to address 20 locations after the next instruction.

References

Philips *Single-chip 8-bit Microcontrollers* User Manual, 1988.

Motorola *MC68020 32-bit Microprocessor User's Manual MC68020UM/AD*, 1985.

9 Interfacing

This chapter is the first of three which describe how memory and peripheral devices can be interfaced to microprocessors. These interfaces allow, for example, the microprocessor to read its instructions from memory or, say, to write to some peripheral; that is, data transfers occur across the bus between the microprocessor and some other device.

In general, these data transfers are instigated by the microprocessor, which puts suitable signals on to the bus; as a result of this the other device responds in a suitable manner. As the microprocessor instigates the transfer, it is the master device; the memory or I/O device is the slave which responds to the signals from the master.

Therefore, if such a slave device is to be connected to a microprocessor, it must be able to respond suitably to the signals output by the microprocessor. This requires a suitable logic circuit to interface the slave to the bus. The aim of this chapter is to introduce the concepts of such interfaces.

Other data transfers can occur across the bus, when interrupts and direct memory access (DMA) are used. Interfaces allowing such transfers are also introduced in this chapter.

9.1 Bus protocols

The bus consists of a series of connections between a master and its slaves. It is divided into three sections; the address bus, which specifies the address of the slave with which the master is communicating; the data bus, on which the data being transferred are put; and the control bus, which carries signals which control the transfer, providing synchronisation between the master and slave, and clarifying the type of data transfer. The various microprocessors have different signals on the bus, so in the following a simple set of signals is assumed; the signals on 'real' devices, the 8051 and 68020, are described later.

When data are transferred between the master and slave, a suitable protocol is required so that the two devices may be synchronised. The three protocols used, synchronous, semi-synchronous or asynchronous, are defined below.

Synchronous data transfers

The synchronous protocol is the simplest of the three methods, and is the least used as there are major problems with it. The following simple set of signals is assumed for the protocol.

The address bus contains the address of the device being accessed; this is a binary number which is set up by the master device to indicate the device with which the master is communicating.

95

The data bus contains the data; these are set by the master device when data are to be written to the slave, and set by the slave device when data are read from the slave into the master.

The control bus contains two signals, write* and strobe*. The * at the end of the name indicates that the signal is active when it is '0'. Thus write* is '0' when data are written to the slave and '1' when data are read from the slave. When strobe* is '0', the other signals on the bus have correct values and data can be transferred.

In the synchronous protocol all data transfers take a fixed length of time; the master instigates the transfer and a fixed time later the master terminates the transfer. The sequence of events for a read transfer is as follows:

- Master outputs address on the bus and sets write* to '1' to indicate a read transfer is to occur.
- When these are stable, master asserts strobe* (sets it to '0').
- The slave at the specified address puts data on to the data bus.
- The master, a fixed time after asserting strobe*, reads the data from the data bus, stores them internally, and then releases strobe*.
- The slave then stops driving the data bus.
- The master can then change the other signals at the start of the next data transfer operation.

These actions are shown in figure 9.1a; the variations of the signals are shown with respect to time. At the start, the address lines change from one set of values to another; the write* changes from its previous state (it may have been '1' or '0') to '1'. Then strobe* is asserted. Later, the slave device puts the data on the data lines (the figure shows the data in an undefined state initially before changing to the correct values dependent on those read from the slave). After strobe* is released, the data change and the other signals can change for the start of the next transfer.

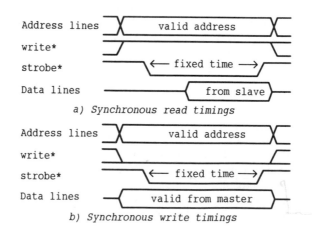

a) *Synchronous read timings*

b) *Synchronous write timings*

Figure 9.1 Timings for synchronous bus protocol

A similar set of actions is used for writing data. The sequence of events is described below, and shown in figure 9.1b.

- The master outputs the address on to the address bus, sets write* to '0' and puts the data to be output on to the data bus.
- When these are stable, the master asserts strobe*.
- A fixed time later, the master releases strobe*.
- The addressed slave, reads the data from the bus, and stores the data internally.
- The master releases the data and can change the other signals at the start of the next transfer.

A key point to note in the above is that it takes time for data to be read from the slave and put on the bus. It also takes time for the slave to store data internally. This is called the *access time*. The length of the access time will vary depending on the slave device from, typically, 20 ns to 500 ns.

This presents a problem; how long should strobe* be on? Clearly, it should be on for as long as the slowest slave device. This, though, is wasteful if most transfers are with faster devices. Therefore, two other protocols are used, where the length of the transfer can be varied depending on the device being accessed.

Semi-synchronous transfers

The semi-synchronous protocol is the same as the synchronous protocol, except there is one other signal, often called wait* (it is also active low), which the slave can assert if it is too slow. If the slave is fast enough, the data transfer occurs in the manner described above. If, however, the slave is too slow, then the slave asserts wait* before the strobe* signal is due to be released, and only releases wait* when it is ready for the transfer to be completed. When the master device is due to release strobe* it first checks wait* and only releases strobe* when wait* is released. Figure 9.2 shows the variation of the signals for transfers using the semi-synchronous bus.

Note, wait* should not be used in the interface of a very slow slave; wait* should only lengthen a transfer time to, say, three times its normal length. This is because a simple CPU cannot do any other action while it is waiting, such as responding to an interrupt. If a device is too slow, then it should provide a status line which the CPU can test under instruction, and only read the data when the status line indicates that the device is ready.

The semi-synchronous protocol is used by many different processors, but it is not infallible. A very fast master device might release strobe* before the slave has asserted wait*. Also, if a slave has been interfaced to a slow master device for which no circuit is needed for generating wait*, and then the master is replaced by a faster version, a wait* circuit may then be needed. Chances are, though, there will be no space on the circuit board for the wait* circuit.

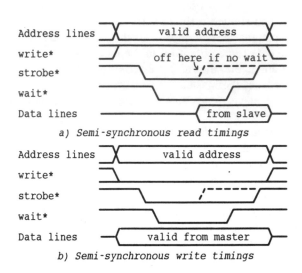

a) *Semi-synchronous read timings*

b) *Semi-synchronous write timings*

Figure 9.2 Timings for semi-synchronous bus protocol

Asynchronous data transfers

The semi-synchronous protocol will not work in all cases; therefore some more modern systems use the asynchronous protocol which automatically adapts the length of the data transfer. This is achieved by the master and slave communicating with each other; they handshake.

The basic idea is simple, the same signals are used as for synchronous transfers, except there is one other signal, acknowledge*, which is asserted by the slave device when the data have been transferred, that is, when the slave device has put the data on to the bus during a read transfer, or when the slave has stored the data during a write transfer. Essentially, acknowledge* is asserted by the slave to tell the master that it can terminate the transfer and release strobe* and the other signals. The sequence of events by which a read transfer occurs is as follows, as shown in figure 9.3a.

- Master outputs address on the bus and sets write* to '1' to indicate a read transfer.
- When these are stable, master asserts strobe*.
- The slave at the specified address puts data on to the data bus.
- The slave then asserts acknowledge*.
- The master reads the data from the data bus, storing them internally, then releases strobe*.
- The slave then stops driving the data bus and releases acknowledge*.
- The master can then change the other signals at the start of the next data transfer operation.

A similar set of actions is used for writing data. The sequence of events is described below, and shown in figure 9.3b.

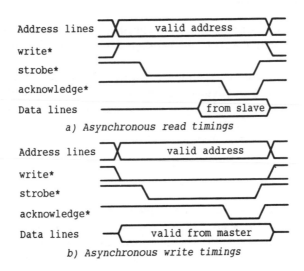

a) Asynchronous read timings

b) Asynchronous write timings

Figure 9.3 Timings for asynchronous bus protocol

- The master outputs the address on to the address bus, sets write* to '0' and puts the data to be output on to the data bus.
- When these are stable, the master asserts strobe*.
- The addressed slave reads the data from the bus and stores the data.
- The slave asserts acknowledge*.
- The master releases the data and can change the other signals at the start of the next transfer.
- The slave releases acknowledge*.

The length of the transfer operation varies with the speed of the slave; a fast device will issue acknowledge* quickly, a slow device more slowly. If a faster master is added, the slave devices will continue to work although the full potential of the faster master will not be realised.

One problem can occur, when the master attempts to transfer data to a slave which does not exist. Then there is no slave to issue the acknowledge signal, so the transfer will continue indefinitely. However, this problem can be solved, and to advantage. If a program has caused the master to address a non-existent slave, it is possible that the program is in error and this should be reported. This is easily achieved. An extra circuit is required which is associated with the microprocessor and which detects when a transfer is taking too long (say 20 times the length of a normal transfer). When strobe* has been asserted for too long, this circuit issues a signal to terminate the cycle and to cause the microprocessor to stop its current program and obey some instructions to handle such an error, typically reporting the error to the user.

9.2 Basic slave interfaces

The above section describes the typical signals provided on a bus which allow data to be transferred along the bus between a master and slave device. In this section some simple circuits are developed which allow some simple slaves to be interfaced to the bus. These circuits will use the signals outlined above.

The simplest of these circuits is an interface of a hexadecimal keypad and seven segment display to the synchronous bus; the interface will then be extended to allow for the semi-synchronous and asynchronous protocols. First these two devices will be introduced and their interface requirements derived.

Interfacing a seven-segment display

A seven-segment display consists of seven rectangular light emitting diodes (LEDs) arranged in the shape of an eight as shown in figure 9.4a, and each light is lit if current flows through it. In addition, such a display often has a small dot which can also be lit (here the dot is on the left of the eight, but some devices have the dot on the right). To display a particular number, the appropriate segments must be lit; all seven are turned on to show an 8, the two down the right side are turned on to show a 1 (as shown in figure 9.4b).

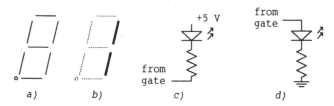

Figure 9.4 Seven-segment light emitting displays

Each LED is connected in the following manner, as shown in figure 9.4c. Its anode is connected to 5 V and its cathode connected via a voltage dropping resistor to a logic gate. If the output of the logic gate is '0', there is a voltage across the LED and resistor, so current will flow through the device and so the LED will shine. If the output is '1', there is no such voltage, so no current will flow and the LED will not shine.

The above arrangement might be considered odd as when the LED shines, current flows through the LED and resistor and into the logic gate. The more obvious arrangement is that shown in figure 9.4d, where the gate is '1' for the LED to shine. However, TTL logic gates can sink more current into their outputs than source current out from their outputs, so the arrangement in figure 9.4c is used.

The value for the resistor can be calculated easily. The LED will shine if the voltage across it is 0.6 V and the current through it is about 10 mA. When the output of the logic gate is '0', its voltage is 0.6 V, so there is 3.8 V across the resistor. Thus the resistor should be about 390 Ω. A smaller resistor will allow a greater current, so the LED will shine more brightly; 270 Ω is a suitable value. Common anode seven-segment displays can be obtained, for which all the anodes are connected together, and this common line is connected to 5 V.

To interface such a display, the logic '0's must be provided. The LEDs cannot be connected directly to the data bus, as the contents of the bus change with each data transfer, so the display will keep changing. Instead, an octal latch is required, whose inputs are connected to the data bus, and whose outputs are connected to the appropriate resistors, as shown in figure 9.5; note the symbol used for a latch. The microprocessor writes a value into that latch so that the appropriate patterns may be displayed. The octal latch is an edge-triggered device containing eight D-type flip flops controlled by a common signal, CP; when CP changes from '0' to '1', the data on the inputs are stored in the flip flops. Note that the data should be stable for a short time before the edge of CP (the *set-up time*) and for a short time after the edge (the *hold time*). A set-up time of 20 ns and a hold time of 0 ns is typical for TTL devices.

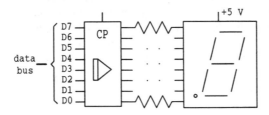

Figure 9.5 Latch and display

The interface must arrange that the control signal of the latch goes from '0' to '1' when the microprocessor is writing data to the latch, that is, when the address bus contains the address associated with that slave, the write* signal is '0' and strobe* is '0'.

Interfacing a keypad

The following properties are assumed for the hexadecimal keypad. It has a status line which is '1' if a key is pressed and '0' otherwise. If a key is pressed then the four data outputs of the keypad indicate the value of the key currently pressed; otherwise these outputs are undefined.

To interface such a device, these five lines must be put on to the data bus when the microprocessor is reading from the address associated with the keypad. This cannot be done by connecting the lines directly to the bus, as sometimes the keypad should be putting data on to the bus, at other times another slave is driving the bus, and the microprocessor drives the bus during write transfers. Instead, the keypad is connected to the bus via an octal buffer which has *tristate* outputs; each output of the buffer is connected to one of the lines on the data bus.

A tristate output is one which can have one of three possible states, the normal '0' and '1', and the high impedance state. In this last state, the output is hardly affecting the line to which it is connected. Many such outputs can be connected to the same line if it is arranged that at most only one output is '0' or '1', with all the others are in the high impedance state. Then that '0' or '1' (a low impedance) is in parallel with many high impedances, which have a negligible effect, so the output in the low impedance state determines the logic value of the line.

An octal tristate buffer is one which has eight of these buffers each of which has a data input, a data output and a common <u>output enable signal</u>. If the output enable, $\overline{OE}$, is '1', all the outputs are in the high impedance state, otherwise, the value on each data output is the same as that on its corresponding input.

Thus the five output lines from the keypad are connected to five inputs of the tristate buffer, and their equivalent outputs are connected to the data bus; the status line is connected via the buffer to bit 7 of the data bus, the values of the key pressed are put on to bits 3 to 0 of the bus; this is shown in figure 9.6; note the symbol used for a tristate buffer. The output enable signal should be '0' only when the the microprocessor is reading data from the buffer, that is, when the address bus contains the address associated with that slave, the write* signal is '1' and strobe* is '0'. In the figure, the unused inputs to the buffer are connected to '0'. Note, all inputs to logic gates should be connected either to '1' or '0'.

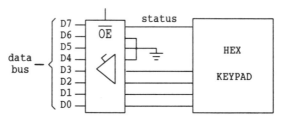

Figure 9.6 Buffer and keypad

Interfacing the keypad and seven-segment display

Clearly, the circuitry required to interface the keypad (that is, to enable the outputs of its buffer) is very similar to that required for interfacing the display (that is, to control the CP signal on its latch). Both require that the address is that associated with the device and that strobe* is '0'; one needs to check that write* is also '1', the other that write* is '0'. Thus the interface of both will be achieved using one circuit. In fact, it is convenient for both devices to have the same address; when the microprocessor writes to that address, data are written to the latch so as to set the display; when the microprocessor reads from that address, the tristate buffer is enabled and the status and data values of the keypad are put onto the data bus.

A block diagram of the interface is shown in figure 9.7. The buffer and latch are connected to the data bus and the control circuit checks the address bus, that strobe* is '0' and the state of write*, so as to control the CP signal of the latch, and the output enable of the buffer, $\overline{OE}$. Both CP and $\overline{OE}$ require that the address is that associated with the devices and that strobe* is '0'. If this is the case, then write* selects whether CP or $\overline{OE}$ should be asserted.

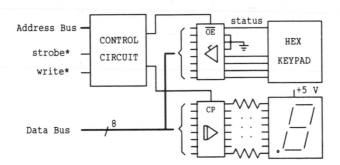

Figure 9.7 Block diagram of interface

A circuit is required whose output indicates if the address is that associated with the device and strobe* is '0'. This is easily achieved by a comparator circuit, as shown in figure 9.8a. The n-bit comparator has two sets of n data inputs and its output is '0' only if both data sets are equal. The address bus and strobe* are connected to one set, and the desired address and '0' are connected to the other, so the output of the comparator, labelled valid*, is '0' only if the desired address is on the bus and strobe* is '0'. Here, the desired address is specified by switches, so that the circuit can be set to work at any address. The timings for the circuit are shown in figure 9.8b, assuming that the address is correct.

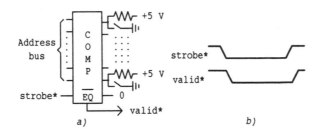

Figure 9.8 Valid address circuit

If valid* is '0', write* is used to assert CP or $\overline{OE}$. During a read transfer, $\overline{OE}$ should be '0', so that the data from the keypad can be put on to the bus via the tristate buffer. For a write operation, CP should also be set '0' while valid* is '0', and when valid* is released, CP will also be released, and at that time the data on the bus will be written into the latch.

Note, the data are written when strobe* is released not when it is asserted, as on some systems the data are not on the bus at the start of a data transfer.

The timings for $\overline{OE}$ and CP are shown in figure 9.9a, and a circuit to achieve them is in figure 9.9b. The complete interface circuit consists of the latch, buffer, comparator and the gates shown in figure 9.9b.

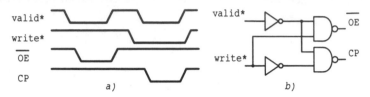

Figure 9.9 Control circuit and timings

Note, in a dedicated system for which there are only a few slave devices, the address comparator need not check all addresses. For example, suppose addresses $F000 to $FFFF (the address numbers are given in hex) are assigned to input/output devices in the system. If the keypad and display are the only input/output devices, then the comparator need only check the address lines A15 to A12. If, however, the system is one where many different devices may be connected, then the whole of the address bus is required. A bus system is one such system, where different devices can be plugged into the bus. For such a system it is a good idea for switches to be used to set the address associated with the interface.

Interface to a semi-synchronous bus

The latch and buffer circuits are fast devices, therefore it is unlikely that a wait* signal will be needed. However, the following simple circuit is described so as to illustrate how a wait* signal could be generated.

This circuit should assert wait* immediately that valid* is asserted, and then release wait* after an appropriate delay, that is, when the data have been transferred. This requires a circuit which can delay a signal; for the following it is assumed that there is a device whose output is the same as its input except that it is delayed by a suitable amount. Figure 9.10a shows the timings of valid*, and figure 9.10b shows how such a device may be used to produce wait*. This circuit is the only addition required to the interface for a synchronous bus.

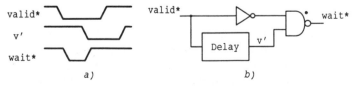

Figure 9.10 Wait generator circuit

The wait* signal should be asserted by the one slave device which is addressed. However, all of the slave interfaces in the system should be able to assert wait*, that is, all slave interfaces should have a 'wait generator' whose output is connected to the wait* line. This output cannot be a 'normal' logic gate as damage is caused when two such gates are connected together and one output is a logic '1' and the other a logic '0'. So, instead a gate with an 'open collector' output is used; and this is depicted by the 'blob' near the output of the gate in figure 9.10b.

An open collector output is essentially a transistor whose collector is open circuit, as shown in figure 9.11a. (Sometimes the output is an FET whose drain is open circuit, hence the gate has an open drain output.) For such a circuit to operate, a resistor must be connected between the collector output and the positive power supply, as in figure 9.11b. Then, if the transistor is turned on, current flows through the resistor and transistor and hence there is a voltage across the resistor, so the output is '0'; if the transistor is turned off, no current flows, there is no voltage across the resistor and the output is '1'.

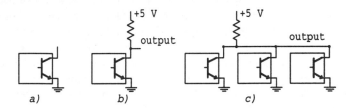

Figure 9.11 Open collector outputs

The advantage of such an arrangement is that many open collector outputs may be connected together, with one resistor to the power supply, as shown in figure 9.11c. If any of the transistors is turned on, current will flow through the resistor and hence the output will be '0'. This is exactly what is required for the wait* signal; any slave interface can pull the signal down to '0'.

Delay circuits

The interface also requires a delay circuit to generate the v' signal shown in figure 9.10. The following describes two techniques for this purpose, one using a monostable and the other a shift register, so as to generate wait*.

Figure 9.12 shows a monostable based circuit and its timings. For most of the time valid* is '1', hence the monostable and its associated D-type flip flop are cleared. When, however, valid* is asserted, the monostable is triggered and its $\overline{Q}$ output goes low for a time determined by the resistor and capacitor. After this time, $\overline{Q}$ goes high which clocks the flip flop, whose Q output goes to '1' and its $\overline{Q}$ output goes to '0'. The $\overline{Q}$ output of the flip flop provides the v' signal, and this is passed to the NAND gate to provide wait*. When valid* returns to '1', the monostable and flip flop are cleared and so wait* is released.

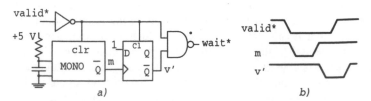

Figure 9.12 Monostable delay circuit

One problem with monostables is that of false triggering; there can be sufficient noise in the circuit to cause the monostable to be triggered at the wrong time. Another problem is that timings using monostables can be inaccurate because of tolerances on the values of resistors and capacitors and because these values can change during operation. Thus, a sufficient margin of error should be allowed when calculating values for these components. For these reasons, the author prefers to use an alternative method.

Figure 9.13 shows a shift register made from two D-type flip flops, its use in generating wait*, and the associated timings. The circuit has as input valid* and a regular clock signal, marked CLK, such as is provided in all microprocessor systems. While valid* is '1', the flip flops are cleared. When, however, valid* is asserted, the flip flops are under the control of CLK. When CLK goes from '0' to '1', the value on each D input is passed to the corresponding Q output. Thus on the first such edge of CLK after valid* is asserted, the Q output of the first flip flop, Q0, becomes '1'; and on the second such edge of CLK, the output of the second flip flop, Q1, becomes '1'. The inverse of Q1 provides v' which is passed to the NAND gate to generate wait*. When valid* is released, the flip flops are cleared and so wait* is released.

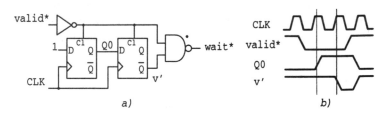

Figure 9.13 Shift register delay circuit

As it cannot be known when valid* will be asserted in relation to CLK, the delay before Q0 becomes '1' is unknown, and hence should be omitted in calculating delays. Instead, the length of the delay before acknowledge* is asserted will be at least one complete cycle of CLK. If a longer delay is required, then a longer shift register is used. For example, if the CLK has a frequency of 16 MHz and hence a period of 62.5 ns, and a delay of 250 ns is required, then a five bit shift register is needed, the Q5 output being used to generate acknowledge*.

Many of the circuits used by the author, therefore, use a standard 8-bit shift register, with the appropriate output used. In the following section, therefore, where an interface to an asynchronous bus is described, the required delay is achieved using a shift register circuit.

Interface to an asynchronous bus

The interface to an asynchronous bus is slightly more complicated than that to a semi-synchronous bus. This requires a circuit which asserts acknowledge* a suitable time after valid* is asserted, and which releases acknowledge* when strobe* (and hence valid*) is released. In addition, the CP signal on the latch should be released when acknowledge* is asserted. This is because, during a write operation, the acknowledge signal is asserted to indicate that the data have been written (which happens when CP is released). In a read operation, acknowledge* is asserted when the slave has put the data on the bus, that is after $\overline{OE}$ has been asserted. The data should then remain on the bus until strobe* is released, so that the microprocessor can read the data. Hence, $\overline{OE}$ should remain asserted until strobe* is released.

Figure 9.14a shows the timing required for valid*, write*, CP, $\overline{OE}$ and acknowledge*. A circuit to achieve these is shown in figure 9.14b, which again uses a shift register delay circuit. The acknowledge* signal, like wait*, is achieved by a gate with an open-collector output. It should be noted that this circuit both asserts acknowledge* at the appropriate time and, during a write operation, releases the CP signal so as to store the data in the latch.

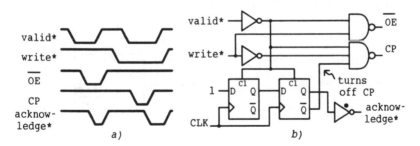

Figure 9.14 Acknowledge generator circuit

Another advantage of using a shift register to generate delays is to handle hold times on edge-triggered devices. Such devices require the data to remain on their inputs for some time after the CP signal is asserted. Suppose the set-up time of a device requires a delay of four clock cycles, and the hold time is the length of one clock period, then the Q4 output of the shift register should be used to turn CP off and the Q5 output to generate acknowledge*. This is shown in figure 9.15.

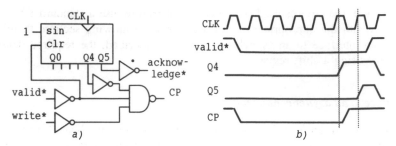

Figure 9.15 Longer delay shift register circuit

Interfacing analog digital converters

The above shows how a simple keypad and latch may be interfaced to a bus. In fact, most of the circuitry is concerned with the interface of a tristate buffer and a latch. This is important as most devices can be considered to be, from the point of view of interfacing, a tristate buffer or a latch. This is here demonstrated by considering the interface of a digital-to-analog converter (DAC) and an analog-to-digital converter (ADC).

A DAC is a device which is loaded with a digital number and which produces an analog signal whose voltage is proportional to that digital number. This requires a latch to store the digital number whose outputs are converted to the analog voltage by suitable conversion circuitry; a block diagram of a DAC is shown in figure 9.16a. Thus the interface to the bus of the DAC is like that of an interface of a latch, so this is described here, and a description of the conversion circuitry is left to chapter 10.

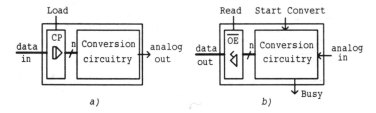

Figure 9.16 Block diagrams of DAC and ADC

An ADC is a device which samples an analog signal and which produces the digital number proportional to the voltage of the analog signal; a block diagram of an ADC is shown in figure 9.16b. For many ADCs this requires a signal telling it to start the conversion, and some time later the digital number is produced and stored in the ADC. That number can then be read by turning on the tristate outputs of the ADC. Another output from the ADC, sometimes called Busy, is the status line which can be used to indicate when the ADC has converted the data.

Although ADCs come in various forms, the digital interface of many devices requires a signal to start the conversion, a means of reading the busy line and of turning on the tristate buffer to read the converted data. It should be noted that the complete interface of an ADC and DAC requires some analog circuitry, providing scaling and buffering. As this chapter is concerned with digital interfaces, such analog processing is left to chapter 10.

For the following interface it will be assumed that the data bus is n bits wide and that the ADC and DAC convert between n-bit data and their equivalent analog voltages. The state of the busy line is found by reading from an address different from that used to read the ADC data. Data are written to the DAC by writing to the first address, and a write to the other address causes the issue of the start convert signal. The next section describes how an ADC, DAC and keypad and display can all be interfaced to a bus.

Interfacing many peripherals

The following describes how many devices may be interfaced to a bus. In the interface of the keypad and display, both devices were assigned the same address, so that the same comparator circuit could be used for both devices, and the write* signal was used to select either the keypad or display. This process can be extended in the interface of many devices. All the devices are assigned similar addresses for which most of the address lines are the same, and hence a comparator circuit can be used to verify that the address bus contains the address of one of these devices. Then, the remaining address lines and write* are used to select which particular device is used.

Figure 9.17 shows a block diagram of an interface of an ADC, a DAC, a keypad and two seven-segment displays to a synchronous bus. This requires a latch for each of the displays, a tristate buffer for the keypad and a 1-bit tristate buffer for the Busy output of the ADC. It is assumed that the DAC contains a latch and the ADC has an internal tristate buffer for its data outputs. The block marked 'valid address' contains a comparator circuit which asserts valid* if the address on the bus is one of those associated with one of the devices and that strobe* is asserted; the comparator compares most of the address lines with their required values and strobe* with '0'. The remaining address lines and write* are used to select one of the devices if valid* is asserted. The other block in the circuit is a bi-directional tristate buffer.

This buffer is often required in a system when there are many devices connected to the data bus. The fan out limit of logic gates specifies the maximum number of devices which may be connected to the output of a gate. For some gates a fan out limit of 20 is possible, though it is often much less for microprocessors and similar devices. The use of the bi-directional tristate buffer means that only one gate is connected to each bit of the data bus, instead of five or six gates. In a small dedicated microcontroller, where there are few devices connected to the bus, the buffer may not be needed. In other systems, however, it will be required.

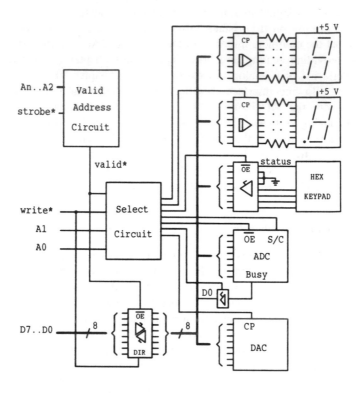

Figure 9.17 Interface of various peripheral devices

The buffer consists of eight pairs of back to back tristate buffers and one such pair is shown in figure 9.18. If data are to be passed from a to b (in the figure), then $\overline{OE1}$ should be asserted; if data are to be passed from b to a, then $\overline{OE2}$ should be asserted. A practical octal tristate buffer has eight of these circuits, with $\overline{OE1}$ and $\overline{OE2}$ common to all pairs, and these are controlled externally by two signals $\overline{OE}$ and DIR. If $\overline{OE}$ is '1' then all outputs are disabled; but if $\overline{OE}$ is '0' then DIR specifies the direction in which data are passed, asserting the appropriate internal signals, $\overline{OE1}$ or $\overline{OE2}$. In the interface circuit, $\overline{OE}$ is conveniently generated by valid* and write* specifies the direction data travel through the buffer, so write* provides DIR.

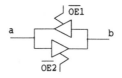

Figure 9.18 Bi-directional tristate buffer

The only other part of figure 9.17 that needs comment is the select circuit. This specifies which device is read from or written to, assuming that valid* is asserted. The interface has three input devices, the keypad buffer, the ADC data and the ADC busy, and three output devices, the two latches and the DAC. In addition, the start convert signal must be generated; it is convenient to do this by writing to one address. Thus there are four addresses to write to and three addresses to read from. The write* signal determines whether a read or write is occurring, so write* and two address lines select the device, as shown by the following truth table:

valid*	A1	A0	write*	action
1	x	x	x·	no device accessed
0	0	0	0	write to DAC
0	0	0	1	read from ADC
0	0	1	0	issue start convert
0	0	1	1	read busy line
0	1	0	0	write to latch for first display
0	1	0	1	read from key pad buffer
0	1	1	0	write to latch for second display
0	1	1	1	no device accessed

This is easily implemented using a three-to-eight decoder. One such device has three enable inputs G1, $\overline{G2a}$ and $\overline{G2b}$, three select inputs, C, B, A, and eight outputs $\overline{Y7}..\overline{Y0}$. The device is enabled if G1 is '1' and $\overline{G2a}$ and $\overline{G2b}$ are '0'. The values on C B A can be considered to be a three bit number in the range 0..7; if the device is enabled and the number on C B A is n then $\overline{Yn}$ is '0' and the other outputs are '1'; if the device is disabled all outputs are '1'. Thus the select circuit can be implemented directly using such a decoder, as shown in figure 9.19.

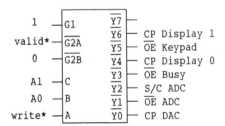

Figure 9.19 Select circuit using 3-8 decoder

The complete circuit contains the comparator circuit to generate valid*, the decoder to select the appropriate device, the tristate buffer and the actual devices with their associated latches or buffers.

The interface to a semi-synchronous bus contains the above plus the wait* generator, exactly as described earlier.

The interface to an asynchronous bus is slightly more complicated. This must generate acknowledge* and, during a write operation, turn off the appropriate CP signal so as to write the data (as was done in the interface for the latch for the display). The acknowledge* signal can be generated using the shift register circuit described earlier. Turning off the control signal is easily achieved by disabling the decoder at the appropriate time, as shown in figure 9.20 which contains the complete circuit for the interface to an asynchronous bus. The Q4 output of the shift register is used to generate acknowledge*, the Q3 output is used to disable the decoder during a write operation (as achieved using the NAND gate connected to the G1 input of the decoder).

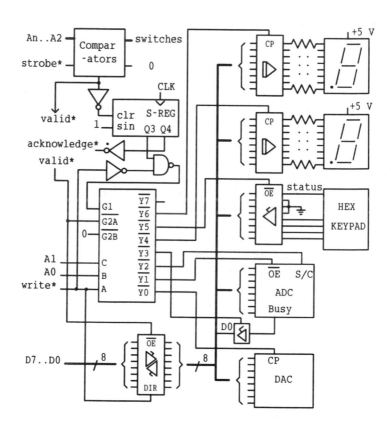

Figure 9.20 Interface of peripherals to asynchronous bus

Interfacing ROM and RAM

The techniques for interfacing peripherals can be easily extended to the interface of memory. This section considers two of the simplest forms of memory used in microprocessor systems, EPROM (erasable programmable read only memory) and static RAM (random access memory). Another form of memory, dynamic RAM, is described in chapter 10.

EPROM is memory which is programmed with appropriate information using a special programming device. In a microprocessor system, an EPROM is a device which consists of many locations in which this information has been stored, and from which the information can be read by the microprocessor. To read from one location, the address of that location must be specified, and then two control signals on the EPROM, $\overline{CE}$ and $\overline{OE}$, should be asserted. When $\overline{CE}$, chip enable, is asserted, the EPROM examines the address lines, determines the location in the EPROM specified by that address and extracts the data in that location, passing them to the inputs of an internal tristate buffer. The $\overline{OE}$, output enable, of the EPROM is used to enable that buffer, and hence output the data from the addressed location on to the data bus. The time when the data are output is determined by three access times; t_{addr}, the access time after addresses are stable; t_{ce}, the access time after the chip is enabled; and t_{oe}, the access time after outputs are enabled. The data will appear at the latest of the following times: time when the address lines are stable + t_{addr}, time when $\overline{CE}$ is asserted + t_{ce} and time when $\overline{OE}$ is asserted + t_{oe}. Note, t_{addr} and t_{ce} are usually about the same and are longer than t_{oe}, as t_{oe} is dependent only upon the delay required to turn the output buffer on.

A static RAM is in many ways very similar to an EPROM, as it has many locations in which information can be stored. However, a RAM can have data read from it and data written to it. Also, most RAM is volatile, that is, it loses its contents when the power supply is removed. As regards interfacing, a typical static RAM has various address lines, a chip enable signal, $\overline{CE}$, an output enable signal, $\overline{OE}$ and a write enable signal, $\overline{WE}$.

To read from a RAM, the required address is specified and $\overline{CE}$ and $\overline{OE}$ must both be asserted. Access times for these are similar to those for an EPROM. To write to a RAM, again the address is specified, as are the data to be written, $\overline{CE}$ is asserted and $\overline{WE}$ is asserted. The data are usually written when $\overline{CE}$ or $\overline{WE}$ is released (compare this with a latch, for which the data are written when the CP signal is released). Access times for writing are similar to those for reading, again that for $\overline{WE}$ is less than that for $\overline{CE}$.

An interface of an EPROM and RAM is considered next, in which it is assumed that both these devices can store 32K bytes of data, hence they both require 15 address lines (A14..A0) to address each location. Address line A15 is used to select which device is accessed; A15 is '0' for the EPROM and '1' for the RAM. The remaining address lines are common for the two devices, as was used for the peripherals.

A block diagram of an interface for one static RAM and one EPROM is shown in figure 9.21. The top address lines and strobe* are passed to a comparator circuit to verify that the address is valid. A15 and write* are used to select the $\overline{OE}$ or $\overline{WE}$ of the appropriate device; this is achieved using a two to four decoder. Note, valid* is connected to the $\overline{CE}$ of both devices; this is done to speed the operation of the circuit, as the access time from $\overline{CE}$ is longer than that from $\overline{OE}$ or $\overline{WE}$ and valid* is asserted before $\overline{OE}$ or $\overline{WE}$. The remaining (lower) address lines are connected to the address bus, and the data

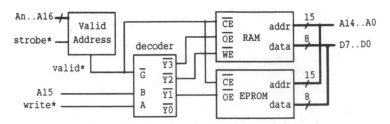

Figure 9.21 Interface of ROM and RAM

lines are connected to the data bus, though sometimes a buffer is required for the data bus (as was used in figure 9.17).

When interfacing to a semi-synchronous bus, extra circuitry is required to generate wait*. In an interface to an asynchronous bus a circuit is needed to assert acknowledge* at which time $\overline{WE}$ should also be released so as to write the data.

The above, therefore, demonstrates the principles and simple circuits involved in interfacing simple peripherals and memories to buses using the synchronous, semi-synchronous and asynchronous protocols.

9.3 Interrupts and direct memory access

The above circuits allow data to be transferred between a microprocessor and a slave device on the instigation of the microprocessor. Sometimes, however, a data transfer is not caused by the microprocessor. Instead interrupts and direct memory access are used; their use will be considered by example.

Interrupts

Consider a system which contains a keypad, such as that described above. To detect keypresses, the microprocessor could continually read from the appropriate address, testing to see if a key had been pressed, and reading the key if it had; this process is termed *polling*. Alternatively, the keypad could tell the microprocessor when a key had been pressed; the keypad would *interrupt* the microprocessor, in response to which the microprocessor would read the value of the key pressed.

One advantage of interrupts over polling is that the interrupting device is serviced soon after it has issued an interrupt, rather than only when the microprocessor notices that the device needs servicing. However, extra circuitry is needed to process the interrupts.

There are various types of interrupt, and microprocessors have various ways of responding to an interrupt. Here a simple circuit for interrupts is shown. This circuit issues an interrupt when a key has been pressed. It is assumed that the microprocessor has a signal, reset*, which is asserted when the system is switched on, or when it is started again, to initialise the system.

Figure 9.22a shows part of a keypad interface to generate an interrupt when a key is pressed; it asserts the interrupt request signal, intreq*. In response to this, the microprocessor clears the request by issuing the interrupt acknowledge signal, intack*. The timings of this are shown in figure 9.22b.

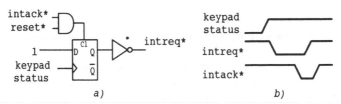

Figure 9.22 Interrupt control circuit

When the status line of the keypad is asserted (when a key is pressed), the '1' on the D input of the flip flop is passed to the Q output, so intreq* is generated. Note, intreq* is an open collector signal, as many devices could issue a request. The intack* signal is connected to the clear input of the flip flop, so this will clear the request. The reset* signal is also used to clear the flip flop, so there is no interrupt request when the system is first switched on or restarted.

Many devices could issue an interrupt, possibly at the same time. A system is needed, therefore, to prioritise these so that the most important device is serviced first. One method used is called daisy chaining; figure 9.23 shows such a system. Here there are two devices capable of issuing an interrupt; both can assert intreq*, as a result of which the microprocessor asserts intack*.

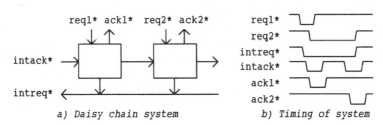

Figure 9.23 Daisy chain priority system

The intack* is passed to the first device; if this has issued an interrupt (its req1* is asserted), then ack1* is asserted to clear req1*, and no signal is passed to the second device. If, however, req1* is inactive, then the intack* is passed to the second device which issues ack2* to clear req2*. Figure 9.23b shows what happens when both devices issue a request; intack* is asserted twice, clearing req1* the first time and req2* the second time.

An alternative method is to use a priority encoder, as shown in figure 9.24. Four possible interrupt requests are shown, intreq3*..intreq0*, and these are input to the encoder. When any one of these is active, the intreq* of the microprocessor is asserted, thereby informing the microprocessor that an

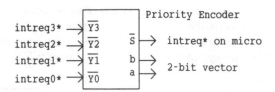

Figure 9.24 Using a priority encoder for interrupts

interrupt request has occurred. On detecting this, the microprocessor examines the two outputs of the encoder which indicate the highest priority of all the active interrupt requests and hence the device which should be serviced. The microprocessor then obeys the appropriate service routine, during which the interrupt request is cleared.

Direct memory access (DMA)

When a peripheral has new data, the data are often stored in memory for later processing. This is often done by the microprocessor obeying a program in which, in one instruction, the data are read from the peripheral into the microprocessor, and in another instruction, the data are written from the microprocessor into a suitable location in memory. This process can be slow. The alternative is for the peripheral to access the memory directly, using a process called direct memory access or DMA.

To achieve this, the peripheral must have access to the bus and be able to instigate its own data transfer operations. As the microprocessor and peripheral cannot both transfer data at the same time, the peripheral must first request that it can control the bus. When the microprocessor accedes to this request, the peripheral can then transfer data. When it has finished transferring data, the peripheral releases its request, as a result of which the microprocessor can again control the bus. Figure 9.25 shows the timing required for such a system, using two control signals, busreq*, which a peripheral issues to request the bus, and busack*, which the microprocessor uses to acknowledge the request.

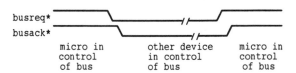

Figure 9.25 Timings of bus request signals

The actual operation of DMA is quite involved and is beyond the scope of this chapter. Most of the work is achieved by special direct memory access controller chips. No more will be said of DMA here.

9.4 Using peripheral interface devices

Associated with many microprocessors are peripheral interface devices, variously called PIOs (parallel input/outputs), PIAs (peripheral interface adapters), PITs (parallel interface timers): in the following the term PIA will be used. These connect to the bus using the techniques described above, but they also provide a number of input/output pins to which other devices may be connected. PIAs are programmable devices, that is, they can be configured to provide a great variety of features. In this section, therefore, the basic principles of their operation are given; details of the use of one specific device are given in a later chapter.

Many of these devices provide two 8-bit ports which can be configured as input or output lines. In addition, associated with each port are 'handshake' lines which handle the transfer of data between the port and the device to which it is connected and which can be used to instigate an interrupt request when a data transfer has occurred. The timer inside such devices is a synchronous counter which can be loaded with an initial value and then set to count down on each rising clock edge it receives. It can be programmed to provide various functions; one typical use is to generate an interrupt at regular intervals; another is to generate a square wave. In the following discussion, a simple PIA is considered which has no timer; it is based on the 6821.

This device has two identical ports and associated with each port are eight input/output lines, two handshake lines and an interrupt request signal (as shown in figure 9.26a). These ports can be used in various ways, although some PIAs provide more facilities than others.

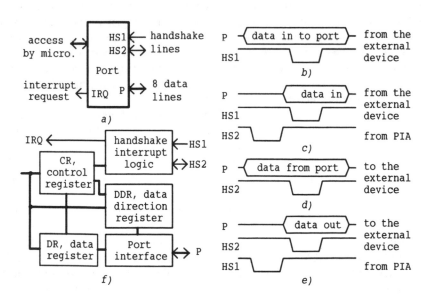

Figure 9.26 PIA ports and operation

In the simplest modes of operation, each port can be programmed to act like a simple buffer or latch; that is, the port can be an 8-bit input port, so at any time the microprocessor can read in the data presented on the port, or the port can be programmed as an 8-bit output port, so the microprocessor can just write data there which will appear on the output lines. In fact, each bit in the port can be configured separately to act as either an input or an output.

One use of a handshake line is to provide a signal to indicate to the PIA that new data have been presented to the port; the timings for this are shown in figure 9.26b, the data are provided by the external device and appear on the port, and then the external device asserts the handshake line for a short time. The PIA can be configured so that the assertion of the handshake line causes an interrupt to be generated, as a result of which the microprocessor can read the data during an interrupt service routine.

A more complex use of handshake lines for inputting data is illustrated in figure 9.26c. This extends that shown in figure 9.26b, in that the PIA also outputs a signal to inform the external device when the PIA is ready to accept the new data. Then the new data can be sent to the PIA by the external device.

The equivalent use of a single handshake line for outputting data is shown in figure 9.26d. Here the data being output are sent to the port and then a strobe signal is output to tell the external device that data have been output.

An extension of this, using two handshake lines for output, is shown in figure 9.26e. The extra handshake line is used by the external device to indicate when it is ready to accept new data. The assertion of this line may generate an interrupt or even instigate a DMA transfer.

These various functions must be programmed, so associated with each port are three programmable registers, as shown in figure 9.26f. The registers are a control register, a data direction register and the data register. The data register contains the data input from or output to the port. The data direction register determines whether data are read from or written to the port: each bit in the register determines the direction of the appropriate bit in the port. The control register determines the actions of the port, specifying how the handshake lines operate and whether interrupts are generated.

A block diagram of the complete PIA is shown in figure 9.27: this shows the internal components of the PIA, the signals used by the PIA to connect with external devices, and the signals used to interface the PIA to a microprocessor. There are two sets of registers for the two ports, and the contents of the registers are accessed via the internal data bus which is connected to the microprocessor's data bus via the buffers in the PIA. The microprocessor must be able to address the internal registers, so as to configure the ports and to read or write data to the ports. The block marked 'chip select logic' is used for this purpose; it has a chip select signal, $\overline{CS}$, which must be '0' to access the device, a read/write signal, R/$\overline{W}$, to indicate whether data are read from or written to the device, and two register select signals, RS1..RS0, which are used to identify the particular register in the PIA. Typically, these register select lines will be connected to address lines of the microprocessor, as shown in the figure, so that the microprocessor accesses the relevant register by reading or writing

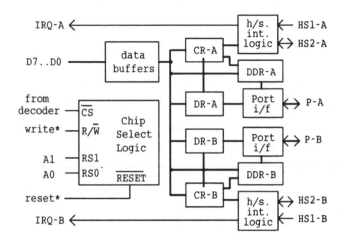

Figure 9.27 Internal structure of PIA

from the appropriate address. The $\overline{CS}$ signal will be generated by a 3-to-8 decoder chip, or similar circuit. In addition, there is a reset signal for initialising the device, and two interrupt request signals, one for each port.

The following examples show how a PIA may be used, that is, certain devices are connected to the ports and handshake lines of the PIA. One problem with using PIAs is that they are often low power devices which cannot drive many devices directly, instead a buffer or amplification circuit is needed. For example, if a seven-segment display were to be interfaced, a latch or buffer would be needed between the PIA and the display; in this case there would be no great advantage in using a PIA, it may be better to connect a latch directly to the microprocessor bus. On the other hand, the chip select logic and interrupt generation circuitry in the PIA may prove more useful. Figure 9.28 shows two uses of a PIA, controlling a stepping motor and a multiplexed ADC.

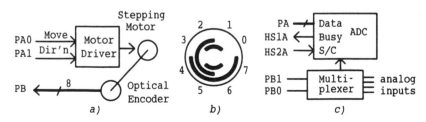

Figure 9.28 Applications of a PIA

The stepping motor system in figure 9.28a may be appropriate to the washing machine controller mentioned in chapters 2 and 3. Many washing machines have a dial which the user can turn to select a particular wash program and which turns around as the wash progresses. The microcontroller controlling the machine needs therefore to be able to determine the position of the dial and to move the dial. This can be achieved by having a motor which can move the dial and an optical encoder mounted on the shaft of the dial for measuring the position.

A suitable motor for this is a stepping motor (see Acarnley) whose shaft can be rotated in discrete steps, and this can be achieved by a suitable drive circuit controlled by the PIA; the PIA can issue a command telling the motor to rotate to the next position, either clockwise or anticlockwise. In the circuit in figure 9.28a, two bits of port A are used; one to specify the direction of the step, the other to cause the motor to step.

The optical encoder is like the system introduced in chapter 4 where there are areas of black and white on to which LEDs shine and behind which receivers are positioned; a black area stops the signal reaching the receiver. Here the areas are Gray coded and arranged circularly (a 3-bit Gray code is shown in figure 9.28b), with the LEDs and receivers positioned along an axis. In figure 9.28a an 8-bit encoder is used, and the digital outputs of the encoder are connected to port B.

The second system, shown in figure 9.28c enables four analog signals to be measured by one ADC. An analog multiplexer selects one of the four channels and passes it to the ADC which operates in the manner described earlier. The Busy and Start convert lines of the ADC are connected to handshake lines of port A of the PIA, and the data lines of the ADC are connected to the data lines on the port. Two bits output from port B are connected to the multiplexer and hence used to select the appropriate analog signal.

The above illustrate two simple means whereby a PIA may be used. The software for these systems is described in chapter 12, where also are given further details of the PIA.

9.5   Microprocessor system

The above describes the slave devices in a microprocessor system. This section describes the remaining circuitry of a microprocessor system, namely the clock and reset circuits.

A microprocessor needs a continuous train of pulses at regular intervals, termed a clock. This is used to provide regular timing and for synchronisation of events, both internal to the processor and externally; indeed, one use of the clock is shown above for generating the delay before acknowledge* is asserted. In a system in which the synchronous protocol is used, the clock is used by the microprocessor to determine the length of time that the strobe* is asserted.

A clock signal is usually generated using a quartz crystal, as this provides more accurate timings than, say, using a resistor and capacitor. Various circuits are available for clocks, but nowadays it is easiest to use clock modules, which contain the crystal and associated circuit.

A reset signal is required to ensure that the microprocessor and the rest of the system are initialised correctly when the system is first turned on, and when the user has pressed the reset button to start the system again, possibly when something has gone wrong. There are, therefore, two parts to this, the power-up circuit and the reset button circuit. Such a circuit is shown in figure 9.29.

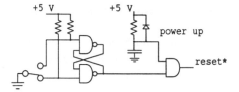

Figure 9.29 Reset circuit

The isr latch is used to debounce the reset button. Switch bounce occurs when a switch is pressed, the switch makes contact, then bounces away, then makes contact again; when it is not making contact, both inputs to the latch are '1' so the latch outputs are held. The resistor and capacitor provide the power-up reset; the capacitor takes time to charge, so reset* is held at '0' for some short time after power is applied.

The complete microprocessor system, therefore, consists of the microprocessor, its reset and clock circuits, and the memory and peripherals. Figure 9.30 shows a block diagram of a small microprocessor system, with ROM, RAM, ADC, DAC, keypad and seven-segment displays. The memory and peripheral control blocks contain the valid address and select circuitry outlined earlier. The rest are just connections to buses.

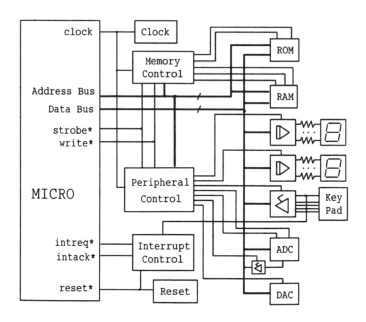

Figure 9.30 Block diagram of microprocessor system

Summary

This chapter has introduced the various methods by which data are transferred within a microprocessor system, using data transfers and the various protocols, interrupts and DMA. A simple set of signals is assumed for these protocols. Also introduced are PIA devices and how they may be used in interfacing. The next chapter describes other devices which can be connected to a bus.

Exercises

1. Show how a monostable and a shift register can each be used in circuits to generate wait*.

2. Design an interface of four seven-segment displays and a keypad to a semi-synchronous bus which uses the signals outlined in this chapter.

3. Design a circuit to interface two EPROMs and two static RAMs to an asynchronous bus.

References

Texas Instruments *TTL Data book.*

D.Lewin and D.Protheroe *Design of Logic Systems* Chapman & Hall 2nd Edn, 1992.

P.P.Acarnley *Stepping Motors: a guide to modern theory and practice* Peter Peregrinus Ltd, , 1982.

Motorola *MC6821 Data Sheet.*

10 Other Hardware

The previous chapter has shown how some slave devices can be interfaced to a microprocessor bus. Essentially such interfaces connect a tristate buffer or a latch to the bus. Most other slave devices also require such an interface. The aim of this chapter, therefore, is to describe some other devices showing how they may be used, but not giving their detailed interface to the bus.

10.1 Dynamic RAMs

Simple memory devices, EPROMs and static RAMs, were introduced in the previous chapter. This section considers another type of memory, dynamic RAM, whose operation is more complicated than that of static RAM, but which can store more information in a given circuit size. Such memory is more likely to be found in a microcomputer than in a small dedicated microcontroller; a microcontroller can often address only 64K of memory, and this is easily provided by modern EPROM and static RAM; a microcomputer may require 16Mbyte of memory and this is best achieved using dynamic RAM.

Like most static RAM, dynamic RAM is volatile, its contents are lost when the power is removed. However, due to the relative simplicity of the memory element (it can be thought of as a capacitor), a dynamic RAM 'forgets' its contents even when the power is maintained (because, in effect, the capacitors discharge). Therefore, dynamic RAMs must be reminded of their contents; the memory must be refreshed (effectively, the capacitors are recharged).

Dynamic RAM operation

Accessing data in dynamic RAM is more complicated than for static RAM. The memory elements are arranged in a matrix which has many rows and columns. To access an element, the row in which the element can be found is specified and the complete row is copied into a buffer inside the RAM; then the column for that element is specified, thereby indicating the particular element in the buffer, and data are read from or written into that element. At the end of the data transfer, the contents of the buffer are copied back into the row in the matrix and this action refreshes that row of elements.

The signals required for such an interface are shown in figure 10.1. First the address lines contain the address of the required row. Then, when these lines are stable, the row address strobe, $\overline{RAS}$, is asserted, as a result of which the specified row is copied into the buffer. Then, the address lines are changed to specify the column address, after which the column address strobe, $\overline{CAS}$, is asserted, and this specifies the required data in the row. For a read operation, the write enable signal, $\overline{WE}$, is held high, and after the access time, the

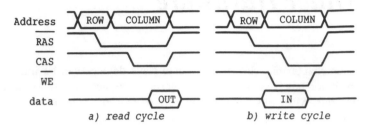

Figure 10.1 Accessing dynamic RAM

specified data appear on the data output. For a write operation, the data to be written should be on the data input and $\overline{\text{WE}}$ held low before $\overline{\text{CAS}}$ is asserted.

Every row in the matrix must be refreshed at regular intervals. For instance all rows in a dynamic RAM with 256 rows must be refreshed every 2 ms, so on average one row must be refreshed approximately every 8 μs. This can be achieved in various ways. For example, every 2 ms, normal computer operation can be suspended and every row in the memory refreshed. Alternatively, every 8 μs, the next row can be refreshed. The second method is more preferable as a microprocessor is not accessing memory all the time, so it is relatively easy to find the short time required to refresh a row.

If it can be guaranteed that every row is accessed each 2 ms period, then no further action is required. In general this is not the case, so two specific refresh operations are used, RAS-only refresh and CAS-before-RAS refresh.

In RAS-only refresh, the address of the row to be refreshed is specified, $\overline{\text{RAS}}$ is asserted and, after the appropriate delay, $\overline{\text{RAS}}$ is released. When $\overline{\text{RAS}}$ is asserted the row is copied into the buffer, and when $\overline{\text{RAS}}$ is released the row is copied back from the buffer thereby refreshing the row. One problem is that the circuit to achieve this must provide the address of the row to be refreshed.

Some modern RAMs circumvent this problem by having a built-in counter which stores the address to be refreshed and the memory needs only to be told when to refresh. This is achieved by asserting $\overline{\text{CAS}}$ and then $\overline{\text{RAS}}$; this action is termed CAS-before-RAS refresh, the timings for which are in figure 10.2.

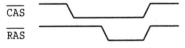

Figure 10.2 CAS before RAS refresh

It is also possible to access many data items from one row by first loading the row, by specifying the row address and asserting $\overline{\text{RAS}}$, and then giving many column addresses. This *page mode* operation is shown in figure 10.3.

Read-modify-write operation is also allowed where in one operation data are read from one location and a new value written there. As shown in figure 10.4, this is achieved by specifying the row address and then the column address in the normal way with $\overline{\text{WE}}$ high, so the data are output and then, while $\overline{\text{RAS}}$ and $\overline{\text{CAS}}$ are asserted, the data to be written are specified and $\overline{\text{WE}}$ is taken low.

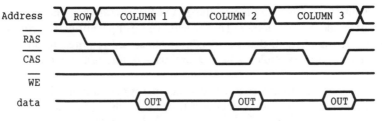

Figure 10.3 Page mode operation

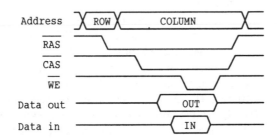

Figure 10.4 Read modify write operation

Dynamic RAM control circuitry

Clearly the interface of dynamic RAM is more complicated than that for static RAM. However, suitable dynamic RAM controllers are available which provide most of the operation. The following, therefore, gives a block diagram for a suitable interface, with an indication of the actions of the controller. This interface does not allow page mode or read-modify-write operation. A block diagram of the interface is shown in figure 10.5, and this is explained below.

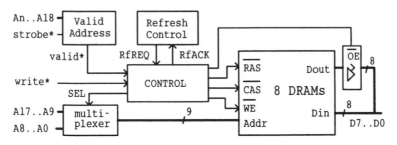

Figure 10.5 Dynamic RAM interface

Many dynamic RAMs are one bit wide, that is, one data item can be read or one written at a time. For a microprocessor system, many such RAMs must be connected in parallel, one connected to bit 0 of the data bus, one to bit 1, and so on. These RAMs often have separate data inputs and outputs. Each RAM, therefore, has many address lines, data in and data out and the control signals, $\overline{\text{RAS}}$, $\overline{\text{CAS}}$ and $\overline{\text{WE}}$. The interface above is for eight dynamic RAMs.

The interface must provide to the RAM the row address at one time and the column address at another. This is achieved using multiplexer circuits. If a 256K bit RAM is used, that is, 18 address lines are required to address each location then, for example, A17..A9 are passed through the multiplexers to provide the row address, and A8..A0 are passed to provide the column address. The signal SEL, in figure 10.5, selects the appropriate address lines.

The interface also requires a circuit to generate the valid* signal, indicating that the address on the bus is one associated with the memory. Using the signals from chapter 9, valid* is asserted if the remaining address lines are correct and strobe* is asserted.

Another circuit is required which determines when the next refresh operation should occur, asserting a signal called RfREQ at this time; another signal, RfACK, is used to clear that request.

The last part of the circuit, marked control, generates the select for the multiplexers and the control signals $\overline{RAS}$, $\overline{CAS}$ and $\overline{WE}$, in response to the signals valid* and RfREQ. The control circuit also generates the RfACK signal to acknowledge RfREQ. If the interface is to a semi-synchronous bus, the control circuit would also generate wait*, or for an asynchronous bus the circuit would generate acknowledge*, when valid* is asserted.

The control circuit acts in a sequential manner, which can be implemented in a sequential logic circuit. If RfREQ is detected, then the circuit goes through the appropriate steps for refresh to occur, asserting $\overline{CAS}$ and RfACK, then asserting $\overline{RAS}$ and releasing RfACK, and so on. If valid* is asserted, then the circuit goes through the steps to ensure that data are read or written; the row address selected, $\overline{RAS}$ asserted, the column address selected, and so on. When either sequence of actions is being obeyed, any assertions of RfREQ or valid* are ignored until the end of the sequence.

This can be implemented in a synchronous circuit; at each clock cycle the appropriate signals are generated. Figure 10.6 shows the sequence of operations. Note that in this example, RfREQ is asserted after valid* is asserted, thereby requesting a refresh while the control signals are being generated; however, this request is not processed until after the processing of valid* is complete. Similarly, when valid* is asserted during the refresh operation, this is not processed until after the refresh is complete. A circuit to achieve this is beyond the scope of this book, but such a circuit is found in dynamic RAM controllers.

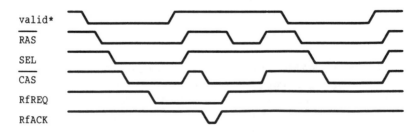

Figure 10.6 Sequence of control signals

10.2 Analog-digital conversion

Analog-digital converters were introduced in the last chapter, and their digital interface to buses was considered. This section describes how these devices work and the analog circuitry required to connect the devices to the outside world. This section includes some elementary analog electronics, including resistors and simple operational amplifiers and requires an appreciation of the laws of Ohm and Kirchhoff. Relevant details can be found in Horrocks.

Digital-to-analog converters (DACs)

A DAC takes n bits of data, representing a digital number, and converts these to their equivalent analog voltage. A converter which generates positive only signals is operating in *unipolar* mode, and one which generates signals which can be positive or negative is operating in *bipolar* mode. An n-bit converter in unipolar mode generates signals in the range 0 V to $(Max*2^n-1)V$, for some value Max, and an n-bit bipolar converter generates signals in the range $-(Max*2^{n-1})$ V to $Max*(2^{n-1}-1)$ V.

An 8-bit converter, for example, might be used to generate voltages in the range 0 to 2.55 V, so the hex number 00 is equivalent to 0 V, 80 to 1.28 V and FF to 2.55 V; or the same converter might be used to produce voltages from -10 V to 9.92 V, where 00 is equivalent to -10 V and FF to 9.92 V; or a 12-bit converter could be used to generate voltages between -5 V to 4.99 V, in which case 000 is equivalent to -5 V, 800 is 0 V and FFF is 4.99 V.

A DAC consists of a latch for storing the n-bit number and a circuit to convert the number to an analog voltage. A simple DAC is shown in figure 10.7. The conversion is achieved by resistors arranged in a summing virtual earth amplifier configuration.

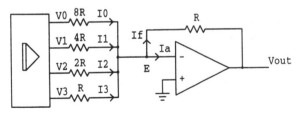

Figure 10.7 Block diagram of a 4-bit DAC

In such a configuration, the voltage at the common connection of all the resistors, marked E in the figure, is sufficiently close to 0 V to be considered as 0 V; it is said to be *virtually earth*. Also, the current Ia, flowing from E into the negative input of the amplifier can be considered to be negligible.

By Kirchhoff's current law, the sum of all currents flowing into point E (that is I0 + I1 + I2 + I3) must equal the current If flowing out of E through the feedback resistor to Vout (as it is assumed that Ia is negligible).

By Ohm's law, $I0 = V0 / 8R$, $I1 = V1 / 4R$, $I2 = V2 / 2R$, $I3 = V3 / R$ and $If = -Vout / R$. Therefore

$$-Vout / R = V0 / 8R + V1 / 4R + V2 / 2R + V3 / R$$
or $-Vout = V0 / 8 + V1 / 4 + V2 / 2 + V3$

The voltages V0..V3 are digital signals, in principle being 0 V or 5 V, so Vout will vary from 0 V to −9.375 V, in the manner required for a converter. V3 is the most significant bit, V0 the least significant bit.

The main problem with the above is that the output of a logic gate is not fixed as 0 V or 5 V; '0' is any value less than 0.8V and '1' is any value greater than 2.8 V. A better circuit is that shown in figure 10.8, where the logic outputs ·from the latch control analog switches which select 0 V or a reference voltage, Vref. If Vref is −5 V, then Vo varies in the range 0 V to 4.68 V, as would be expected in a 4-bit converter, as $4.68 = 5*(2^4-1)/2^4$.

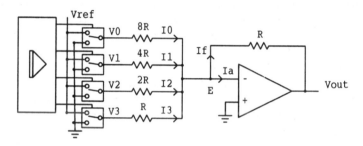

Figure 10.8 DAC using voltage controlled switches

Although the above has many practical applications, it is seldom used when more than 6 bits are required. The main reason is the difficulty in manufacturing resistors for such a wide range of values sufficiently accurately. Instead, an R-2R ladder network is used.

Consider figure 10.9a, which contains three resistors, one of value R and two of value 2R. The 2R resistors are in parallel, so that half of the current flowing through the R resistor to point P will flow down one 2R resistor, the other half will flow through the second 2R resistor. The net resistance of two 2R resistors in parallel is R, hence, the net resistance from point P′ to earth is 2R, being the sum of the resistance from P′ to P and that from P to earth.

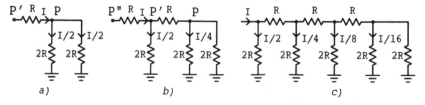

Figure 10.9 R-2R networks

Now consider figure 10.9b, the right hand half of which is the circuit shown in figure 10.9a whose resistance between P′ and earth is 2R. Thus any current flowing from P″ to P′ will 'see' two paths of equal resistance 2R, hence half of the current will flow down each path. So, if the current from P″ is I, that down the left most 2R resistor is I/2 and that through the other two 2R resistors is I/4. The net resistance from P″ to earth is, like that from P″ to earth, 2R. Therefore this circuit can be extended using more resistors of values R and 2R to generate other fractions of I. Figure 10.9c shows a network in which currents of I/2, I/4, I/8 and I/16 are generated.

Figure 10.10 shows how the above can be made into a practical DAC. The currents generated by the ladder network are each passed to switches which are controlled by the outputs of the latch; thus, the currents flow to earth or the virtual earth. All the currents flowing into the virtual earth are then summed and passed through the feedback resistor, so the output voltage is proportional to the sum of the currents, and is hence determined by the logic signals from the latch. R-2R ladders are used as the basis of most DACs in this manner.

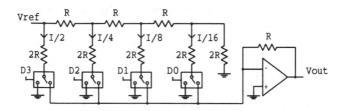

Figure 10.10 Practical R-2R ladder DAC

Analog-to-digital converters (ADCs)

An analog-to-digital converter generates an n-bit digital number proportional to the analog signal on its input. There are many forms of ADC, though only three will be described here.

Figure 10.11 shows the block diagram of two types of ADC, the counter ramp and successive approximation ADCs. A latch contains a 'guess' as to the n-bit digital number. This number is converted using a DAC to its equivalent analog voltage. This voltage is compared with the analog voltage being measured, the result of which is used to change the value in the latch. The ADC has a start convert signal which starts the guesses, and generates a busy signal until the answer is found.

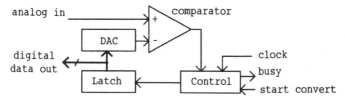

Figure 10.11 Block diagram of ADC

In a counter ramp ADC, the latch is a counter which is cleared to 0 at the start of the conversion, so the lowest value is output by the DAC. If the DAC output is less than that of the analog input to the ADC, then the counter is increased. The output from the DAC therefore ramps up from 0 until it just exceeds the ADC input. The digital number equivalent to the analog input is thus the output of the counter.

One problem with this system is that it can take a long time to measure the voltage. Also, the conversion time varies with the voltage being measured. A better solution is to use the successive approximation method.

Here, for a 4-bit converter, the first guess of the digital number is (in binary) 1000. If the DAC output is greater than the analog input, then the answer requires bit 3 to be 0, so the number is converted to 0000. Next, bit 2 is set, the guess being 1100 or 0100 depending on the first test. The guess is passed to the DAC, compared with the analog input, as a result of which, bit 2 may be left at 1 or cleared to 0. Then bit 1 is tested in the same manner, and then bit 0. Thus, after 4 cycles, the answer is produced.

For an n-bit converter, the ADC converts in n iterations, whereas for a ramp converter, the ADC can take up to 2^n iterations. The successive approximation method is used therefore in many situations. However, for some applications, an even faster method is needed. Here flash converters are used.

An n-bit flash converter has 2^n-1 comparators, each one of which compares the analog input with a particular reference voltage, generating a logic 1 if the analog voltage exceeds the reference. The comparator with the highest reference voltage whose output is a 1 determines the n-bit digital result. This is best explained by example, so consider a 2-bit converter, which requires 2^2-1 comparators. The table below shows the possible digital results and their analog equivalent voltages for a 2-bit ADC for some nominal Vmax:

d1	d0	Voltage
0	0	0
0	1	Vmax/4
1	0	Vmax/2
1	1	3*Vmax/4

Thus the answer should be 11 if the analog voltage exceeds, say, 5×Vmax/8, it should be 10 if the voltage exceeds 3×Vmax/8, 01 if it exceeds 1×Vmax/8 and 00 otherwise. The resistor chain in figure 10.12a generates these voltages. These are fed to the comparators, as shown in figure 10.12b, the outputs of which are fed to a priority encoder logic circuit which generates the equivalent digital number. The truth table for a priority encoder is shown in figure 10.12c.

Flash converters operate very rapidly. However, many comparators may be required; for example, 255 comparators are needed for an 8-bit converter. Thus, most applications use the slower successive approximation devices.

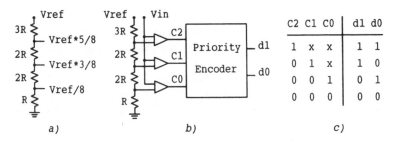

C2	C1	C0	d1	d0
1	x	x	1	1
0	1	x	1	0
0	0	1	0	1
0	0	0	0	0

a) b) c)

Figure 10.12 Circuitry for flash ADC

Multiplexed ADC

As the circuitry for ADCs is relatively complicated, some devices are provided which can convert many analog signals. This is achieved by having a multiplexer to select one of the analog signals. The interface for such a device, therefore, must specify to the multiplexer which signal is required and then issue the start convert signal.

Sample and hold

A successive approximation ADC takes a significant time to convert the analog input. It is important that the input remains constant during the conversion time. If, however, the signal is changing too rapidly, then it may be necessary to latch the analog signal. This is achieved by a sample-and-hold device, which is essentially a device which stores an analog signal.

Voltage scaling and buffering

An ADC will typically convert a signal which is in the range 0 to 2.5 V; similarly a simple DAC will generate a signal in the range 0 to 2.5 V. If, however, voltages in other ranges are required, say between +5 V and –5 V, suitable scaling is required. This can be achieved using operational amplifier circuitry. More details can be found in Stonham. Such circuitry also provides buffering of the ADC and DAC, providing some protection for the devices.

10.3 Communication systems

Computers are often connected to other computers or to such devices as printers or terminals. These connections allow information to be transferred between the devices; data can be shared by computers; text or graphics can be shown on a printer or terminal. Communication is usually achieved by a simple parallel link, a simple serial link, or over a network. These communication systems and associated controlling circuitry are described in this section.

Parallel communication

A parallel communications link is one in which many bits of data, often 8, are sent from one device to another. The link uses the logic signals found inside a computer which do not have the power be sent over great distances. However, such a link can connect a computer and a printer up to a few metres distant.

Many microcomputers are provided with a Centronics parallel port. This defines a standard connection to which many manufacturers conform, thereby allowing computers and printers to be connected. The main connections on the port are as follows. There are 8 data output lines and a strobe signal which indicates that the data lines contain valid data. The data and strobe signals are output from the port. The device being sent the data can issue a signal, acknowledge, to indicate when it is ready and able to accept new data.

Figure 10.13 shows the timings of these signals. When acknowledge goes low to indicate that data can be sent, the microcomputer can put the new data to be output on to the data lines; then, when these data are set, strobe is asserted; strobe is released at least 3 ms later. Sometime later, when the other device has processed the data, acknowledge is pulled low for 3 ms to indicate that new data can be sent.

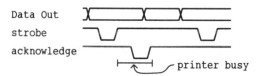

Figure 10.13 Signals for parallel port

Figure 10.14 shows a block diagram of latches which can be used to control these signals. The main latch stores the data being output in a normal data transfer operation. The second output latch provides the strobe signal; the microprocessor writes '0' using one write operation, and '1' a short time later. The input latch is used to store the acknowledge pulse; this is necessary as the microprocessor may not notice the pulse. The input latch is set when strobe is asserted and cleared by acknowledge; its output is passed to the data bus via a tristate buffer. This latch could also be used to generate an interrupt. Alternatively, a PIA (see section 9.4) could be used to provide the port.

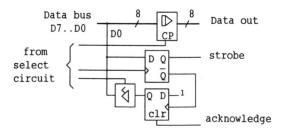

Figure 10.14 Circuit for parallel port

Serial communication

There are some problems with parallel communication. First, the data can be sent over only short distances and second many wires are required to carry the information. Serial communication, however, circumvents these problems. Here one bit of data is sent at a time, so fewer wires are required, and special driver and receiver circuits are used which amplify the signals sent and so allow them to be sent over longer distances. Sending data serially has the disadvantage that the data are sent more slowly than for parallel communication, as only one bit is sent at a time. However, as many of the devices with which a computer communicates operate more slowly than computers, this is often not a significant problem.

In its simplest form, serial communication requires two wires, one which is used to send data and an earth link, as shown in figure 10.15a. In *simplex* communication, data can be sent in one direction along the data wire. Data can be sent in both directions with such a system (*half duplex* communication), if it can be guaranteed that the devices at both ends of the wire do not attempt to send data at the same time. A more practical system, called *full duplex*, has three wires, one for data in one direction, a second for data in the other direction, the third wire being earth; this is shown in figure 10.15b. In addition, many serial communications links also have handshake lines. These are status lines which tell the transmitting device whether the receiving device is ready to accept new data. A five wire system with handshake is shown in figure 10.15c. Some systems have even more handshake lines.

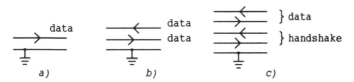

Figure 10.15 Connections for serial communication

When data are to be transferred, the transmitter first checks that the receiver is ready, and then sends the data, one bit at a time. There is the problem, though, that the receiver must know when data are being sent. This is achieved by one of two methods, *asynchronous* and *synchronous* communication.

Asynchronous communication

Figure 10.16a shows the data format used to send a byte of data using the asynchronous method. When no data are sent, the data line is in the inactive (high) state. Then, when a byte is to be sent, the data line is pulled low for a fixed time. This is termed the start bit; the presence of this is used by the receiver to detect that data are about to be sent. Then the data are sent one bit at a time, starting with bit 0. For each bit, the data line is held at '1' or '0' for the same length of time as the start bit. Then, the data line is held high for 1,

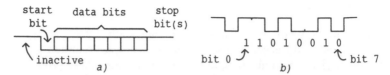

Figure 10.16 Waveform for asynchronous communication

1.5 or 2 times the bit time; these are termed the stop bits. Figure 10.16b shows the state of the data line when the hex number 4B is sent.

The length of each bit time determines the speed at which data are sent. This speed is termed the baud rate, the number of bits per second. A common speed is 9600 baud; if there are one start bit and one stop bit, this allows a maximum of 960 bytes to be sent per second.

Sending data in this manner is relatively straightforward. A parallel-in serial-out shift register is loaded with the data, and at regular intervals, determined by a clock signal, the data are shifted out.

Receiving the data can be achieved by a serial-in parallel-out shift register. There is a problem: as the clock signal is not transmitted, when should the data down the line be clocked into the shift register? The best time to sample the data is half way through each bit time, not at the start or end of the bit time as then the data may be changing. These times can be determined by the receiver having a clock sixteen times as fast as that used by the transmitter; the data line is sampled on each edge of this clock. Eight clock cycles after the data line is found to be a 0 is about the middle of the start bit; sixteen clock cycles later is the middle of bit 0, and so on. In this way, the receiver knows when to sample the data, and hence clock the data into the shift register.

This is beginning to sound complicated. However, special circuits have been produced which can transmit and receive data in this manner. These devices are often called UARTs (universal asynchronous receiver transmitters) or ACIAs (asynchronous communications interface adapters).

These devices can often be programmed to vary the number of data bits sent, the number of stop bits, to add parity in transmission and to check the parity of the data when receiving, and to generate interrupts; some also can have their baud rate set, although this is often set by an external clock circuit. This programming is achieved by writing appropriate data into the control register internal to the device. In addition, the status of the device, for example whether data have been received or whether the device at the other end of the link is ready, can be read from the internal status register. For transmitting, the device has a transmit data register, into which the data are written; and data received are stored in the receive data register.

A block diagram of a UART is shown in figure 10.17. This contains the registers mentioned above, plus shift registers for receiving and transmitting data, a buffer for the internal data bus and chip select circuit. The control register and associated circuitry control the operation of the shift registers. The chip select circuit acts much like the decoders used in chapter 9, allowing data

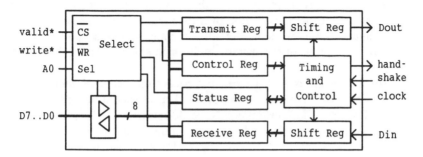

Figure 10.17 Block diagram of UART

to be written into the control or transmit register or read from the status or received data register. If the chip select $\overline{CS}$ is active, the write $\overline{WR}$ and select SEL signals determine which register is accessed; in an interface to a bus these three signals would be generated by valid*, write* and an address line. The UART is provided with a clock signal which should be 16 times the baud rate.

A UART such as the above can be used to transmit or receive data serially. These devices, however, use normal logic signals and so do not allow the data to be sent further than for parallel communication. However, special buffer devices are used to boost the signals to travel over greater distances.

Various standards are used which specify the levels of signal over communications links and the actual signals transmitted. One of the most common is RS-232-C, in which '0' is nominally 12 V and '1' is −12 V; such high voltages allow signals to be sent over relatively long distances. Another standard is the 20 mA current loop; in which a 20 mA current indicates a '1' and no current a '0'. Other standards include RS-422, RS-423 and RS-449. More details about these standards can be found in McNamara and in Cullimore. A practical communications interface will use the associated driver/receiver devices to convert between the TTL logic levels of the UART and those required by the standard.

Although asynchronous communication is mainly used to connect computers together or with printers, a recent innovation is to connect computers to musical instruments such as keyboards, synthesisers and drum machines. The MIDI system uses the asynchronous protocol, with a fixed 31250 baud rate, with logic levels determined by a 5 mA current loop.

Synchronous communication

One problem with asynchronous communication is that ten bits are sent for each eight bits of actual data; this is inefficient, but not a problem if data are sent relatively infrequently. If, however, large amounts of data are to be sent, a better system is required, one which uses a synchronous communication protocol. The basic concept is simple; the various data to be sent are grouped together, with additional information, into a *packet*. Then the packet is sent.

With asynchronous communication, the start bit at the beginning is used to indicate the start of the transmission of a byte and to synchronise the receiver and transmitter. Similarly, a packet also contains a unique pattern for this purpose; for one protocol the pattern is the data stream 01111110. It is then assumed that the devices will remain synchronised for the complete packet, so the rest of the packet is sent. Part of the packet may contain address values, indicating where the data came from, or to where it should be written; another part will allow errors in transmission to be detected.

More information on synchronous communication can be found in Cullimore. Devices are available, similar to UARTs, which allow data to be transmitted in this way.

Local area networks

Asynchronous and synchronous links allow data to be transmitted between two machines. Sometimes, however, information needs to be sent between many machines; or a relatively expensive device, like a PostScript laser printer, needs to be shared by many computers. This is best achieved using a *local area network*, or LAN.

A LAN consists of various devices which are located in the same site and which are connected together; whereas networks connecting systems further apart are called *wide area networks*. The two most common configurations of LANs are *ring* networks and *bus* networks like Ethernet.

In a ring system, such as that shown in figure 10.18a, various devices are connected in a ring. Each node on the ring is connected to a computer, printer or similar device; the node interfaces the device to the network. The action of the node is to receive data from the previous node and pass them to the next node, and to allow data to be passed between its device and the LAN.

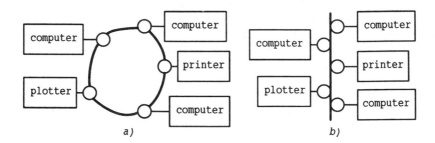

Figure 10.18 Local area network configurations

In operation, typically, one packet of data is sent around that ring, using a synchronous protocol, although some systems use many packets. This packet can contain addresses, indicating the nodes from where data are received and to where data are to be sent, the actual data, and control information here called packet empty and packet read. Initially the packet is empty.

When a device wishes to transmit data, it passes to the node the data and the address of the device to which the data should be sent. The node then waits for the packet to come around the ring. If that packet is not empty, the node just passes the packet to the next node. If, however, the packet is empty, the node loads the data into the packet, loads its own address and the destination address and marks the packet full. The packet continues around the node until it reaches its destination. Here, if the node is able to accept the data, the data are loaded from the packet and sent to the associated device, and the packet is marked read. The packet is then passed on. When the packet returns to the transmitter node, the packet is marked empty, so that another node can load the packet. If the packet was marked read, the transmitter knows that the data were received, otherwise it knows that another attempt should be made to send the data at a later stage. The data will also be sent again if the error checking on the packet indicates that the data have been corrupted in transmission.

In a bus system such as Ethernet, there is a common link which all the nodes read continually and on to which all nodes can write (see figure 10.18b). When a node sees that the link has a packet addressed to it, the node reads the packet. If a node has data to transmit, it waits until there are no data on the link, then it writes its packet, which is then read by the destination node. It is possible that two nodes will at the same time see that the link is not used and both then write data. Such a *collision* can be detected by the transmitter both writing on to the bus and reading back the data there. If the data on the bus differ from the data being sent there is a collision. The transmitters then both stop sending and, a random time later, look again to see if the packet can be sent. The delay before looking again is random so it is unlikely that both devices will look again at the same time.

This sounds complicated, but again suitable interface devices are available for interfacing microprocessors to bus and ring networks. More details about networks and their implementation can be found in books such as Guy's.

10.4 Disks

Disks are a form of memory on to which data can be stored and from which data can be read. These devices can, in general, store more data than ROM or RAM, but accessing the data is much slower. Disks come in various forms, including floppy and hard disks, which use magnetic storage techniques, and the more modern laser-based optical disks. Floppy and hard disks are described here; more details on these and optical disks can be found in Bradley.

The principle behind magnetic storage techniques, whether used on disks or on magnetic tape, is straightforward. Data are stored as magnetic fields on a magnetic surface which travels relative to a head which has a coil wound round it, as shown in figure 10.19. When the medium passes the head, the magnetic field induces currents in the coil, the direction of which indicate that a logic 1 or 0 has been read. Writing data is achieved by putting currents in the coil which induce fields to be put on the magnetic surface. The magnetic fields

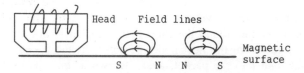

Figure 10.19 Principle of operation of magnetic recording

must not be too strong or too close together, as then one field will affect its neighbour. If the fields are too weak then they may not be detected. Various encoding methods are used to maximise the amount of data stored and to ensure that the data can be read reliably. Two systems will be explained here; others can be found in Bradley.

The frequency modulation (FM) system stores a synchronising clock and data in regular intervals, as shown in figure 10.20a. At the start of each interval, a magnetic logic 1 is stored for a quarter of the interval; this is the clock. If the data for the interval is a logic 1 then a 1 is stored in the third quarter, otherwise the quarter is blank.

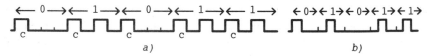

Figure 10.20 Timings of two disk formats

The above method is only 50% efficient as each data bit has an associated clock signal. Therefore modified frequency modulation (MFM) is often used; this is shown in figure 10.20b. The period for each data item is half that of FM, so twice as much data can be stored as for FM. In MFM, '0' is indicated by a pulse in the first third of the interval, and '1' is indicated by a pulse in the middle third. However, if a '0' follows a '1', then the magnetic pulse for the '0' is too close to that of the previous '1'; thus a '0' following a '1' is indicated by there being no pulse at all.

The above formats define magnetic logic levels. The next stage is to consider how the data are arranged on disks. The data are stored in packets, as is used in synchronous communication, with addresses, data, control and error checking information being stored in each packet. When a disk is 'formatted', the packets are set up and areas of the disk are allocated for each packet.

A floppy disk consists of a circular sheet of magnetic material, which can revolve around its centre, housed in a plastic envelope. Concentric tracks are arranged on the sheet, and these tracks are divided into sectors, as shown in figure 10.21a. One packet is stored in each sector. The disk revolves continually, typically at 300 r.p.m. To access a sector, the head is moved radially until it is over the appropriate track, and then the system waits for the disk to have rotated such that the appropriate sector is under the head.

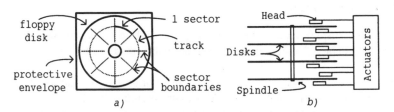

Figure 10.21 Floppy and hard disks

A hard disk consists of several circular magnetic surfaces mounted on rigid backings, as shown in figure 10.21b. Each surface has an associated read/write head. Like floppy disks, hard disks have the data stored in sectors on concentric tracks, and the heads move radially. Hard disks rotate more rapidly, up to 3000 r.p.m., so accessing data is faster than for floppy disks. Also, hard disks can store more data; a floppy disk storing 1.4M byte is typical in a modern microcomputer, but so are 200M byte hard disks.

Normally, a hard disk resides permanently in the computer, whereas a floppy disk can be removed. Microcomputers contain floppy disk drives, which contain the heads and the motors for rotating the disk and the interface to the microprocessor. The disk can be inserted into and removed from the drive.

The exact organisation of disks varies between computers, depending upon the operating system of the computer. Certain tracks are sometimes used to store the operating system; these are called system tracks. Other tracks, the so-called directory tracks, contain information specifying the location of data on the disk. Normally the data are stored in separate files, each having its own name, and each file can be stored in many sectors. The directory track often contains the name of the file as well as the addresses of the sectors in which the file is stored. To access a file, therefore, the directory tracks must be read to find the locations of the file and then the head or heads must be moved to the position of the file sectors.

Control of disks is complicated, but once again suitable controller devices are available which do much of the work. The controller is directed by software, which interprets the directory sectors so as to determine the locations of the files. The interface of a disk drive and a microprocessor uses these controllers and, as data are read from the disk in packets, many interfaces use direct memory access to transfer data between the disk and memory for processing by the microprocessor.

10.5 Displays

Display devices are used to output information to the user. They come in various forms, and in this section a number of devices are described, from simple LEDs to graphics systems. More details about these and other displays can be found in Bradley.

LED and LCD displays

The simplest display type is the seven-segment light emitting display described
in the last chapter. Similar displays are available made out of liquid crystals,
LCDs. Both technologies can come in this segment format and as rectangular
arrays of dots, as shown in figure 10.22a; by illuminating the appropriate dots,
characters can appear, such as the 'A' shown in figure 10.22b. Some units are
available in which the appropriate patterns of dots must be written for the
character to be displayed, such as the pattern for the seven-segment displays.
Others allow the ASCII character to be specified, and the display has a suitable
memory which converts such data to the pattern of dots. This can be
accomplished by the circuit shown in figure 10.22c. The memory contains the
required pattern for each of the eight rows, for each character. Thus three bits
are used to specify the row, and these are generated by a counter; eight bits
are used to specify the character. These 11 bits are passed to the address lines
of the memory, and the data from the addressed location in the memory are
used to illuminate the row of dots whose address is specified by the counter.

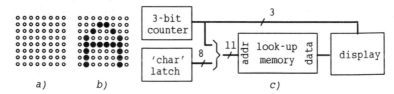

Figure 10.22 Character dot displays

CRT displays

Larger displays exist, having many more rows of dots. Such displays can be
made from liquid crystals, though still today the most common form is the
display based on the cathode ray tube or CRT, like that found in televisions.
The basic operation of a CRT is shown in figure 10.23.

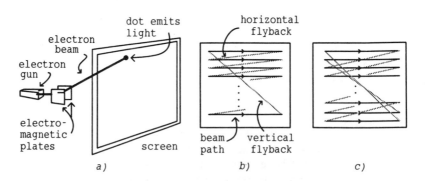

Figure 10.23 Operation of CRT display

The CRT has many dots arranged on a rectangular grid at the front of the screen. An electron gun is used to fire a beam of electrons at this grid, normally in a raster scan, that is, the beam is fired at the start of the first row, then it scans across the row, then it is moved to the start of the next row, scanned across that row, and so on (see figure 10.23b). Electromagnetic coils are used to direct the beam. The intensity of the beam is varied during this scanning process; if the intensity of the beam is high when it is fired at a particular dot on the screen, that dot emits bright light for a short time, a lower intensity beam yields less light. The scanning process is repeated continually, and if the display is redrawn at least 30 times a second the picture appears to be constant.

In the UK, a standard TV picture consists of 625 lines, one half of which is redrawn 50 times a second; every odd line is drawn in one pass of the beam, every even line drawn in the next pass (see figure 10.23c). This process in known as *interlacing*. One problem with an interlaced image is that each dot is only redrawn 25 times a second, so it can appear to flicker. This is why some early microprocessor systems did not use interlace; instead the display had only 300 lines and each line was redrawn in each pass of the beam. (In the USA, a TV has 525 lines drawn 60 times a second, so interlace is not a problem.) Modern computer displays can have over 1000 lines, but these require more advanced CRTs than those found in standard TVs; these are more expensive.

Computers show images on such a display. These images may consist of characters (a text image) or it may be a picture (a graphics display). As the display of a picture is easier, this will be considered first.

Graphics displays

Figure 10.24 shows a block diagram of a graphics system which redraws the picture many times a second. It has a memory in which an image of the picture is stored. A byte may be stored for each dot, indicating the intensity of the dot from black to white (colour will be considered later). The first location in the memory contains the required intensity for the first dot in the the first row, and so on. This memory should thus be read serially, each value read being passed to a video driver which controls the intensity of the beam; this contains a digital-to-analog converter, DAC, as well as other circuitry to ensure the correct signal levels. Careful timing is required to ensure that the intensity of the beam is set when the beam is fired at the correct dot. The beam must also be turned off when it is directed from the end of one row to the beginning of the next. This is also achieved by a suitable controller circuit, which generates addresses for the RAM and hence the data at appropriate times.

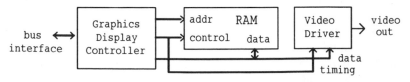

Figure 10.24 Block diagram of graphics display

How fast is the memory accessed? If about 300 lines are to be drawn every 20 ms, then it takes about every 60 μs to draw each line. Each line contains the data describing that line as well as some synchronisation and periods where the beam is turned off while it is redirected to the start of the next line. Figure 10.25 shows the timings of a line of video. The 'porches' are times where the beam is turned off and the 'sync' pulse is used to tell the system when the line starts (like the start bit in asynchronous communication). The rest of the time, about 50 μs, is used to display the data. If the display is 256 dots across the screen, then the memory must be read every 200 ns.

Figure 10.25 Timing of one line of video

There is the complication, though, that the computer will often want to change the image being displayed, that is, the data in the memory must be changed. As the display process is almost continual, there is little time in which the memory is not being read, so writing new data can be complicated. However, once again the controller performs the necessary actions.

In fact, the action of the controller can be simplified by the use of so-called video RAMs. These are like normal dynamic RAMs except that a row of data can be copied from the main matrix into a buffer, and this buffer can act as a shift register, the data from the buffer being output serially, which is exactly the form required for the display. While such serial access is occurring, the normal random access to the memory is possible, so new values can be written into the memory.

Colour display is achieved by an extension to the above. Instead of there being one dot at each position there are three, capable of emitting red, green or blue light, and instead of one electron beam, there are three, one exciting all the red dots, one the green dots and one the blue dots. The memory must contain the data for each of the three sets of dots.

Character displays

Character displays can show only characters and these can be achieved using the above system. When a character is to be placed at a particular position, the microprocessor simply writes the image of that character in the appropriate locations in the memory. If each character is made up of eight rows each having eight dots, then 64 values must be written into the memory. As it is often required that the whole display is scrolled up a line, the data about each character must be copied from one part of memory up one line. This can result in much manipulation of data in the display, the resulting system being slow. Thus, a faster system is often used.

Often the memory for character displays contains only the ASCII value of each character in the display. The modification of such a display requires the manipulation of only one byte per character, not 64 dots for each character.

The display of the characters is more complicated. Each character must be converted into the corresponding output pattern to appear at the appropriate position on the display. The patterns are generated using a look-up table in a memory, as explained in the earlier section on dot displays, but other circuitry is required to ensure that the patterns are generated at the correct time. Figure 10.26 shows a block diagram of the circuitry for displaying the image. This circuit gives a black/white display, but this can be extended to provide colour.

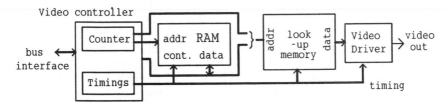

Figure 10.26 Block diagram of character display

The display requires that the first character in the top line is accessed first and the first row of this character is then displayed. Then the first row of the the remaining characters in the top line are displayed in turn. Then, the second row of all characters in the top line must be output, and so on. Thus, if the image of each character contains 8 rows, the memory containing the characters must be scanned eight times for each character position.

Assuming that each character is displayed by 8 rows of 8 dots, the look-up table contains 8 bytes for each character, one byte for each row. The value of the appropriate row in the character is output from the look-up table into a shift register, and this is then output serially to the video driver.

A counter is used to scan the memory containing the characters, so as to generate the value to be passed to the look-up table. The bottom three bits of the counter are passed to the look-up table so as to specify which row in the character is to be displayed, the remaining bits of the counter are passed to the address lines of the character memory, and the character at that address is output and passed to the look-up table. Care is required to ensure that the timing for the system is correct, but again suitable controllers are available.

10.6   Video input

The above section describes how video data can be output from memory to a suitable display. Some computing systems, however, require video data from a camera to be input back into a computer. This requires circuitry to take the video signal, extract the data from that signal and then store the data in a memory called a frame store. The stored data can then be processed suitably. Such a system is shown in figure 10.27.

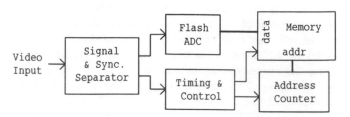

Figure 10.27 Block diagram of frame store

The first part of the system is the signal and sync. separator. This extracts the synchronisation pulses, so the rest of the system can tell when each line of data is about to be received, and then passes the signal (which contains the data) to an analog-to-digital converter. The ADC converts the incoming signal into its equivalent digital number, and this is then stored in memory. The ADC must be fast; for an image of 256 dots per line, the ADC must convert data every 200 ns. Thus a flash ADC is used. The address in which the data are stored is set by a counter, and the whole operation of the circuit is controlled by a suitable timing and control circuit.

Once a complete image is stored, the microprocessor can then access the memory. Thus the above circuit needs extending to allow such access. Note, some of the video RAMs described earlier which have a built-in shift register for outputting data can be used here. Some of these devices allow data to be both shifted out and shifted in to the register. Hence the data from the ADC can be passed to the serial input of the register and, when the register is full, the whole register is copied into the main body of the RAM.

Summary

This chapter has described some other devices which may be interfaced to a microprocessor. The next stage is to consider the interface of these and other devices to some actual systems, namely the 68020, the 8051 and the STE bus.

Exercises

1. Extend figure 10.12 to generate a 3-bit flash ADC.

2. For the dynamic RAM interface, design a circuit to generate RfREQ every 8 µs; this should be cleared when RfACK is asserted. Assume the existence of a suitable clock signal.

3. Design a circuit which interfaces a graphics display controller (GDC) to a synchronous bus like that described in chapter 9. The GDC can be programmed to provide various graphical functions; both commands and data are written to and read from the GDC. Assume the following signals used for the GDC interface: D7..D0, the 8-bit data bus; $\overline{CS}$, chip select, this is asserted when the

GDC is to be accessed; R/$\overline{\text{W}}$, read/write, this is '0' if data are to be written to the GDC; and SEL, which selects whether data or commands are written to or read from the GDC.

4. A UART is another device which has data and commands written to it and read from it. The signals used to interface it are the same as those for the GDC described above. Design a circuit which interfaces both the GDC and the UART to a bus running the semi-synchronous protocol.

5. Design an interface of a 12-bit ADC and 12-bit DAC to a microprocessor running the asynchronous protocol which has only an 8-bit data bus. Figure 10.28 shows how latches are used to control the data.

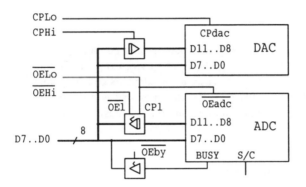

Figure 10.28 Latches for interfacing a 12-bit DAC and ADC

For the DAC, the upper four bits of the data to be converted are written to one address, being stored in one latch. Then the remaining eight bits are output to the second address, to be passed with the values in the latch to the DAC.

For the ADC, the start convert is issued and the busy line is read in the manner described in chapter 9. When the data are to be read, the $\overline{\text{OE}}$ of the ADC is asserted by reading from one address, and the lower eight bits of the data are put on the microprocessor data bus, the upper four bits being stored in a latch. These remaining four bits are read by reading from a second address.

References

D.H. Horrocks *Feedback Circuits and Op Amps* Chapman & Hall, 1987.
Ian Cullimore *Communicating with Microcomputers* Sigma Press, 1987.
J. McNamara *Technical Aspects of Data Communication* Digital Press, 1981.
A.C. Downton *Computers and Microprocessors* Chapman and Hall, 1992.
Alan Bradley *Peripherals for Computer Systems* Macmillan Press, 1991.
C.G. Guy *Data Communications for Engineers* Macmillan Press, 1992.
R.J.Mitchell *Microcomputer Systems Using the STE Bus* Macmillan Press, 1989.

11 Practical Interfaces

The principles by which slave devices can be interfaced to microprocessors have been described, as have a variety of slave devices. The aim of this chapter is to show how some of these devices can be used in some typical systems, as opposed to the simple idealised system described in chapter 9. Three systems are described, the 8051, the 68020 and the general purpose STE bus. These were chosen as they illustrate three very different systems. The simplest of the three, the 8051, is described first.

11.1   8051 interfaces

The 8051 is a single chip microcomputer, containing the microprocessor, its own ROM, RAM and input/output devices, to which other devices may be connected. In the simplest case, a few devices can be connected directly to the pins of the 8051. However, if extra memory is required, or many devices are to be connected, then suitable interfaces must be designed. In this section, therefore, different circuits will be derived for various cases.

8051 external connections

Figure 11.1a shows the external connections of the 8051. Most of these external connections are four 8-bit ports, ports 0..3. These are general purpose input/output lines, but port 3 can be reserved for some specific functions, and ports 2 and 0 can be used to generate address and data buses.

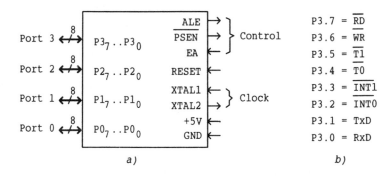

Figure 11.1 External connections to 8051

Figure 11.1b lists the functions of port 3. Bits 7 and 6 provide the signals $\overline{RD}$ and $\overline{WR}$ which are strobes used for reading from and writing to external RAM. Bits 5 and 4, T1 and T0, can be used to provide the clock signal for the

146

two counters in the 8051. Bits 3 and 2, $\overline{INT1}$ and $\overline{INT0}$, are two interrupt request inputs. Finally, bits 1 and 0, provide TxD and RxD, the transmitter and receiver data lines for the serial communications device in the 8051.

When external memory is connected to the 8051, port 2 is used to provide the upper half of a 16-bit address bus, A15..A8, and port 0 provides a multiplexed address/data bus; when the address latch enable signal, ALE, is active, port 0 provides the lower half of the address bus, A7..A0, otherwise port 0 is the bi-directional data bus, D7..D0.

The 8051 has separate program memory and data memory, both of which can be internal or external to the 8051; program memory is stored in ROM, data memory is stored in RAM. Certain control signals are used for reading from ROM, and others for accessing RAM; both use ports 2 and 0 to provide the address and data buses.

For the 8051, which has a 4K internal ROM, if the address being read is in the range 0..0FFFH and the EA input is '1', the internal ROM is read. Otherwise, if EA is '0', or the address is above 1000H, external ROM is read, in which case the $\overline{PSEN}$ signal is asserted, and this is used to enable the ROM.

For reading from external RAM, the signals $\overline{RD}$ and $\overline{WR}$ from port 3 can be used to control the $\overline{OE}$ and $\overline{WE}$ signals on the RAM. If a RAM is to be used for storing both programs and data, $\overline{RD}$ and $\overline{PSEN}$ can be ANDed together, to generate the $\overline{OE}$ signal on the RAM; $\overline{OE}$ is thus asserted if either signal is asserted. When many peripherals are connected to the 8051, they are memory-mapped into the RAM address space and hence their interface uses the $\overline{RD}$ and $\overline{WR}$ signals.

The other connections to the 8051 are the two crystal clock inputs, a suitable crystal is connected across these; the active high reset input, RESET; and +5 V and 0 V.

8051 bus timings

The 8051 uses the synchronous bus protocol; the time for any data transfer operation cannot be varied by any external device. When reading from ROM, the $\overline{PSEN}$ strobe is active for three clock cycles; when accessing RAM, the $\overline{RD}$ or $\overline{WR}$ strobe is active for six clock cycles. Figure 11.2a shows the bus timings for reading external ROM and figure 11.2b shows the bus timings for reading from and writing to external RAM memory.

At the start of the cycle, ports 0 and 2 are given the address being accessed, and when the ALE signal is released, the address on port 0 should be latched.

When $\overline{PSEN}$ is asserted, the ROM should be enabled so that it puts on to the bus the data at the specified address. If, however, $\overline{RD}$ is active, the RAM should put its data on to the bus. For a write operation, the data are put on the bus just before $\overline{WR}$ is asserted, and the RAM should store the data when $\overline{WR}$ is released.

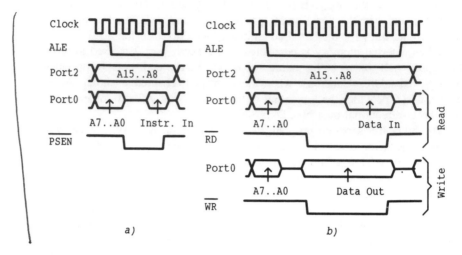

Figure 11.2 Bus timings for the 8051

Connecting to ports

The following shows how an 8-bit ADC and an 8-bit DAC can be interfaced to the 8051. In this example, these devices can be connected directly to the ports of the 8051 because they are the only two external devices in the system. Figure 11.3a shows a block diagram of the system.

The data lines of the DAC are connected directly to port 0 and the data lines of the ADC are connected directly to port 1. The control signals for these devices are connected to bits on port 2, thereby providing the CP signal for loading the DAC, the S/C signal to start the conversion of the ADC, the Busy signal of the ADC, so that the 8051 can test to see if the conversion is complete, and the $\overline{OE}$ signal for reading the ADC.

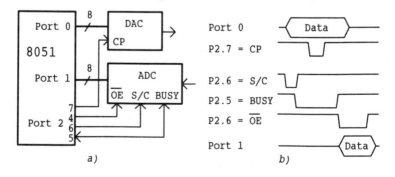

Figure 11.3 Interfacing directly to the ports of the 8051

Figure 11.3b shows the timings of these signals. For the DAC, the data to be output are written to appear on port 0, then the CP signal is asserted and then it is released, at that stage the DAC stores the data. For the ADC, the S/C signal is asserted and then released, the 8051 then tests the Busy line until the conversion is complete; then the $\overline{OE}$ of the ADC is asserted so that the data appear on port 1, the data there are read, and then $\overline{OE}$ is released.

Connecting external memory

The next circuit shows how external ROM and RAM can be connected to the 8051. In this interface, a 32K ROM is connected at addresses 0..7FFFH, and a 32K RAM is connected at addresses 8000H..FFFFH; the RAM is arranged here so that both programs and data can be read from the device.

The interface is shown in figure 11.4. A latch is used to store the lower half of the address bus from port 0; the latch is controlled by ALE. Address lines A14..A0 are connected to the ROM and RAM, as are the data lines D7..D0. The remaining gates control the devices. The $\overline{CE}$ of the ROM is asserted when A15 is '0', and the $\overline{CE}$ of the RAM is asserted when A15 is '1'. The $\overline{OE}$ of the ROM is asserted when $\overline{PSEN}$ is active, that is, when the 8051 is reading an instruction in external memory. It should be remembered that a ROM will only output data when both its $\overline{CE}$ and $\overline{OE}$ signals are active. The $\overline{OE}$ of the RAM is asserted either when $\overline{RD}$ is asserted (when the 8051 is reading external RAM) or $\overline{PSEN}$ is asserted (when the 8051 is reading external ROM). The $\overline{WE}$ of the RAM is asserted when the $\overline{WR}$ signal is active, which occurs when the 8051 is writing to external RAM.

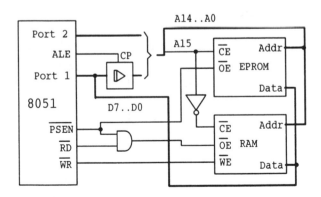

Figure 11.4 Connecting external memory to the 8051

Connecting many peripherals

This section considers the interface of many devices to the 8051, too many to be connected directly to the ports. Instead these devices are connected as external memory mapped peripherals in external data address space, that is, the interface uses the $\overline{RD}$ and $\overline{WR}$ signals.

The interface is of a keypad, two seven-segment displays, an ADC and a DAC. It is assumed that no external ROM or RAM is needed. Four addresses are required for these devices; these are listed in the following truth table.

Addresses	Read Action	Write Action
0	ADC Busy	Issue ADC S/C
1	ADC data	DAC data
2	Keypad	Display2
3		Display1

Figure 11.5 shows a block diagram of the circuit. Again a latch controlled by ALE stores the two relevant address lines from port 0 (only two are needed because the system contains only four devices), and these lines are used to select the different devices. Two two-to-four decoders are used for the selection purpose, one being enabled by $\overline{RD}$ and used to select one input device, and the other being enabled by $\overline{WR}$ and used to select one output device. (The signals KeyPress and RdKey are used in the next section.)

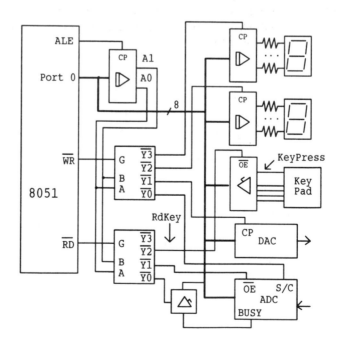

Figure 11.5 Interface of many peripherals to the 8051

Miscellaneous circuitry

The following contains a few other parts of an 8051 system; the clock and reset signals, the handling of interrupts and the serial communications port. Relevant circuitry is shown in figure 11.6. The clock signal is achieved by connecting a crystal and associated capacitors across the two pins XTAL1 and XTAL2. The reset signal is achieved using a resistor and capacitor; initially the capacitor is discharged, so RESET is '1' thereby resetting the device, but when the capacitor is charged, RESET becomes '0'.

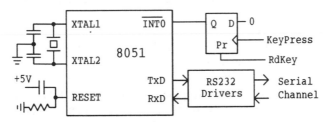

Figure 11.6 Miscellaneous circuitry

The D-type flip flop in figure 11.6 is used to issue an interrupt when a key is pressed on the keypad, that is, when the KeyPress signal (from figure 11.5) is asserted; when this occurs, the Q output of the flip flop is asserted, so the $\overline{INT0}$ line of the 8051 is asserted. When the 8051 responds to this interrupt request it must read the value of the key pressed and clear the interrupt request; this is achieved in one action, as the signal enabling the buffer of the keypad, RdKey, which causes the value of the key pressed to be put on to the data bus, is also connected to the preset signal of the flip flop, thereby releasing the interrupt request.

The serial communications lines, RxD and TxD from port 3, should be connected to suitable driver circuitry, to convert between normal logic levels and those required by RS-232 (or similar). In the interface shown only serial data lines are shown, but if handshake lines are also required then two lines from port 1 could be used, again via suitable driver circuitry.

The above completes the description of various 8051 interfaces. In chapter 13, some assembly language programs are described which use these circuits. Details on the configuration of the ports are described in appendix 2, and these can be found, together with more information on the 8051 in the relevant technical reference manual.

11.2 68020 interfaces

The 68020 is a 32-bit microprocessor, more complicated than the 8051. It can address more memory and is typically used in a microcomputer system, though it can be used as an advanced controller. In this section, two 68020 systems will be described, a dedicated controller and a more general microcomputer.

Many 68020 systems also contain coprocessors, for example, the MC68881, the floating point coprocessor, and the MC68851 memory management unit. The former performs fast floating point operations, the latter is used to organise the memory of the system. Both are beyond the scope of this book.

68020 overview

The 68020 is a complicated processor. Therefore, before explaining in detail the external connections of the device, an overview is given of the machine and its operation.

The 68020 is a 32-bit device which can address 2^{32} bytes of data using the asynchronous protocol. In any operation, the processor can request a transfer of one, two, three or four bytes of data between itself and a slave, though, in fact, as shall be demonstrated, the slave is able to transfer less data if that is appropriate. The 68020 can also respond to interrupt and DMA requests.

As explained in chapter 8, the 68020 can operate in either supervisor or user mode, and certain facilities are available only in each of the modes. For example, some memory can be designated as supervisor memory and some as user memory. In addition, like the 8051, the 68020 can distinguish between program and data memory. Special function code signals from the 68020 are used to specify the area of memory being accessed, though the system can be designed to ignore these signals and allow access to all memory regardless of whether the machine is in supervisor or user mode.

68020 memory accessing

The 68020 can read up to 4 bytes of data at one time. This means that data transfers can be complicated. The following explains the principle of operation. The 32-bit data bus, D31..D0, can be considered to be four 8-bit buses, D31..D24, D23..D16, D15..D8 and D7..D0. Slave devices are connected to these buses. Often, memory is connected to all of the four buses, thereby allowing 32-bits of data to be transferred at one time. Many peripherals, however, are only 8 bits wide; these can be connected to D31..D24. Similarly, 16-bit devices can be directly connected to D31..D16.

The 32-bit address bus, A31..A0, specifies the address of one byte only. If one byte of data is to be transferred, then the address is the address of that byte; if many bytes are to be transferred, then the address is the address of the first byte. The size signals, SIZ1 and SIZ0 are used by the 68020 to specify how many bytes are to be transferred.

Figure 11.7a shows how memory can be connected to all four 8-bit data buses. Note that A31..A2 are common to all memories, but A1 and A0 are not connected. This is because the address specifies the address of one byte; A1 and A0, in this case, are used to specify one of the four memory banks. A1, A0, SIZ1 and SIZ0 determine which of the memory banks should be enabled.

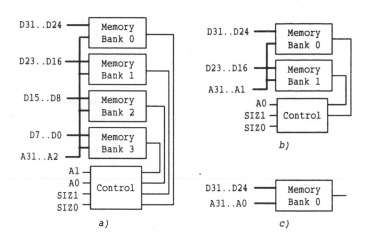

Figure 11.7 Connecting memory to the 68020

Figure 11.7b shows how 16-bit wide memory can be connected to the 68020. Here memory are connected to two of the 8-bit data buses, and A31..A1 are common to both memories. A0, effectively, selects one of the two memory banks. A0, SIZ1 and SIZ0 determine which memory banks are enabled.

Figure 11.7c shows how memory can be connected to one 8-bit data bus only. Note that A31..A0 are connected to the memory, as it must be possible to address one specific byte within the memory.

Consider the system in figure 11.7a. If the 68020 wishes to read the byte at address 65, then A1 and A0 specify that the data are in memory bank 1 and A31..A2 specify the one location within that bank. If the 68020 wishes to read 16-bits starting from address 66, that is the bytes at addresses 66 and 67, then A1 and A0 indicate that these data are in memory banks 2 and 3, and A31..A2 again specify the particular locations in these banks. Similarly, if the 68020 wants to read 4 bytes from address 64, that is, it wishes to read the data at addresses 64, 65, 66 and 67, as A31..A2 are the same for these four addresses, all memory banks are enabled, and again A31..A2 specify the particular location within each bank.

Now suppose that the processor wishes to read 4 bytes from address 66, that is, the data at addresses 66, 67, 68 and 69. These cannot be read in one attempt as A31..A2 are not the same for all these addresses. Instead, two data transfers are required; the first reads the two bytes from addresses 66 and 67 by enabling memory banks 2 and 3; the second reads the two bytes from addresses 68 and 69, by enabling banks 0 and 1. The 68020 automatically instigates these two transfers.

Consider the system shown in figure 11.7c. If the 68020 wishes to read one byte from address 65, then the memory bank is enabled and the data at the specified address is put on to the data bus. But, what if the 68020 wishes to read two bytes from address 66? As only 8-bits of the data bus are being used, only one byte can be transferred at a time, so the 68020 must request two transfers, one from address 66 and then one from 67. But how can the 68020 tell that two transfers are needed? The answer is in the use of the data acknowledge signals, $\overline{\text{DSACK1}}$ and $\overline{\text{DSACK0}}$. These are used to tell the 68020 that data have been transferred correctly, as is usual in the asynchronous protocol, as well as the number of bytes which have been transferred. Thus, when the 68020 wishes to read the data at addresses 66 and 67, the $\overline{\text{DSACK}}$ signals are set to report that only one byte has been transferred from the first address; as a result, the 68020 will instigate another transfer from address 67. Similarly, if the 68020 wishes to read four bytes starting from address 66, the $\overline{\text{DSACK}}$ signals will indicate that only one byte has been transferred, so the 68020 will instigate separate transfers to addresses 67, 68 and 69.

For the case in figure 11.7b where only 16 bits of the data bus are used, if the 68020 wants to read four bytes, the $\overline{\text{DSACK}}$ signals will be used to indicate that only two have been read and, as a result, the 68020 will start another transfer for the remaining two bytes.

Interrupts

The 68020 allows various levels of interrupt which effectively indicate the importance of an interrupt. The 68020 will only respond to an interrupt request if it has a high enough level. Software is used to specify the level above which interrupts will be serviced, and when the 68020 is servicing an interrupt of one level it will ignore any request unless it is at a higher level.

The three interrupt priority level signals, $\overline{\text{IPL2}}..\overline{\text{IPL0}}$, are asserted by slave devices wishing to set an interrupt at a given level. The following table indicates what these signals mean.

$\overline{\text{IPL2}}$	$\overline{\text{IPL1}}$	$\overline{\text{IPL0}}$	Interrupt level
0	0	0	7 (non maskable)
0	0	1	6
0	1	0	5
0	1	1	4
1	0	0	3
1	0	1	2
1	1	0	1
1	1	1	0 (no request)

The 68020 'recognises' an interrupt request if the signals on the $\overline{\text{IPL}}$ lines are constant for at least two clock cycles. However, it is best if a circuit instigating an interrupt asserts the $\overline{\text{IPL}}$ lines and holds them until the 68020 acknowledges the request.

The acknowledgement is first achieved by the assertion of the interrupt pending signal, $\overline{\text{IPEND}}$, which indicates that the 68020 will respond to the interrupt request, but only when it has finished its current operation; for example, if the 68020 is reading from memory when an interrupt occurs, the 68020 will not respond to the interrupt until after the data have been successfully read.

Then, the 68020 will issue an interrupt acknowledge operation in which the interrupting device tells the processor how to find the address of the service routine. There are two possible responses by the interrupting device. First, it can return an 8-bit vector, as in a normal read data transfer, putting the data on to the data bus and asserting the $\overline{\text{DSACK}}$ signals; the 68020 then uses this number, call it n, and the service routine address is the nth item in a list stored in an area of memory called the exception vector table. Alternatively, the interrupting device can assert the autovector signal, $\overline{\text{AVEC}}$, in which case the vector is determined by the 68020 as being the value of the interrupt priority level, call it i, and the address of the service routine is the ith item in another list in the exception vector table. More is said about this table in chapter 13.

Bus arbitration

When another device wishes to control the bus, it must request the 68020 to stop using the bus, in response to which, at the appropriate moment, the 68020 acknowledges the request and allows the other device to control the bus. Three signals are used for this purpose, bus request, $\overline{\text{BR}}$, bus grant, $\overline{\text{BG}}$, and bus grant acknowledge, $\overline{\text{BGACK}}$; their timings are shown in figure 11.8.

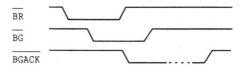

Figure 11.8 Bus arbitration signals

When the requesting device issues the bus request signal, $\overline{\text{BR}}$, the 68020 asserts the bus grant signal, $\overline{\text{BG}}$. At the end of the current data transfer operation, all outputs from the 68020 except those for bus arbitration are put in the tri-state condition (to allow the other device to drive the bus). Then the device requesting the bus releases $\overline{\text{BR}}$ and asserts the bus grant acknowledge signal, $\overline{\text{BGACK}}$, to indicate that it has control of the bus. In response to this, the 68020 releases $\overline{\text{BG}}$. The other device is now in control of the bus. When it has finished using the bus, the device releases $\overline{\text{BGACK}}$, and the 68020 can retake control of the bus, unless another device is requesting the bus.

If there are many devices wishing to request the bus, external arbitration circuitry is required to decide which device should control the bus when the 68020 has relinquished control.

68020 external connections

Figure 11.9 shows the external connections to the 68020. The description below explains the actions of those signals which are required for normal operation. Figure 11.10 shows the timings of these signals when they are used for transferring data between the microprocessor and a memory or peripheral.

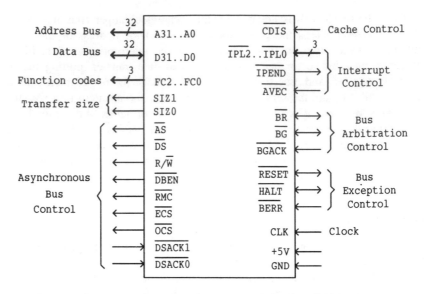

Figure 11.9 External connections to the 68020

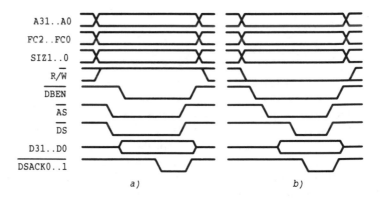

Figure 11.10 Timing of 68020 bus signals

The address bus, A31..A0, defines the address of the slave being accessed.

The function code signals, FC2..FC0, are used to define the type of transfer, as indicated by the following table.

FC2	FC1	FC0	Transfer type
0	0	0	Undefined - reserved for future use
0	0	1	User data space
0	1	0	User program space
0	1	1	Undefined - reserved for future use
1	0	0	Undefined - reserved for future use
1	0	1	Supervisor data space
1	1	0	Supervisor reserved space
1	1	1	CPU space

The user/supervisor data spaces specify memory allocated for storing data in user/supervisor mode. The user/supervisor program spaces are memory allocated for storing programs in the appropriate mode. CPU space is used for special data transfers, for example, those involved in responding to interrupts, or for transfers to the coprocessors. In a CPU space transfer, additional information about the transfer can be found in the address bus; for example, when acknowledging an interrupt, all bits in the address bus are 1, except bits 3..1 which contain the level of the interrupt being serviced.

The data bus, D31..D0, contains the data being transferred.

SIZ1 and SIZ0 indicate the size of the data being transferred, as defined by:

SIZ1	SIZ0	Size of transfer
0	0	4 bytes
0	1	1 byte
1	0	2 bytes
1	1	3 bytes

$R/\overline{W}$, read/write, indicates the direction of data transfer.

$\overline{AS}$, address strobe, indicates that the address bus contains valid information, and that the functions codes, SIZ1, SIZ0 and $R/\overline{W}$ are correct.

$\overline{DS}$, data strobe, indicates in a read operation that the addressed slave should put data on to the data bus; and in a write operation this indicates that the 68020 has put valid data on to the data bus.

$\overline{DBEN}$ is data bus enable; if a significant number of devices are connected to the data bus, then bi-directional tristate buffers should be connected directly to the data bus, and $\overline{DBEN}$ provides the enable for these buffers and $R/\overline{W}$ the direction. Buffers may not be required in all systems.

$\overline{DSACK0}$ and $\overline{DSACK1}$, the data transfer and size acknowledge. These signals are asserted by a slave to indicate that data have been transferred and the amount of data, according to the following table:

$\overline{DSACK1}$	$\overline{DSACK0}$	Meaning
0	0	32 bits of data successfully transferred
0	1	16 bits of data successfully transferred
1	0	8 bits of data successfully transferred
1	1	No data transferred yet

BERR, Bus error, is used to indicate to the 68020 that there is an error in the data transfer. One use of this is when the 68020 has addressed a slave which does not exist; a separate circuit notes that a transfer operation has lasted too long and asserts $\overline{BERR}$ to stop the transfer.

$\overline{RMC}$, Read modify write cycle, indicates that the current operation is a read modify write cycle, that is, the data at the specified address are read and new data written in their place. No more is said here about RMC.

$\overline{ECS}$, external cycle start, gives an early indication that a data transfer is to occur; no more is said of this here. $\overline{OCS}$, operand cycle start, is a similar signal.

$\overline{RESET}$, this bi-directional signal is either output by the 68020 to reset other devices in the system, or by another device in the system (like a reset button) to reset the 68020. Note, a device asserting $\overline{RESET}$ should hold the signal low for at least 520 clock periods.

$\overline{\text{HALT}}$, this bi-directional signal is used to halt the operation of the system. Again this may be invoked by the 68020 or any other device in the system.

$\overline{\text{CDIS}}$, cache disable, is used to stop the 68020 using its cache memory.

The interrupt control signals, interrupt priority level ($\overline{\text{IPL2}}..\overline{\text{IPL0}}$), Interrupt pending ($\overline{\text{IPEND}}$) and Autovector ($\overline{\text{AVEC}}$) were described in the section on interrupts and the bus arbitration signals, bus request ($\overline{\text{BR}}$), bus grant ($\overline{\text{BG}}$) and bus grant acknowledge ($\overline{\text{BGACK}}$) were given in the bus arbitration section.

The above completes a description of the important signals and functions of the 68020. The next stage is to consider the design of a 68020 system.

Example 68020 controller system

The following describes a 68020 based microcontroller. This is similar to that produced for the 8051, and could be used in an application where the 8051 is too slow, or when 8051 software development facilities are not available.

The system has a microprocessor, EPROM, static RAM, a hex keypad, a seven-segment display, an 8-bit ADC, an 8-bit DAC and 8 digital input lines and 8 digital output lines. The memories will be 32-bits wide, the peripherals 8-bit wide. The 68020 can address 2^{32} locations, which is far more than is needed. For minimal addressing, however, the following memory map is used:

Address Range (in hex)	Device
00000000-3FFFFFFF	EPROM
40000000-7FFFFFFF	RAM
80000000-FFFFFFFF	Peripherals

The peripherals only require 4 addresses: these will be:

Address	Action	
0	Write to DAC	Read from ADC
1	Issue start convert	Read ADC busy
2	Write to display latch	Read from keypad
3	Write to output lines	Read from input lines

A block diagram of the system is shown in figure 11.11. The peripherals have an 8-bit data bus which is connected to D31..D24 of the 68020 via a bi-directional buffer. Each memory is connected to A31..A2 and to the appropriate part of the data bus. The system is controlled by three blocks.

The first, marked valid cycle, checks to see that the strobes are correct, and that the function code signals indicate that the current operation is not an interrupt acknowledge. In which case, the circuit uses A31 and A30 to determine whether a memory or peripheral transfer is occurring, controlling the bi-directional buffer appropriately. Figure 11.12 shows a block diagram of this circuit, its inputs and outputs. The circuit is best implemented in a programmable logic array (PLA), whose functions are determined by the following truth table (using the abbreviations in figure 11.12), in which the 'not 7' under the function codes means that the codes should not all be 1, that is, an interrupt acknowledge operation is not occurring, and the signal MA is generated by the memory control circuit (described later) to turn $\overline{\text{WE}}$ off early.

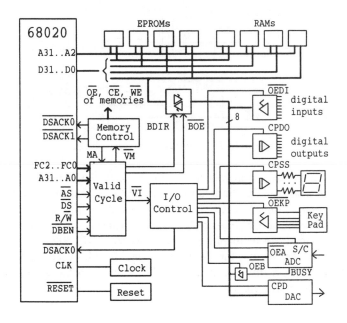

Figure 11.11 Block diagram of 68020 system

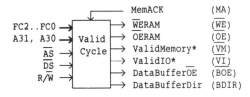

Figure 11.12 First control circuit

FC2..0	A31	AS	DS	R/W	DBEN	MA	WE	OE	VM	VI	BOE	BDIR
not 7	0	0	0	0	x	0	0	1	0	1	1	x
not 7	0	0	0	0	x	1	1	1	0	1	1	x
not 7	0	0	0	1	x	0	1	0	0	1	1	x
not 7	1	0	0	0	0	x	1	1	1	0	0	0
not 7	1	0	0	1	0	x	1	1	1	0	0	1
not 7	1	0	0	x	1	x	1	1	1	0	1	x
			else				1	1	1	1	1	x

The second control circuit enables the appropriate peripheral device, as shown in figure 11.13. This uses the ValidIO enable signal from the first PLA, and using A1, A0 and R/W̄ to select the appropriate device, using a decoder circuit as usual. The circuit also includes a shift register to generate the delay before data acknowledge is generated and the signal to turn off the latch control

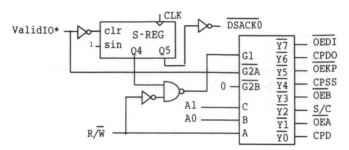

Figure 11.13 Peripheral control circuit

signals. Note, as the peripherals are 8-bit devices, the control circuit should generate an acknowledge indicating that only 8-bits of data have been transferred; that is, only $\overline{\text{DSACK0}}$ is asserted by this circuit.

The third control circuit enables the appropriate memory, taking into account the signals from the first PLA, A30, A1, A0, SIZ1 and SIZ0, and generating the chip enable for each ROM and RAM. Again, a PLA is best utilised to implement this circuit. Figure 11.14 shows a block diagram of the memory and its control circuit.

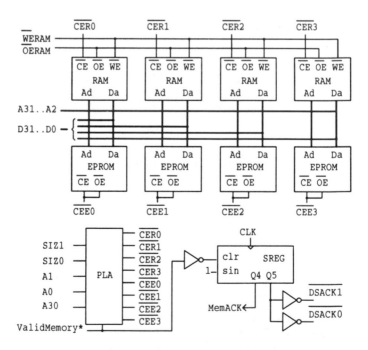

Figure 11.14 Memory control circuit

The $\overline{\text{OE}}$ and $\overline{\text{WE}}$ of the RAMs are common to all the RAMs, being basically controlled by the R/$\overline{\text{W}}$ signal from the 68020. In addition, the $\overline{\text{WE}}$ signals are turned off when the acknowledge signals are generated; hence the signal marked MemACK from the shift register in figure 11.14 is an input to the first PLA circuit in figure 11.13. The $\overline{\text{CE}}$ of each RAM, and the $\overline{\text{CE}}$ and $\overline{\text{OE}}$ of each EPROM are controlled by the PLA in figure 11.14.

When memory is connected to the 68020 in four 8-bit blocks, the SIZ0 and SIZ1 signals indicate how many bytes are to be accessed, and A1 and A0 indicate the address of the first byte. These four signals, therefore, indicate which of the four memory blocks should be enabled; that is, in figure 11.14, which of the $\overline{\text{CERn}}$ or $\overline{\text{CEEn}}$ signals should be asserted. The truth table below indicates which memory block(s) should be enabled (the signal $\overline{\text{CEn}}$ is the active low chip enable for block n);

SIZ1	SIZ0	A1	A0	$\overline{\text{CE0}}$	$\overline{\text{CE1}}$	$\overline{\text{CE2}}$	$\overline{\text{CE3}}$	transfer size
0	0	0	0	0	0	0	0	4 bytes
0	0	0	1	1	0	0	0	
0	0	1	0	1	1	0	0	
0	0	1	1	1	1	1	0	
0	1	0	0	0	1	1	1	1 byte
0	1	0	1	1	0	1	1	
0	1	1	0	1	1	0	1	
0	1	1	1	1	1	1	0	
1	0	0	0	0	0	1	1	2 bytes
1	0	0	1	1	0	0	1	
1	0	1	0	1	1	0	0	
1	0	1	1	1	1	1	0	
1	1	0	0	0	0	0	1	3 bytes
1	1	0	1	1	0	0	0	
1	1	1	0	1	1	0	0	
1	1	1	1	1	1	1	0	

The PLA in the memory control circuit implements the above separately for the RAMs and EPROMs; the $\overline{\text{CE}}$ on the RAMs are asserted if A30 is 1 and the first PLA indicates that a valid memory transfer is occurring, the $\overline{\text{CE}}$ on the ROMs are asserted if A30 is 0 and a valid memory transfer is occurring.

Example 68020 microcomputer system

Next a 68020 based microcomputer is described. This is a general purpose computer on which various programs can be developed and executed. Such a machine has a graphics display (on which text can also be shown), a full ASCII keyboard, a serial interface, disks, printer port and memory. An overview will be given of the whole system and some of it will be described in detail.

The hard disk will contain much of the operating system, but the computer will need instructions for starting the system, telling it to read the operating system from the disk. Therefore, the computer will not require much EPROM, but it will need much RAM; 16 Mbytes of dynamic RAM will be provided.

It is assumed that the display, disk and serial channels will be controlled by associated controller devices. The printer port and keyboard will be controlled by a parallel interface timer (a PI/T) which is like the PIAs described earlier.

A block diagram of the system is shown in figure 11.15. Separate control is provided for the memory and peripherals and, as for the microcontroller, a circuit marked valid cycle is used to verify that a data transfer cycle is in operation. This circuit also detects when an interrupt acknowledge cycle occurs.

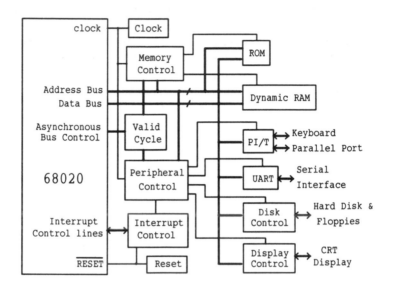

Figure 11.15 Block diagram of 68020 microcomputer

The memory control has two parts, a circuit similar to that developed earlier enabling the appropriate memory blocks, and a more complicated circuit controlling the dynamic RAM. This second circuit generates the $\overline{RAS}$ and $\overline{CAS}$ signals in the manner described in chapter 10.

The peripheral circuits used are those designed specifically for the 68020. One of these will be described, the MC68681 DUART (dual UART); this illustrates the principles required in interfacing the other devices. A block diagram of the device is shown in figure 11.16; more details on the devices can be found in the manufacturer's data sheet.

The DUART contains two serial interfaces, both capable of transmitting and receiving data. It therefore has two transmit data lines, TxDA and TxDB, and two receive lines, RxDA and RXDB. In addition, it has 8 digital output data lines and 6 digital input lines. These can be used for hardware handshake signals or other purposes. Interrupts can be generated by signals on these lines, or on reception or transmission of data, or when there is an error in transmission (for example a parity error). The baud rate of transmission and reception can be programmed.

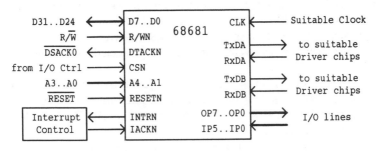

Figure 11.16 Interfacing the DUART

The device is clearly quite complicated. As it is has many programmable features, some means is needed whereby the desired features can be specified. This is achieved using various internal registers, which can have data written to them and read from them. Thus the device has an interface to the microprocessor to allow the programming. This interface consists of 8 data lines; 4 address lines, to address the specific data registers; the R/WN signal (read/not write); a chip select signal, CSN; the data acknowledge signal, DTACKN; and the reset input, RESETN. The N at the end of these names indicates that they are active low. These signals are compatible with those from the 68020, so they can be connected directly (or via buffers). The one exception is the chip select. This is asserted when the 68020 specifically addresses the DUART; so the peripheral control circuit (of figure 11.15) generates the CSN signal if the 68020 is addressing the DUART.

The last part of the circuit is the interrupt control. The DUART can generate an interrupt request, INTRN, and in response to an acknowledge from the 68020 in which the DUART's IACKN signal is asserted, the DUART outputs a vector on to the data bus, and generates the DTACKN signal. The other peripheral devices can also generate such interrupts. Thus the 68020 interface of figure 11.15 also has a block marked interrupt control; this is shown in figure 11.17.

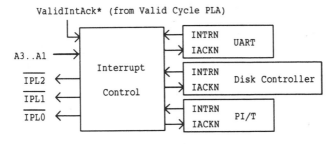

Figure 11.17 Interrupt control circuit

This circuit receives the INTRN signals from each device and generates the appropriate IACKN when the 68020 issues an interrupt acknowledge cycle.

When an INTRN is asserted, the control circuit asserts the interrupt priority level signals, $\overline{IPL2}..\overline{IPL0}$. The values asserted determine the priority of the interrupt. When the 68020 responds to such an interrupt, it issues an interrupt acknowledge operation (a cycle which can be detected as the three function code signals are all logic 1), and the level of the interrupt being responded to is found in address lines A3..A1. The Valid Cycle PLA generates a signal when an interrupt acknowledge is generated, and the interrupt control circuit uses the address lines to determine which IACKN signal to assert. The logic to produce this is left to the reader as an exercise.

The above gives an overview of a 68020 microcomputer, illustrating how standard devices can be connected together. It should be noted that the interface of the PI/T and other peripheral circuits to the 68020 is very similar to that given above for the 68681. Next a different system, the STE bus, is described.

11.3 STE bus interfaces

A general purpose computer can be configured to perform one of many tasks by being provided with the required facilities. These facilities include a suitable program and appropriate hardware, both the required slave devices and the microprocessor(s). Thus a system is required which allows various slave devices and microprocessors to be connected together. The above descriptions of the 8051 and 68020 show one problem with such an arrangement; the processors have different bus signals, so the interface of a slave to a 8051 is significantly different from that to a 68020. The solution to this problem is a modular bus system.

A bus system consists of the bus and a number of modules which can be plugged into the bus. A predefined set of signals is used on the bus, and all devices connected to the bus must conform to those signals. Thus, slave devices are interfaced to the bus in the normal manner, but microprocessors must also be interfaced suitably, with the signals from the microprocessor transformed into those required for the bus. A block diagram of such a system is shown in figure 11.18. This shows a system with two microprocessor boards and three memory or peripheral boards, but the number of boards can vary.

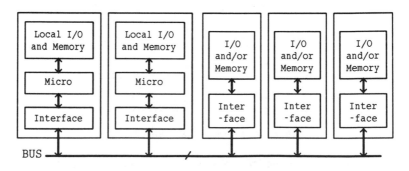

Figure 11.18 Microprocessor bus system

Many different bus standards have been proposed since the mid 1970s. One of the best is the STE bus; it is accepted by industry; it is approved by the IEEE, so manufacturers conform to the standard; it is relatively cheap; it is well defined in terms of the timings of the bus signals and the required power supplies; it is easy to interface slave devices; and the bus is manufacturer independent, that is, it is easy to connect many different microprocessors to the bus. In fact, there are many similarities between the signals on the STE bus and the 68020; but that just shows that these two systems are well designed.

STE allows the connection of memory and slaves to the bus, providing facilities for interrupts and bus requests. Memory and peripherals are distinguished, whereas peripherals are memory mapped for the 68020. STE has only an 8-bit data bus and only 20 address lines, so it is designed for relatively small systems. However, an advanced processor like the 68020 can still be used to advantage on the system; the bus can be used for connecting peripherals and 32-bit wide memory can be put on to the same board as the processor.

STE allows up to three bus masters, that is devices which can instigate transfers across the bus. Only one device is a bus master at any time. An STE system has a default master, which is the master initially; an arbiter, which handles requests from other devices to be bus master; and a system controller, which generates the clock and reset signals and terminates data transfers which take too long (normally because a non-existent slave is being addressed).

STE bus signals

The following describes the signals used on the bus; their timings for data transfers are given in figure 11.19. Note, five types of data transfer are allowed; memory read and write, peripheral read and write, and vector fetch (interrupt acknowledgement). Data transfers are instigated by the current bus master.

A19..A0, the address bus. For memory transfers all lines are used; for peripheral transfers A11..A0 are used; and for vector fetches A2..A0 are used.

D7..D0, the data bus.

CM2..CM0, the command lines, determine the type of data transfer, as indicated by the following table (the reserved types should not be used).

CM2	CM1	CM0	Transfer type
0	0	0	Reserved
0	0	1	Reserved
0	1	0	Reserved
0	1	1	Vector fetch cycle
1	0	0	Peripheral write
1	0	1	Peripheral read
1	1	0	Memory write
1	1	1	Memory read

From the above it can be seen that CM0 is effectively the write* signal.

ADRSTB*, address strobe, which is asserted when the address bus is valid.

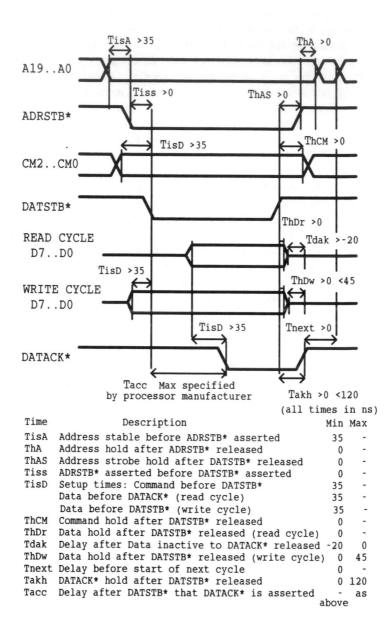

Time	Description	Min	Max
TisA	Address stable before ADRSTB* asserted	35	-
ThA	Address hold after ADRSTB* released	0	-
ThAS	Address strobe hold after DATSTB* released	0	-
Tiss	ADRSTB* asserted before DATSTB* asserted	0	-
TisD	Setup times: Command before DATSTB*	35	-
	Data before DATACK* (read cycle)	35	-
	Data before DATSTB* (write cycle)	35	-
ThCM	Command hold after DATSTB* released	0	-
ThDr	Data hold after DATSTB* released (read cycle)	0	-
Tdak	Delay after Data inactive to DATACK* released	-20	0
ThDw	Data hold after DATSTB* released (write cycle)	0	45
Tnext	Delay before start of next cycle	0	-
Takh	DATACK* hold after DATSTB* released	0	120
Tacc	Delay after DATSTB* that DATACK* is asserted	-	as above

Figure 11.19 Bus timings for STE data transfers

DATSTB*, data strobe. In a read operation, the assertion of DATSTB* means that the command lines contain valid information and that the addressed slave should put data on to the data bus. In a write operation, an active DATSTB* means that the command lines and the data bus contain valid data.

DATACK*, data acknowledge, is asserted by the addressed slave when it has put the data on the bus in a read operation, or when it has stored data in a write operation.

TFRERR*, transfer error, is asserted when there is an error in the current data transfer; typically when a non-existent slave is accessed.

SYSCLK, system clock, is a 16MHz clock which can be used by slave devices for timing purposes. SYSCLK is not synchronised with any bus signals.

SYSRST*, system reset, can be asserted by any device and it can be used to initialise any device.

ATNRQ7*..ATNRQ0*, attention request lines, can be asserted by any device which wishes to attract the attention of the bus master. The normal use for these is interrupts. The signals are level triggered, that is, a request is generated when the signal is low, and ATNRQ0* has the highest priority.

In response to the assertion of ATNRQn*, the master can issue a vector fetch cycle, at address n (in the range 0..7), and the addressed device returns a vector to indicate the device which issued the request. This is called an *explicit response*. The attention request is cleared by such an action. Alternatively, normal data transfer operations can be used to clear the request and to provide any identification of the source. This is called an *implicit response.*

As some microprocessors cannot generate interrupt vector fetch operations, any slave which generates attention requests must allow an implicit response, but need not respond to an explicit response.

BUSRQ1* and BUSRQ0*, the bus request signals, are asserted by any device wishing to take control of the bus. In response to such a request, the appropriate bus acknowledge signal, BUSAK1* or BUSAK0*, is asserted when the current master has relinquished control of the bus. The bus request signal remains asserted until the device has finished using the bus.

Example peripheral interface

This section considers some simple interfaces of slave devices to STE. The first connects a seven-segment display, a hex keypad, an ADC and a DAC to STE. These devices are peripherals, so they will be connected as STE peripherals.

The complete digital interface is shown in figure 11.20; this is just an extension of such interfaces given in chapter 9. The latch and buffers are as normal; a shift register provides the acknowledge signal, DATACK*, and via the NAND gate, the signal to turn off the decoder in a write operation; and CM0 provides the write signal. Note, however, that CM0 inverted is passed to the decoder and the direction signal of the buffer; this is to ensure that the CM0 is connected to one device only, which is good practice as it minimises the loading of bus signals.

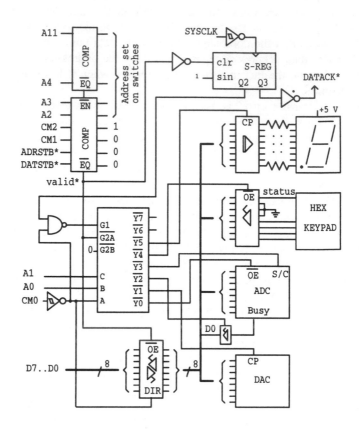

Figure 11.20 Interface of some I/O devices to STE

The main difference between this and the circuits in chapter 9 is in the comparator circuit used to verify that the data transfer is one associated with this circuit, that is, to determine the valid* signal. Here, valid* should be asserted if the address is correct (A11..A2 match the values set on switches) and a peripheral transfer is occurring (CM2 is 1, CM1 is 0, ADRSTB* is 0 and DATSTB* is 0).

One practical point; the STE specification states that SYSCLK, DATACK*, ADRSTB*, DATSTB* and TFRERR* should be connected to logic devices which have Schmitt trigger inputs, so as to reduce the effects of noise; it is recommended that other signals should be connected to such inputs. In the above circuit, the comparators used and the tristate buffer have such inputs.

Figure 11.19 shows the timings of the STE bus signals, with specific timing requirements. For example, ADRSTB* is asserted at least 35 ns after the address is stable, and DATACK* should, in a read cycle, be asserted at least 35 ns after the data have been put on the bus. The following description shows how such timing requirements are used to determine which output of the shift register is used for generating DATACK*.

For this the following maximum timings are assumed. The time for data to propagate through the buffers is 15 ns; the time for an output of the tristate buffer to be turned on is 10 ns; the time for signals to propagate through the decoder is 30 ns; the set-up time for the latch is 20 ns; the hold time for the latch is 0 ns; the set up time for the DAC is 50 ns; the hold time for the DAC is 10 ns; and the time for output of the ADC to be turned on is 60 ns.

For this circuit, the slowest devices are the DAC and ADC. The timing for DATACK* will thus be determined on the basis of the timing requirements of the ADC and DAC.

The minimum delay after valid* is asserted before DATACK* is calculated by estimating when the data from the ADC appear on the STE data bus. Relevant timings are illustrated in figure 11.21a. First valid* is asserted, and later the decoder outputs are turned on as a result of which the ADC will then put the data on to the internal data bus, and later the data will be on the STE bus. Thus the delay before DATACK* is generated is the sum of the propagation delay through the decoder (30 ns), the time to turn the ADC outputs on (60 ns), the propagation delay through the bi-directional buffer (15 ns) and the 35 ns delay required by STE after the data appear; the delay is 30 + 60 + 15 + 35 = 140 ns. Note the time taken for the bi-directional buffer to be turned on can be ignored as this occurs at the same time that signals are passed through the decoder.

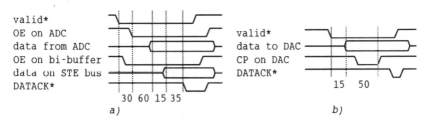

Figure 11.21 Calculating the delay for DATACK*

SYSCLK is a 16 MHz signal, whose period is 62.5 ns. A delay of 140 ns is thus at least three clock cycles. Therefore DATACK* can be generated using the Q3 output of the shift register.

When writing to the DAC, the delay is calculated by determining when the data appear at the DAC plus the set-up time for the DAC: see figure 11.21b. Thus, the minimum delay after valid* is asserted that the CP input of the DAC is released is the sum of the propagation delay through the bi-directional buffer and the set-up time of the latch; the delay is thus 15 ns + 50 ns = 65 ns. Given the hold time requirement for the DAC, DATACK* should be asserted at least 10 ns later. The delay of 65 ns is greater than one clock cycle, so the Q2 output of the shift register can be used to turn off the decoder so providing the set-up time for the DAC, and Q3 can be used to generate DATACK*.

Figure 11.22 shows the extra circuit required to generate an attention request when a key is pressed on the keypad. This contains the flip flop circuit described in chapter 9 which is set when a key is pressed to generate an attention request. Links are provided to allow the attention request to be connected to the appropriate ATNRQ*. Note that the ATNRQ* is cleared when the $\overline{Y4}$ output of the decoder is asserted. The above provides an implicit response only. A vector fetch is not needed here as only one device on the board can issue an interrupt request.

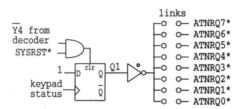

Figure 11.22 Extra circuit to allow interrupts

Example memory interface

The following describes a circuit interfacing a 32K EPROM and 32K RAM to STE; the circuit is shown in figure 11.23. Again this is an extension of a circuit given in chapter 9. The EPROM, RAM, buffers and shift register are as used in the earlier circuit, but the circuit for generating valid* is different.

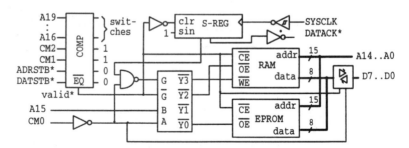

Figure 11.23 Memory interface to STE

The valid* signal should be asserted if the remaining address lines are correct (A19..A16 match the switch settings) and a memory cycle is occurring (both CM2 and CM1 are 1 and both ADRSTB* and DATSTB* are 0).

As regards the timing of DATACK*, the following timings are assumed, in addition to the timings given earlier. For the EPROM, the access time from $\overline{CE}$ is 200 ns and that from $\overline{OE}$ is 150ns. For the RAM, the access time from $\overline{CE}$ is 200 ns, that from $\overline{OE}$ is 130 ns, the set-up time for $\overline{WE}$ is 110 ns and the hold time for $\overline{WE}$ is 0 ns.

Although $\overline{\text{CE}}$ is asserted with valid*, the time delay through the decoder plus the access times from $\overline{\text{OE}}$ are less than the $\overline{\text{CE}}$ access time. Therefore, the $\overline{\text{CE}}$ access times can be used for calculating the DATACK* delay.

For a read operation, the delay before DATACK* is asserted is the sum of the memory access time, the delay through the buffer and the 35 ns STE data bus set up time; the delay is 200 + 15 + 35 = 250 ns. This is 4 clock cycles, so Q4 of the shift register can be used.

For a write operation, the delay before $\overline{\text{WE}}$ is released is the delay through the buffer plus the $\overline{\text{WE}}$ set-up time (15 + 120 ns). Thus Q3 can be used to turn off the decoder and Q4 to generate DATACK*.

68020 on STE

This section considers how the 68020 can be connected as a bus master on STE. As STE has only an 8-bit data bus and a 20-bit address bus, it is best if the 68020 has 32-bit memory on the same board, and uses STE primarily for peripherals. It is useful, though, to have some on-board I/O so that a system can be built with relatively few boards; the 68020 STE board the author uses has on-board DUART and PI/T. A suitable memory map for the 68020 is shown below; this is like that described in the 68020 microcomputer system.

Address Range	Device
00000000 - 3FFFFFFF	ROM
40000000 - 7FFFFFFF	RAM
80000000 - 8FFFFFFF	STE memory
90000000 - 9FFFFFFF	STE I/O
A0000000 - AFFFFFFF	On board I/O

A block diagram for the circuit is like that for the microcomputer in figure 11.15. The main difference is that the disk and display controllers are absent, and in their place is the STE interface. The circuit is shown in figure 11.24.

The interface consists of four parts; buffers for the STE address bus, data bus and the control signals like CM2 and DATSTB*; a control circuit which takes the signals from the 68020 and converts them to those required by STE; an interrupt control circuit, for handling the attention requests; and the bus arbitration circuit, for processing bus requests.

The output enable of the buffers is controlled by the bus arbitration circuit. When the 68020 is the bus master, these buffers are enabled. However, when another device controls the bus, that second device is generating data transfer operations, so these buffers must be disabled.

The control circuit in the PLA is relatively straightforward, for example, $\overline{\text{AS}}$ is effectively ADRSTB* when an STE address is accessed, $\overline{\text{DS}}$ is effectively DATSTB* and CM0 is R/$\overline{\text{W}}$.

The interrupt control circuit is shown in figure 11.25. This generates an INTRN, uses an IACKN signal compatible with those used in figure 11.17 and it generates a suitable interrupt vector; the circuit operates as follows.

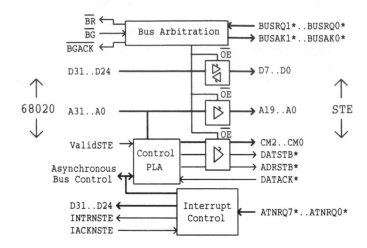

Figure 11.24 Block diagram of 68020 to STE interface

Eight attention requests can be generated on STE, but the 68020 can handle only seven at maximum (when the three IPL signals are not all high). Thus all STE attention requests generate one interrupt priority level, by issuing the INTRNSTE signal to the control circuit in figure 11.17. When the 68020 acknowledges the interrupt, the IACKNSTE signal is asserted, and the circuit of figure 11.25 puts the appropriate vector on to the data bus. This vector is in binary %11111aaa where aaa is the number in the range 0..7 of the attention request. A priority encoder device forms aaa from the eight ATNRQ* signals, and when IACKNSTE is asserted, these values are stored in a latch whose tristate outputs are connected to the data bus; the outputs are enabled when IACKNSTE is asserted and $\overline{\text{DSACK0}}$ is also asserted.

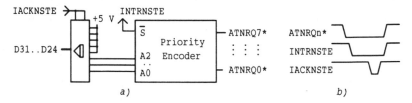

Figure 11.25 Interrupt control circuit

It should be noted that the above is a simple solution to interrupt control as this circuit generates the vector, rather than generating a vector fetch cycle in which the device on the bus produces the vector. Thus this circuit allows only implicit responses to attention requests. A more comprehensive circuit would generate both implicit and explicit attention requests. One of the exercises at the end of the chapter considers how vector fetch cycles could be generated.

The final part of the 68020 circuit is a bus arbiter which allows the 68020 to be the default bus master, that is, the 68020 is the master when the system is first operated, and other devices can request control of the bus. These requests come from the BUSRQ1* and BUSRQ0* lines. When one of these is asserted, a request is issued to the 68020 to stop driving the bus; when the 68020 does so, the appropriate BUSAK* signal is generated. The circuit to achieve this and suitable timing diagrams are shown in figure 11.26.

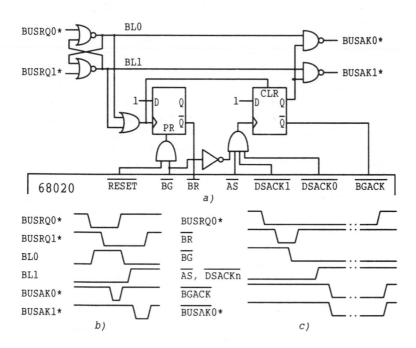

Figure 11.26 Bus arbitration circuit

The two BUSRQ* signals are connected to an ISR latch. This is needed when both BUSRQ* signals are asserted; the first one to be asserted sets the latch one way, and this remains set, even when the other BUSRQ* signal is asserted, until the first signal is released. This is shown in figure 11.26b.

If either BUSRQ* signal is asserted, the first D-type flip flop is set, and this generates the $\overline{BR}$ signal on the 68020. In response to this, the 68020 issues $\overline{BG}$, and this clears $\overline{BR}$. Then, when the current 68020 data transfer operation terminates, that is, when $\overline{AS}$, $\overline{DSACK1}$ and $\overline{DSACK0}$ are all inactive, $\overline{BGACK}$ is asserted and the appropriate BUSAK* is asserted; if BUSRQ1* is asserted, then BUSAK1* is asserted. The requesting STE device is now the bus master. When the BUSRQ* signal is released, the BUSAK* and $\overline{BGACK}$ signals are also released, and the 68020 is again in control of the bus. This is shown in figure 11.26c.

8051 on STE

The 8051 is designed to be used as a dedicated controller. Therefore, it might be thought that it could not be used on STE. Indeed, because the length of a data transfer for the 8051 is fixed, it is very difficult to make the 8051 a master on STE. However, there is one way in which the 8051 can be used, and that is as an *intelligent slave*.

An intelligent slave is an STE slave circuit, that is, it is one which cannot instigate data transfers on the bus, but which contains a microprocessor which can process data. The results of this processing can then be passed to the main microprocessor on the system, by the microprocessor instigating normal data transfer operations. A possible use for this would be for the 8051 to sample an analog signal many times and compute the fast Fourier transform of the data.

A block diagram of the system is shown in figure 11.27a. The 8051 has external memory and peripherals (the extra memory could be used to store the data being processed) and a suitable channel for communicating with the STE bus. This channel could be a shared memory, that is, a memory whose contents can be accessed by either the 8051 or the STE processor (see Mitchell 1989). Alternatively, a bi-directional latch could be used. One such device used by the author is shown in figure 11.27b. Data can be written into each latch from the appropriate data bus, and the outputs from each latch can be read by enabling the tristate outputs of the latch on to the appropriate data bus. Status signals are available indicating when data are stored in the latch, and when the data have been read, so that the next data item can be written.

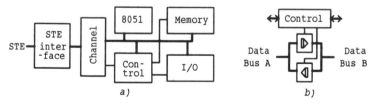

Figure 11.27 Block diagram of 8051 intelligent slave

Summary

This chapter has described how devices can be connected to the 8051 and 68020 microprocessors and to the STE bus. In so doing, circuits have been produced showing the hardware of some microprocessor systems. The hardware, of course, is only one part of the system. Therefore, the next few chapters consider the software for these systems. The final chapter describes the testing of both the hardware and software.

Exercises

1. Design a logic circuit to enable the appropriate memory banks given the SIZ1, SIZ0, A1 and A0 signals from the 68020.

2. Outline a strategy whereby the 68020 on STE could issue vector fetch cycles if that was required. Extend figure 11.25 to incorporate your strategy.

3. Design an 8051 based intelligent slave on STE which uses a bi-directional latch for communicating between the 8051 and the STE bus. Assume the following for this device: each side has a bi-directional 8-bit data bus; a signal CP, on the rising edge of which the data input are stored in the latch to be read by the other side; an output enable signal, $\overline{OE}$, which is asserted when the data are being read; and two status signals, DR and CS which, respectively, indicate that there are data in the latch from the other side which can be read, and that the other device has read the last data byte sent. The 8051 and the microprocessor on STE should be able to read DR and CS.

4. Design an interface of a 12-bit ADC and 12-bit DAC to a) the 8051, b) the 68020 and c) the STE bus. See the exercise in the previous chapter.

5. Design an interface of the graphics display controller and UART described in the exercise in the previous chapter to a) the 68020 and b) to the STE bus.

6. Design an interface to the STE bus of two 32K static RAMs and two 32K EPROMs for which the following timings should be assumed. The EPROM access times from $\overline{CE}$ and $\overline{OE}$ are, respectively 300 ns and 160 ns; the RAM access times from $\overline{CE}$ and $\overline{OE}$ are 150 ns and 120 ns and the set-up time for $\overline{WE}$ is 70 ns. This interface should assert DATACK* as early as possible, that is, different delays should be used for an access to the EPROM and the RAM; show that the circuit conforms to the timing requirements of the STE specification.

References

Philips *Single-chip 8-bit Microcontrollers User Manual* 1988
Motorola *68020 Technical Manual, MC68020UM/AD* 1985.
SCN68681 *Dual Asynchronous Receiver / Transmitter [DUART] Data Sheet* Signetics, 1985.
R.J.Mitchell *Microcomputer Systems Using the STE Bus* Macmillan Press, 1989.
IEEE *STEbus Specification* IEEE 1000, 1987.

12 Computer Instructions

The structure and operation of microprocessor systems have been described, as have the ways in which information is represented and processed within a microprocessor. The aim of this chapter is to describe in more detail the types of instruction provided in most microprocessors and then to show how they can be used to form short programs which utilise the hardware described in the previous chapters. This is to be accomplished using as an example the simple imaginary microprocessor described in chapter 8, as this allows the principles to be established. The next chapter gives more details on the two 'real' microprocessors, the 68020 and the 8051.

As a reminder, this imaginary microprocessor has a data register, DREG, an address register, AREG, a status register, FREG, a program counter, PC and a stack pointer, SP. These are described more fully in chapter 8, where the instruction fetch and execute operations are also given.

12.1 Instruction types

Microprocessors have a wide variety of instructions, some are simple and others are more complicated. However, they can be classified into various types: data transfer, branching, arithmetic, logical, and shifting. In the following sections details are given of the various instructions found in many microprocessors. It should be noted that the manufacturers of microprocessors have different ideas as to the instructions which should be provided and the ways in which they are represented. One example is the short names (the assembly language *mnemonics*) which are used to represent the instructions; another is the order of the parameters associated with the instruction. Here these differences are highlighted and an indication given of the way in which they are used in the imaginary microprocessor.

Data transfer instructions

Data transfer instructions cause information to be transferred between components within the computer system, usually between a register in the CPU and a memory or input/output location. These instructions are given various names depending on the microprocessor; some typical instructions are given below, containing the instruction mnemonic, the register and the address of memory or peripheral.

```
MOV reg, addr    ; move data from address into a register
LD reg, addr     ; load data from address into a register
```

The above are identical in action; so are the next two.

176

```
MOV addr, reg   ; move data from a register into address
ST reg, addr    ; store data from register into address
```

Note in the above that the move instructions specify *MOV d,s*, that is, the data should be moved from the source, s, to the destination, d. The assembly language for some microprocessors require the order of s and d to be *MOV s,d*, so it is important to check which is appropriate. Also in the above, data are moved between a register and memory; some microprocessors have instructions where data are moved from register to register, or from memory to memory.

The assembly language for some microprocessors includes the register in the instruction mnemonic. For example:

```
LDA addr        ; load register A from data at given address
STA addr        ; store contents of register A into address addr
```

For systems with memory mapped peripherals, that is, where peripherals are addressed just like memory but are allocated different addresses, the above instructions are used. However, those systems which treat memory and peripherals separately often have special instructions for handling peripherals.

```
IN reg, addr    ; input data from peripheral address into register
OUT reg, addr   ; output data from register to peripheral
```

Note that the flags of the microprocessor may be affected as a result of these move operations. For example, on some microprocessors the zero flag will be set (to a logic 1) if the data transferred were zero, or cleared (to a logic 0) if the data were non zero; similarly the state of the negative flag would be determined by the sign of the data transferred. On other microprocessors, however, the flags are not changed by data transfer instructions.

For the imaginary microprocessor, it is assumed that peripherals are memory mapped, and that the mnemonics LD and ST will be used for reading and writing data between the microprocessor and memory or peripherals. Also, the zero and sign flags will be affected by a data transfer operation.

Branching instructions

Branching instructions are used to provide conditional operation, to allow the microprocessor to obey actions a number of times and to allow subroutines to be called. Most microprocessors therefore are provided with simple branch instructions, which cause the microprocessor to obey code starting at a different location (this is also called an *unconditional branch*); *conditional branch* instructions, where such a branch occurs only if a particular condition is true (that is, the flags in the status register have specific values); instructions to branch to a subroutine, where the contents of the PC are saved prior to a branch; and instructions which allow the microprocessor to return from a subroutine. The conditional and unconditional branch instructions are sometimes termed *jump* instructions, and the branch to subroutine instructions are sometimes termed *call* instructions.

The following lists some examples of the conditional and unconditional jump instructions. First are those with 'jump' mnemonics.

```
JP addr         ; jump to given address: PC is loaded with addr
JP Z, addr      ; if zero flag is true, jump to address
JP C, addr      ; if carry flag is true, jump to address
JP NV, addr     ; if overflow flag not true, jump to address
JP MI, addr     ; if minus (sign flag set), jump to address
```

Where the instructions are called branch, the above are represented by:

```
BRA addr        ; branch always to addr
BEQ addr        ; branch to addr if result equal to zero
BCS addr        ; branch to addr if carry flag set
BVC addr        ; branch to addr if overflow flag cleared
BMI addr        ; branch to addr if minus flag set
```

The various microprocessors provide different conditions. Most allow the explicit testing of one flag, like BCS above where the condition is whether the carry flag is set, or BVC where the test is whether the overflow flag is cleared. If one positive number is subtracted from another, the carry flag is set if the first number is less than the second; thus the BCS instruction can be used. However, many modern microprocessors allow tests on combinations of flags; and these are needed, for example, to determine whether one two's complement number is less than another.

The following lists all the conditions which can be tested in many microprocessors, giving the mnemonic and meaning as well as an indication of the flags which are tested to determine the condition (note EOR is exclusive-or). These conditions can be used in the *Bcond* or *JP cond* instructions.

```
CC    carry clear            NOT (C)
CS    carry set              C
EQ    equal                  Z
GE    greater or equal       NOT (N EOR V)
GT    greater than           NOT Z AND NOT (N EOR V)
HI    high                   NOT (C) AND NOT (Z)
LE    less than or equal     Z OR (N EOR V)
LS    low or same            C or Z
LT    less than              N EOR V
MI    minus                  N
NE    not equal              NOT (Z)
PL    plus                   NOT (N)
VC    overflow clear         NOT (V)
VS    overflow set           V
```

Some microprocessors also have the true condition, which can be used to provide an unconditional jump; for completeness the false condition can also be provided, yielding a jump which never takes place!

On most microprocessors, the branch to subroutine instructions save the PC on to the stack, in the manner described in chapter 8. The instructions to call a subroutine and return are given various names, for example:

```
BSR addr     ; branch to subroutine at given addr
JSR addr     ; jump to subroutine at given addr
CALL addr    ; call subroutine at given addr
RET          ; return
RTS          ; return from subroutine
```

CALL and RTS are used in the examples in this chapter. Some microprocessors have conditional subroutine calls, so the following may be allowed:

```
JSR PL, addr   ; jump to subroutine if result is positive
```

Another use of the stack is to store the registers of the microprocessor when a subroutine is obeyed. One philosophy to adopt when programming is that at the end of a subroutine no register should appear to have been changed unless a result is returned in that register. For example, if the action of a subroutine is to read the value of the key pressed on a keyboard, one register should be changed so as to contain the value of that key. If in the course of operation of that subroutine, another register had to be used temporarily, then at the start of the subroutine the value of the register should be saved and at the end it should be reloaded, just as the PC is saved when a subroutine is called and reloaded at its end.

Saving a register can also be achieved using the stack, and two instructions are usually provided. One causes data to be pushed on to the stack, the other causing data to be pulled (or popped) from the stack. The push instruction saves data the same way that the PC is saved, with the stack pointer, SP, being decremented and the register contents stored at the address pointed to by SP; and the pull instruction loads the register and then increments the SP. These instructions are of the form:

```
PUSH reg   ; push register on to stack
PULL reg   ; pull register from stack
POP reg    ; pop register from stack
```

Notice that it is important for there to be the same number of pushes as pulls. For example if the subroutine contained:

```
PUSH reg
< rest of subroutine >
RTS
```

the return instruction would return to the address found at the top of the stack, which is the contents of the register. This can cause problems as the PC may be loaded with the address of memory containing data not instructions.

Another use for the stack is to pass information to and from subroutines. In high level language terms, these are the parameters passed to a procedure. For example, if a subroutine is to output a character, the value to be output is pushed on to the stack before the subroutine is called. Similarly, a subroutine which reads a value from a keypad might put the value read on to the stack. More details on this are given in chapter 14.

On some microprocessors there is a separate stack for data and subroutine calls; the registers are pushed on to the data stack, the PC on to the system stack. This means that the problem above is avoided as the PC will be loaded with the correct return address. However, it may mean that registers contain unexpected data, and this may be a more difficult bug to find.

Other microprocessors have a system stack and a user stack. The former is the stack used when the program is in system mode, and this normally occurs when the computer is running its operating system; the user stack is used by application programs. In this way, it is hoped that stack errors in the user program cannot cause the operating system to crash.

Arithmetic instructions

The arithmetic instructions provided are those which implement the operations described in chapter 7. In general, these instructions take data from a register, process the data, and then return the result into that register and set the flags in the status register according to the result. The flags that are affected are zero, carry, overflow and sign. The instructions are listed below, followed by suitable explanatory comments; the instructions perform arithmetic on integer data.

```
ADD reg, addr   ; add to register the data at the given address
ADC reg, addr   ; add to register the data and state of carry flag
SUB reg, addr   ; subtract data from register
SBC reg, addr   ; subtract data and carry flag from register
CMP reg, addr   ; compare register and data
MUL reg, addr   ; multiply register by data
DIV reg, addr   ; divide register by data
NEG reg         ; negate (two's complement invert) register
INC reg         ; increment register
DEC reg         ; decrement register
DA reg          ; decimal adjust register
```

Note, in the assembly language of some microprocessors the order of the addr and reg is reversed, so that the add instruction might be:

```
ADD addr, reg   ; add data at given address to the register
```

If the mnemonic includes the register, the following may be found:

```
ADDA addr       ; add data at given address to register A
```

Some microprocessors allow the contents of one memory location to be added to the contents of another.

The ADC or add with carry instruction is required in various situations, the most common being as follows. Suppose two 16-bit numbers are to be added together on an 8-bit microprocessor. In this case the least significant bytes of the two numbers should be added, and then their most significant bytes added. However, if there is a carry from the first addition, it should be added into the sum of the most significant bytes, as shown by the following example:

```
  00000000 11000000
+ 00000000 01000000
  00000001 00000000
```

Thus, the 16-bit addition is achieved by the following, assuming that the high byte is at a given address and the low byte at the next address:

```
ADD reg1, addr+1    ; add least significant data to reg low
ADC regh, addr      ; add most significant data to reg high
```

The SBC or subtract with carry instruction is used in a similar manner; 16-bit subtraction is achieved by:

```
SUB reg1, addr+1    ; subtract least significant data to reg low
SBC regh, addr      ; subtract most significant data to reg high
```

The compare instructions perform the subtract operation, affect the flags accordingly, but leave the register unchanged. Thus the instruction:

```
CMP reg, addr
```

will leave the register unchanged, but set the zero flag if the register and data are the same and set the carry, overflow and sign flags appropriately.

The multiply and divide instructions often only perform unsigned integer operation, but some microprocessors allow both signed and unsigned operation. Typical mnemonics for signed and unsigned multiply are MULS and MULU.

The negate instruction converts a positive two's complement number to its equivalent negative number, or vice versa. This is achieved by inverting the bits in the number and adding one.

The decimal adjust instruction is used for BCD arithmetic. To add two BCD numbers the instructions are:

```
ADD reg, addr
DA reg
```

The DA instruction adds 6 to the appropriate nibls if needed. Most micro-processors have a special flag in the status register (called a half carry flag) which the DA instruction tests in order to determine whether any addition is required. Some microprocessors do not have a DA instruction, but instead can be set to operate in binary or BCD mode. If in BCD mode, any addition will add the data and automatically do any necessary adjustment.

Logical instructions

The logical instructions usually take data from a register, process the data and return the result in the register and set the flags accordingly. These are:

```
AND reg, addr    ; and the register and data at the given address
OR   reg, addr   ; or the register and data
EOR reg, addr    ; exclusive-or the register and data
BIT reg, addr    ; test specified bits in the register
COM reg          ; compliment register (invert each bit)
CLR reg          ; clear the register (set each bit to '0')
```

These require little comment. AND performs the *and* operation on each bit in the register with the corresponding bit in the other data. OR performs the logical *or* of each pair of bits. EOR performs the *exclusive-or* of each pair of bits; the exclusive-or of two bits is '1' if they differ. BIT ands the register with the data, setting the flags appropriately, but leaves the register itself unchanged (compare the CMP instruction). In some microprocessors, the BIT instruction specifies the particular bit to be tested; for example, *BIT reg, 3* sets the zero flag depending on whether bit 3 of the register is '1' or 0'.

The following examples illustrate the AND, OR and EOR instructions:

```
     00011011          00011011          00011011
AND  10110001      OR  10110001     XOR  10110001
     00010001          10111011          10101010
```

Shifting and rotating instructions

The required shifting functions are described in chapter 7, namely providing shift left and arithmetic or logical shift right. The actions of these instructions are shown in figure 12.1a, b and c; the rectangles represent bits, C is the carry flag and the arrows show how the data are moved. The mnemonics are:

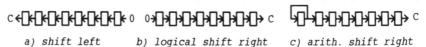

```
a) shift left      b) logical shift right    c) arith. shift right
```

```
   d) rotate left          e) rotate right through C
```

Figure 12.1 Shift and rotate operations

```
LSL reg    ; logical shift left of register
LSR reg    ; logical shift right of register
ASR reg    ; arithmetic shift right of register
```

The LSL instruction shifts all data in the register one place to the left, the top bit is shifted into carry, and '0' is shifted into bit 0. LSR shifts the register to the right, bit 0 is shifted into carry, and '0' is shifted into the top bit. ASR shifts the register to the right as for LSR, but leaves the top bit unchanged, thus retaining the sign of the number. ASR should be used on two's complement numbers, LSR on positive only numbers. Some microprocessors allow the number of shifts to be specified in the instruction; for example, the instruction *ASR reg, 3* shifts the register to the right three times.

The rotate instructions are similar, except the bit shifted from one end of the register is shifted into the other end. An example of rotate left is shown in figure 12.1d. Typical mnemonics for these are:

```
ROL reg    ; rotate register to the left
ROR reg    ; rotate register to the right
```

The rotate through carry instructions are similar, except that the carry flag is shifted into one end of the register and the bit shifted from the register is put into the carry flag; rotate right through carry is shown in figure 12.1e. For example, if carry = 1 and reg = 00010010, then after a ROLC, carry will be 0 and reg will be 00100101. The mnemonics are:

```
ROLC reg    ; rotate register to the left through carry
RORC reg    ; rotate register to the right through carry
```

One use for these instructions is when shifting 16-bit numbers on an 8-bit microprocessor. To shift left such a number, the lower byte should be shifted left, the top bit being shifted into carry, and then the top byte should be rotated left, with the bit shifted from the lower byte (and now in carry) being shifted into bit 0 of the higher byte. The following shifts to the right a 16-bit number stored in registers regl and regh:

```
LSL regl    ; shift regl, its top bit going into carry
ROL regh    ; rotate regh, the bit from regl is put into bit 0
```

12.2 Addressing modes

In the above description, instructions were specified by *LD reg, addr*, which loaded the register from the memory at the given address, or *ADD reg, addr*, which added the data at the specified address to the register. These instructions specify the data to be processed by giving the address of the data. Most microprocessors provide various ways in which the address of the data can be specified; these are termed *addressing modes*. The following describes various common addressing modes. Note, different assemblers specify addressing modes in different ways. Thus the following describes the principles behind the operations and the syntax used in the imaginary microprocessor; the syntaxes required for the 'real' microprocessors are given in the relevant sections.

Absolute addressing

This mode is also called direct or extended addressing. It is the mode used in the above examples; the instruction explicitly contains the address of the data.

```
LD reg, addr
```

will load the given register with the data at the address addr.

The binary for the instruction, called the op-code, must be large enough to include the complete address. For a typical 8-bit microprocessor with a 16-bit address, the op-code will be three bytes, the first specifying that the instruction is load using absolute addressing, the other two bytes containing the address.

Page mode

Some microprocessors have an addressing mode which contains the address using fewer bytes. This is achieved by storing one part of the address elsewhere; typically the upper half of the address is stored in a special register.

On 8-bit microprocessors, the 64K address space is often considered to contain 256 pages, each containing 256 bytes. Thus a page mode instruction specifies the address within the given page, and so the address in the instruction needs to be only 8 bits long. Thus the instruction could be:

```
LD reg, > addr
```

where the > specifies that page mode addressing is used, and is needed so that an assembler decoding the instruction can tell which mode is used, and hence produce the correct op-code.

When the microprocessor obeys the instruction, the required data are fetched by the microprocessor putting this half address on to the lower half of the address bus, and the data from the special register on to the upper half of the address bus. Then the data are read from memory in the usual manner.

This mode requires the upper half of the address to be set by loading the register with the page address, which is achieved using another instruction. However, if much of the data being processed are stored in a 256 byte page, this register need be set only once. Thereafter, the operation of the computer will be quicker using page mode operation than absolute mode, as each instruction will be one byte shorter, and so will take less time to fetch.

Some microprocessors have zero page mode. Here the upper half of the address is always zero. For microprocessors with a 32-bit address, the address can be specified by a shorter number in a similar manner.

Immediate addressing

In immediate addressing the data being processed are given explicitly in the instruction. As the data are immediately available when the instruction has been read, rather than having to be read from memory, the mode is called immediate.

```
LD reg, #data
```

will load the register with the given data. The # symbol is often used to specify that immediate addressing is being used. The data to be loaded can normally be specified in various ways, decimal, hexadecimal, binary or as a character:

```
LD reg, #65          ; load register with 65
LD reg, #$41         ; load register with hex number 41, i.e. 65
LD reg, #%01000001   ; load register with binary number (also 65)
LD reg, #'A'         ; load register with character A (also 65)
```

The assembler processing the above will convert the data specified in whichever form into the appropriate binary number. The % tells the assembler that a number is being specified in binary, a $ (or sometimes an &) indicates that a hexadecimal number is specified. If the register is 8-bit, then the data will be 8-bit, but if a 16-bit register is being loaded, the data will be 16-bit, and so on.

Register indirect addressing

In the above addressing modes the address of the data can be determined when the programmer writes the program. On other occasions the required address can be specified only when the program is running. This can be achieved using register indirect addressing. Here, the address of the required data is stored in a register (typically an address register).

```
LD reg, (areg)
```

loads the register with the data at the address contained in areg. The address register is put in brackets to specify the mode. Another use of the mode is when a particular location is accessed many times; the register is loaded with its address once and then the data at that address are accessed at various times. Note that this indirect addressing is sometimes specified by:

```
LD reg, @areg
```

Offset register indirect addressing

This is an extension of the above. Here the address of the data is found by adding some value to the contents of a register. For example,

```
LD reg, 3 (areg)           or
LD reg, (3, areg)
```

specifies that the register be loaded with data at the address found by adding 3 to the value in the address register. If areg contains 5, then *LD reg, 3 (areg)* loads reg with the data at address 8. Similarly,

```
LD reg1, reg2 (areg)       or
LD reg1, (reg2, areg)
```

loads reg1 with data at the address found by adding the contents of reg2 to the value in the address register. So, if reg2 contains 10 and areg contains 125, then *LD reg1, reg2 (areg)* loads reg1 with the data at address 135.

Auto-increment and auto-decrement

When processing various data in a list, the first item is processed, then the second, then the third, and so on. This can be achieved by:

```
LD reg, (areg)
INC areg
```

However, an addressing mode is often provided where the address register is automatically incremented or decremented. Then the above can be achieved by:

```
LD reg, (areg)+
```

and if the memory area is to be examined in reverse order, the auto-decrement mode can be used:

```
LD reg, -(areg)
```

Note that the above examples are of post-increment and pre-decrement operation; that is, the address register is incremented after the data have been transferred, or the register is decremented before the data have been transferred. These operations are the same as those required for the push and pull instructions. Thus, if SP is the stack pointer, then:

```
PUSH reg     is equivalent to ST reg, -(SP)
PULL reg     is equivalent to LD reg, (SP)+
```

Some microprocessors also allow pre-increment and post-decrement operation. Others allow the amount by which the register is incremented and decremented to be specified. This is needed, for example, if each data item is 16-bits, as the address register should be incremented by 2 bytes to move to the next 16-bit item.

Relative addressing

In this mode, the address of the data is specified relative to the current position in the program; the address is offset from the program counter. Thus this is a special case of offset indirect addressing.

Relative addressing is often used for branching instructions. Consider the following instruction, a branch to the address defined by the name *label*.

```
BRA label
```

The op-code for the instruction contains two parts; one specifies the branch instruction, the second is a two's complement number. When the instruction is obeyed, the PC has this two's complement number added to it. Note, the value is added as part of the execute part of the fetch-execute cycle; this occurs when the instruction has been fetched, and hence the offset is added to the address after the current instruction.

A programmer writing in machine code has to calculate the appropriate offset value; this is an error-prone process. If the program is subsequently changed, and an extra instruction added between the current instruction and the destination of the branch, then the offset must be recalculated.

Such a problem does not occur when writing in assembly language. When the assembler is analysing such an instruction, it first works out the address associated with label, then it calculates the difference between that address and the current address, and finally it generates the op-code containing the instruction code and this difference. If a new instruction is added, the assembler is then run over the new program, and the offsets are calculated automatically.

Relative addressing, of course, is specifying an address relative to the address of the current instruction, that is, relative to the contents of the PC. Thus, for example, another example of relative addressing is:

```
LD reg, 3(PC)     ; load reg with data at address in PC + 3
```

Inherent, implied and register addressing

Some instructions have no data to be specified; for example, the instruction *NOP* does nothing. All the data are inherent or implied in the instruction.

Other instructions process a register, like *LSR reg*, which performs logical shift right on the given register. Also, consider *LD reg1, reg2*, which transfers data from one register to another. Here the addressing mode is sometimes called register.

Orthogonality, CISC and RISC

During the evolution of microprocessors, various instruction sets have been provided and the number of instructions and addressing modes have varied. The following describes the different facilities.

Some processors have many instructions, including some specialist ones for moving large blocks of data or searching for data within a block of memory. The Z80 and Z8000 have such facilities. One notable feature of these processors is that relatively few addressing modes are provided, and these modes can be used only with specific instructions.

Other processors, notably the 6809 and 68000, have fewer instructions, but more addressing modes. Also, most addressing modes can be used with most of the instructions. An instruction set which allows the instructions to be used in the same manner, that is, with the same addressing modes, is said to be *orthogonal* or regular.

At one time it was believed that the power of a computer could be increased by providing more instruction types. Now, however, it is recognised that fewer instructions with more addressing modes is a better strategy. This has led to the development of reduced instruction set computers (*RISCs*), as opposed to complex instruction set computers, *CISCs*.

A RISC has a number of simple instructions. These instructions can operate very quickly. As the machine has few instructions, the design of the computer is made more easy. Thus a fast computer can be quickly designed and built. One such RISC device is the ARM device from Acorn, details of which are in Downton.

12.3 Example programs

The following examples describe assembly language programs for use on the simple imaginary microprocessor system outlined at the end of chapter 3 and described in more detail in chapters 8 and 9. The system contains the microprocessor, memory, a keypad, seven-segment displays, an ADC and a DAC. The programs contain the appropriate instructions and *pseudo-operations* in which definitions are made of data and constants to help make the program easier to read. As with all good programs comments are also included.

Seven-segment display example

The first program waits for the user to press a key on the hex keypad, reads the key (getting a value in the range 0 to 15 corresponding to the key pressed) and displays the appropriate value on a seven-segment display. The following is assumed about the system.

The keypad is accessed by reading from address (in hex) $FF02. Here, bit 7 is '0' if a key has been pressed, in which case bits 3 to 0 contain the value of the key pressed.

The seven-segment display is also at address $FF02. The data value written to that address directly determines the state of the segments on the display. '0' must be written to any bit if the associated segment is to shine. Figure 12.2a shows which bit corresponds to which segment (and to the extra dot). Figure 12.2b shows the binary numbers required to display each of the hex numbers 0..9, A..F and the data patterns produced on the display by the output of these numbers.

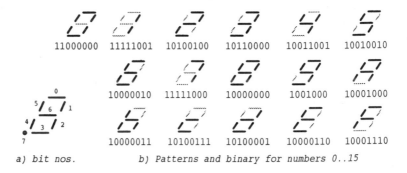

a) bit nos.   b) Patterns and binary for numbers 0..15

Figure 12.2 Seven-segment displays and associated codes

Algorithm development

This section shows the stages by which the program is developed. The problem can be broken down into a series of actions, which themselves can be considered in more detail. The basic actions are:

```
wait for a key to be pressed and read key
convert key value to that needed for seven-segment display
display it
```

The microprocessor should loop continually doing this. The above actions can be implemented as subroutines, so the main part of the program is:

```
loop:   CALL ReadKey    ; call the subroutine ReadKey
                        ; which reads the value into Dreg
        CALL Convert    ; convert data in Dreg to required pattern
        CALL DisplayIt  ; and output value in Dreg to the display
        BRA loop
```

The ReadKey subroutine can be considered next. This should continually read from the keyboard address until bit 7 is '0'. At that time, bits 3 to 0 contain the value of the key; these can then be identified by clearing the upper 4 bits. Thus ReadKey is:

```
ReadKey:      ; read value entered at keypad into Dreg
     LD Dreg, KeyPadAddress   ; read value from keypad address
     BMI ReadKey             ; jump back if key is not pressed
     AND Dreg, #%00001111    ; clear top bits
     RTS                     1 return from subroutine
```

When Dreg is loaded with the value of the keypad, flags are set depending upon that value. One flag, the sign flag, will be set if the value read is negative,. that is, if bit 7 is '1'. The BMI instruction (branch if minus) causes the microprocessor to branch if the sign flag is set. Thus the microprocessor will branch back if a key has not been pressed. The AND instruction ands each bit in the Dreg with the corresponding bit in the data value. Thus bits 7 to 4 of the Dreg will be anded with '0', so these bits will become '0', and bits 3 to 0 will be anded with '1', so they will not change. Thus, Dreg will contain a number in the range 0 to 15 corresponding to the value of the key pressed.

The Convert subroutine must take the value and convert it into the appropriate pattern required to illuminate the seven-segment display. This is best achieved using a look-up table. This table is a number of data bytes stored sequentially in memory, as shown in figure 12.3. The first byte contains the pattern to display 0, the following byte contains the pattern for 1, and so on. Thus, if Table is the label defining the address of the look-up table, then at address Table + 0 is the pattern to show 0, at address Table + 1 is the pattern to show 1, and so on, so that at address Table + n is the pattern to show the number n. This can be implemented by loading the address register with the address of the table, and then using the offset register indirect addressing mode.

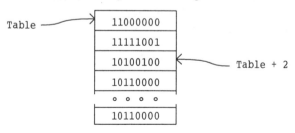

Figure 12.3 Look-up table

```
LD Areg, #Table          ; load address of table
LD Dreg, Dreg (Areg)     ; index to Dreg'th element in table
```

Note that the first instruction uses the immediate addressing mode, not the absolute mode. This is because Areg should be loaded with the address of the table, not the data at that address.

The *LD Dreg, Dreg(Areg)* instruction loads Dreg with the data at the address found by adding the contents of Dreg to Areg. This address is the address of the table plus the value of the key, which is the address of the pattern for that key.

This subroutine uses Areg temporarily, it does not return any value in Areg; it does, however, use Dreg and return a result there. Using the philosophy mentioned earlier of leaving a register unchanged unless a result is returned there, the Areg should be pushed at the start of the subroutine and pulled at the end. The convert routine becomes thus:

```
Convert:   ; Convert 0..15 in Dreg to pattern for display
           PUSH Areg              ; save Areg
           LD Areg, #Table        ; load address of table
           LD Dreg, Dreg (Areg)   ; index to Dreg'th element in table
           PULL Areg
           RTS
```

The table must be implemented. This consists of a series of data bytes. These are defined by a pseudo operation called *DefByte*. All the values following a *DefByte* are bytes of data. In this case, the data are the patterns required for displaying the numbers, as defined in figure 12.2b; the % preceding these numbers indicates that they are defined in binary, not decimal. The assembler generates the binary values of these data, just as it generates the binary values of instructions. The table is thus defined by:

```
Table:   DefByte %11000000, %11111001, %10100100, %10110000
         DefByte %10011001, %10010010, %10000010, %11111000
         DefByte %10000000, %10010000, %10001000, %10000011
         DefByte %10100111, %10100001, %10000110, %10001110
```

Note here that the bytes are defined in binary, as this is the most appropriate form as the state of each bit is important. The bytes could, however, have been defined in decimal, hex, octal or even as ASCII characters. The method used to represent the values should be the one easiest for humans.

The DisplayIt subroutine hardly needs to be a subroutine; it is achieved by simply writing the value of the pattern to the address of the display.

```
DisplayIt:   ST Dreg, DisplayAddress
             RTS
```

Thus the subroutines of the program have been written. A few other aspects are needed. The first of which is to load the stack pointer with a suitable value, that is, to an area where there is some RAM. If it is assumed that the program itself is to be put in RAM, then the stack can be an area of memory at the end of the program. As the stack grows downwards (because the SP is decremented by each call and push instruction), space must be defined at the end of the program, at the end of which is the initial start of the stack. This space is achieved by another pseudo operation, *DefSpace*:

```
DefSpace 20      ; define space for 20 bytes
Stack:           ; put label at default top of stack
```

and the stack pointer is initialised at the start of the program by:

```
LD SP, #Stack
```

The addresses for the key pad and display need to be defined. The equate pseudo operation is used:

```
KeyPadAddress EQU $FF02
```

defines that the name KeyPadAddress has the value of $FF02. Note the $ preceding the number; this indicates that the number is in hex not decimal.

Also required is a definition of the start address of the program. If it is assumed that RAM starts at address $4000, then the program can be origined by another pseudo operation, *ORG*:

```
ORG $4000
```

This defines the current address; the assembler will generate the next op-code or data item starting at that address. Two other pseudo-operations are used; *HEADING* gives a title to the program, and *END* is used to mark the end of the program.

The program is shown below. It should be noted that the following has the minimum in terms of comments. The reader should refer to a good book on software engineering (for example, that by Somerville) on the use of comments.

```
HEADING ReadAndDisplay          ; this is the name of the program
;       Program written by Richard Mitchell, 20/6/94
;       This program continually reads the keys pressed on the
;       hex keypad and displays them on the seven-segment display
;       as each key is pressed.
ORG $4000                       ; program starts at address 4000
        KeyPadAddress EQU $FF02  ; define appropriate addresses
        DisplayAddress EQU $FF02
Start:
        LD SP, #Stack           ; load stack pointer
loop:   CALL ReadKey            ; read from keypad into Dreg
        CALL Convert            ; convert value in Dreg to pattern
                                ; required for seven segment display
        CALL DisplayIt         ; output value in Dreg in display
        BRA loop                ; jump back to do again
ReadKey:  ; wait for key to be pressed, then read value into Dreg
        LD Dreg, KeyPadAddress ; read value from key pad
                              ; bit 7 is 1 if key not pressed
                              ; value of key pressed in bits 3 to 0
        BMI ReadKey            ; jump back if key not pressed
        AND Dreg, #%00001111 ; clear top bits, so have value of key
        RTS
```

```
Convert:         ; converts 0..15 in Dreg to seven-segment pattern
       PUSH Areg
       LD Areg, #Table        ; load address of table
       LD Dreg, Dreg (Areg) ; index to Dreg'th element in table
       PULL Areg
       RTS

Table:    ; this defines the 16 patterns for showing the hex
          ; characters on the seven-segment display
          ; the order of patterns is that for 0, that for 1, etc.
       DefByte %11000000, %11111001, %10100100, %10110000
       DefByte %10011001, %10010010, %10000010, %11111000
       DefByte %10000000, %10010000, %10001000, %10000011
       DefByte %10100111, %10100001, %10000110, %10001110

DisplayIt:  ; store value in Dreg into the seven-segment display
       ST Dreg, DisplayAddress
       RTS

       DefSpace 20    ; define space for 20 bytes for the stack
Stack:                ; label for initial top of stack

END
```

Analog-digital conversion

This example contains a few simple routines for using the analog-to-digital converter (ADC) and the digital-to-analog converter (DAC) described in chapter 9. For these the following operation is assumed.

The data format used for these devices is 8-bit complementary offset binary, as explained in chapter 7. Thus the lowest analog voltage has the equivalent binary number 00000000, and the highest voltage has the equivalent of the binary number 11111111.

The DAC converts such an 8-bit digital number into its equivalent analog value. The DAC is controlled by writing to address $FF00. The byte written there is stored in the DAC and converted to the equivalent analog voltage.

The ADC converts the input analog voltage to its equivalent 8-bit digital number. To do so, it must first be told to start the conversion; this is achieved by writing to address $FF01. Then, the program must wait until the conversion is complete; this is achieved by reading from address $FF01, and bit 0 will be '0' when the ADC has converted the data. Then the converted value can be read by reading from address $FF00.

The following subroutine outputs the value in the Dreg register to the DAC:

```
DACOutput:      ; output value in Dreg to the DAC
       ST Dreg, DACAddress
       RTS
```

A routine to read the ADC is more complicated:

```
ADCInput:       ; convert analog input of ADC to digital form
                ; put result in Dreg
        ST Dreg, StartConvertAddress    ; issue start convert
ADClp: LD Dreg, ADCStatus               ; read status line
        AND Dreg, #1                    ; test bit 0
        BNE ADClp                       ; jump back if it is '1'
        LD Dreg, ADCAddress             ; read converted value
        RTS
```

The above is straightforward; the start convert is issued, then the status is read and bit 0 tested until it is '0', and then the converted data are read.

The basic operation has been described. The following subroutine uses these rotuines to output a square wave whose period is dependent upon the value input initially from the keyboard. This value is used as a counter which is decremented until it reaches zero. The value is stored in a memory location and the *DefSpace* operator is used to define space for this value.

```
SquareWave:     ; subroutine to output a squarewave
                ; whose period is determined by a
                ; the value entered at the keypad
        CALL ReadKey        ; read value from keypad, into Dreg
        ST Dreg, DelayValue ; store value in memory
        LD Dreg, #0         ; load Dreg with initial value, 0
SQLoop:                     ; this is the loop
        CALL DACOutput      ; output minimum value
        CALL Delay          ; delays depending on value in Dreg
        COM Dreg            ; change Dreg from 00 to FF or FF to 00
        BRA SQLoop          ; branch back to start of loop

Delay:          ; this produces a delay whose time is determined
                ; by the value entered earlier on the keypad
        PUSH Dreg
        LD Dreg, DelayValue ; load delay value
Dlp:    CMP Dreg, #0        ; is Dreg zero ?
        BEQ DelayEnd        ; end subroutine if so
        DEC Dreg            ; decrement reg
        BRA DLp             ; and continue loop
DelayEnd:
        POP Dreg
        RTS

DelayValue: DefSpace 1    ; define space for one byte variable
```

12.4 Interrupt example

The principles of interrupts were described in chapter 8, namely that another device can issue an interrupt request signal to the microprocessor, in response to which the microprocessor stops obeying its current program and obeys an interrupt service routine, after which it returns to the main program. Here these principles are shown in action.

The following program extends the square wave program above so as to use interrupts. The idea is that the program outputs a square wave whose period is specified, as before, by a value input on the keypad, but the period can be adjusted during the operation of the program. This is achieved by arranging that the above program is interrupted when the user presses a key; the key should be read, the delay value changed accordingly, and then the program continued.

The hardware mechanism by which an interrupt is generated is as follows (which is consistent with the system described in chapter 9). The keypad interface circuit asserts a logic signal, an interrupt request, which asks the microprocessor to stop its current action and service the request. In this case, the microprocessor jumps to the address of the service routine whose action is to read the value of the key pressed, thereby cancelling the interrupt request signal, and to store this value in the memory location called DelayValue (this being the value used to determine the frequency of the square wave). The service routine is thus:

```
KeyPadRoutine:    ; interrupt service routine
    PUSH Dreg                ; as always, the register is saved
    LD Dreg, KeyPadAddress   ; read value of key pressed
    AND Dreg, #%00001111     ; clear top four bits
    ST Dreg, DelayValue      ; store value in memory
    PULL Dreg
    RTI          ; return from interrupt (back to main program)
```

For this example, it is assumed that the look-up table method is used to determine the address of the service routine and that a maskable interrupt is instigated. Thus, at the start of the program the address of the service routine must be set and then interrupts should be enabled. If the appropriate address in the look-up table is specified by the constant IRQJump, then these actions are achieved by:

```
    LD Areg, #KeyPadRoutine  ; address of service routine
    ST Areg, IRQJump         ; install in look-up table
    EI                       ; enable interrupts
```

Note that it is important to specify the address of the interrupt service routine before interrupts are enabled in case of an interrupt soon after the start of the program. The above should go at the start of the program. The complete program is thus:

```
HEADING InterruptSquareWave

; Richard Mitchell, 19/6/94

; This program outputs a squarewave whose frequency is set by
; values entered at the keypad. During operation, any key pressed
; on the keypad will cause the program to be interrupted as a
; result of which the frequency of the squarewave could change

    KeyPadAddress EQU $FF02  ; define address of keypad
    KeyIntEnable EQU $FF03   ; and address to enable interrupts
    DACAddress EQU $FF00     ; and address of DAC
```

```
ORG $4000      ; start address of program
        LD SP, #Stack          ; first set up stack pointer
        LD Areg, #KeyPadRoutine ; load address of service routine
        ST Areg, IRQJump       ; install it in look-up table
        LD Dreg, #5            ; load initial value required
        ST Dreg, DelayValue    ; to set default value for delay
        EI                     ; enable interrupts

        LD Dreg, #0            ; load minimum value
SquareWave:                    ; the main loop of the square wave
        CALL DACOutput         ; output to DAC
        CALL Delay             ; delay depending on value input
        COM Dreg               ; invert value output
        BRA SquareWave         ; repeat the process

KeyPadRoutine:                 ; interrupt service routine
        ; this reads the value entered at keypad and stores it
        ; in the memory location which determines the period
        ; of the squarewave
        PUSH Dreg
        LD Dreg, KeyPadAddress ; read value of key into bits 3..0
        AND Dreg, #%00001111   ; clear top four bits
        ST Dreg, DelayValue    ; store value in memory
        PULL Dreg
        RTI

Delay:     ; this subroutine generates a delay whose length
           ; is determined by the value entered at the keypad
        PUSH Dreg
        LD Dreg, DelayValue    ; load value for length of delay
DLoop: CMP Dreg, #0            ; is Dreg zero ?
        BEQ DEnd               ; end subroutine if so
        DEC Dreg               ; decrement reg
        BRA DLoop              ; and continue loop
DEnd:  POP Dreg
        RTS

DACOutput: ; output value in Dreg to DAC
        ST Dreg, DACAddress
        RTS

DelayValue: DefSpace 1         ; define space for delay variable
            DefSpace 20        ; define space for stack
Stack:
END
```

Software interrupts

Many microprocessors have instructions which, when executed, cause the PC and some registers to be pushed on the stack, and the PC loaded with the address of a suitable routine. At the end of this routine, the microprocessor can return to the program. That is, the microprocessor acts just as if it was interrupted. These instructions, therefore, are called software interrupts. These can be used for reporting errors, for calling routines in the operating system of the computer which provide useful functions, and sometimes for setting breakpoints for testing purposes. No more is said of these here.

12.5   Programming a PIA

This section briefly considers the software for a PIA and uses as examples the two hardware configurations given in section 9.4. PIAs can be configured to provide many different actions; here a simple PIA, the 6821, is considered, which has two almost identical ports, A and B, each of whose actions are programmed using their three registers, the control register, CR, the data register, DR, and the direction register, DDR. The port A registers are CRA, DRA and DDRA, those for port B are CRB, DRB and DDRB; in the following, for example, CR is used to indicate either CRA or CRB. These registers control the data lines on the port and the two hanshake lines, HS1A and HS2A or HS1B and HS2B, and whether an interrupt is generated on IRQA or IRQB.

The control register, CR, can be read from or written to by the microprocessor. Bits 7 and 6, which cannot be written to directly by the microprocessor, are set by actions of HS1 and HS2, respectively, and cleared when the microprocessor reads from the DR. Other bits in CR control these actions. Bits 1 and 0 control the effect of HS1, and whether interrupts are enabled or disabled, according to the following table:

```
bit 1 0 |    Action
--------+------------------------------------------------------
    0 0 | bit 7 set on negative edge of HS1; interrupts disabled
    0 1 | bit 7 set on negative edge of HS1; interrupts enabled
    1 0 | bit 7 set on positive edge of HS1; interrupts disabled
    1 1 | bit 7 set on positive edge of HS1; interrupts enabled
```

Bits 5, 4 and 3 control the effect of HS2. If bit 5 is a 0, then HS2 is an input and bits 4 and 3 have the following effect.

```
bit 4 3 |    Action
--------+------------------------------------------------------
    0 0 | bit 6 set on negative edge of HS2; interrupts disabled
    0 1 | bit 6 set on negative edge of HS2; interrupts enabled
    1 0 | bit 6 set on positive edge of HS2; interrupts disabled
    1 1 | bit 6 set on positive edge of HS2; interrupts enabled
```

If, however, bit 5 is a 1, HS2 is an output and the effects of bits 4 and 3 are:

```
bit 4 3 |    Action
--------+------------------------------------------------------
    0 0 | pulse appears on HS2A/B, ends when bit 7 of CR is set
    0 1 | pulse appears on HS2A/B, lasting one clock period
    1 0 | 0 output to HS2A/B
    1 1 | 1 output to HS2A/B
```

Note that for CRA, the negative pulse on HS2A is generated when the microprocessor has read from DRA, and for CRB, the pulse on HS2B occurs when the microprocessor has written to DRB.

Bit 2 of the CR selects whether the DR or the DDR is accessible. Each bit in the DDR controls the direction of data for the port: a 1 indicates that the bit in the port is an output, a 0 indicates that it is an input. The DDR and the DR registers can be read from or written to.

The memory map for the registers is shown below, where PIABase is the base address of the PIA:

Address	Register accessed
PIABase	DRA or DDRA (as selected by bit 2 of CRA)
PIABase+1	CRA
PIABase+2	DRB or DDRB (as selected by bit 2 of CRB)
PIABase+3	CRB

For the stepping motor example, bits 0 and 1 on port A control the motor, bit 0 the direction and bit 1 the movement, and the encoder is connected to port B. Thus port A should be configured as a port with two bits as output and port B should be set as an input. The code to initialise the device is:

```
CLR Dreg
ST Dreg, PIABase+1    ; clear CRA: bit 2 = 0, so can set DDR
LD Dreg, #3
ST Dreg, PIABase      ; set bits 0 and 1 to be output
LD Dreg, #4
ST Dreg, PIABase+1    ; set bit 2 of CRA, so can read DRA
CLR Dreg
ST Dreg, PIABase+3    ; clear CRB, allow access to DDRB
ST Dreg, PIABase+2    ; set all bits of port B are input
LD Dreg, #4
ST Dreg, PIABase+3    ; allow access to DRB
```

Then, the direction for the stepping motor is determined by setting bit 1 of port A for clockwise, and clearing bit 1 for anticlockwise.

```
LD Dreg, PIABase      ; read port
OR Dreg, #1           ; set bit 1, i.e set clockwise
ST Dreg, PIABase      ; write value back to port
```

Then the motor can be set to move by setting then clearing bit 0 of port A.

```
LD Dreg, PIABase      ; read port
OR Dreg, #1           ; set bit
ST Dreg, PIABase      ; write it to port
AND Dreg, #$FE        ; clear bit 0
ST Dreg, PIABase      ; write it to the port
```

The position of the encoder is read by the following instruction

```
LD Dreg, PIABase+2    ; read port B, ie motor position
```

The second application is the multiplexed ADC. Here port A controls the ADC, the data being read from the port data bits and the handshake lines controlling the Busy and Start convert signals. Port B controls the multiplexer. For port A, bits 1 and 0 should be 1 and 0, so bit 7 of CCR is set when the Busy line is asserted; bit 2 should be 1 so that DRA can be accessed; and bits

5, 4 and 3, should be 111, so the start convert line is inactive, and bit 3 should
be cleared and then set to issue the start convert signal. Port B should be
configured to provide 3 output bits. The initialisation code is as follows

```
LD Dreg, #%00111110
ST Dreg, PIABase+1       ; set CRA
CLR Dreg
ST Dreg, PIABase+3       ; set CRB
LD Dreg, #3
ST Dreg, PIABase+2       ; set bits 1 and 0 to be outputs
LD Dreg, #3
ST Dreg, PIABase+3       ; allow access to DRB
CLR Dreg
ST Dreg, PIABase+2       ; initialise port B to 0
```

Then the code to read from channel of the ADC whose number is in Dreg
is as follows:

```
      ST Dreg, PIABase+2       ; output to channel
      LD Dreg, #%00110110
      ST Dreg, PIABase+1       ; write to CRA, to assert HS2A
      LD Dreg, #%00111110
      ST Dreg, PIABase+1       ; release HS2A
loop: LD Dreg, PIABase+1       ; read CRA: bit 7 = 1 if converted
      BPL loop                 ; so jump back if not converted
      LD Dreg, PIABase         ; read ADC data and clear CRA bit 7
```

Note, in this case, it is not worthwhile generating an interrupt when the
conversion is complete because ADCs will typically operate in a few
microseconds. If, however, the ADC is much slower, the PIA could be
programmed to issue an interrupt when the ADC has converted and the action
of the service routine would be to read the data.

Summary

This chapter has described the typical instructions and addressing modes
provided in computers, and some example programs have been written which
use some simple peripheral devices. The next chapter considers the instructions
and addressing modes of the 68020 and 8051 microprocessors.

Exercises

1. Write a subroutine which allows the user to enter an 8-bit hex value, by
typing two hex keys. As each key is pressed, the value entered should be
displayed on the seven-segment displays; the first key press should be shown
on the first display, at address $FF02, and the second at address $FF03.

2. Use the above in a subroutine which outputs a square wave whose amplitude
is set by the 8-bit value input in the keypad.

3. Write a subroutine which uses the ADC to read an analog voltage and then shows the 8-bit digital result as two hex digits on two seven-segment displays.

4. Assume that the example computer system also has an analog comparator which compares two analog voltages and reports on bit 7 at address $FF01 whether the first voltage exceeds the second. This is to be used together with the DAC to make a form of ADC in the following manner.

The voltage to be measured is connected to one input to the comparator and the DAC output to the second. Initially 0 is output to the DAC. The program should loop, incrementing the value output to the DAC, until the comparator indicates that the second voltage exceeds the first voltage. At that stage, the value output from the DAC. is just above the analog voltage being measured. This is simulating a ramp ADC, as described in chapter 10.

Write a subroutine to perform the above which outputs the result as two hex digits on the two seven-segment displays.

5. A more efficient algorithm to do the above is as follows which loops 8 times and in the rth time around the loop it decides whether the answer should have bit 8-r set. This is a simulation of an 8-bit successive approximation ADC, as described in chapter 10. The algorithm is:

```
    answer := 0;
    whichbit := 8;
label:
    Decrement whichbit
    set bit number whichbit in answer
    output to the DAC
    IF bit 7 at $FF01 = 1 THEN clear bit whichbit in answer
    IF whichbit <> 0 THEN jump back to label
```

Write a subroutine to implement the above outputting the result on the two seven-segment displays.

6. Explain how you would connect a keypad to a PIA such that an interrupt could be generated when a key was pressed. Write the code to initialise the PIA and the interrupt service routine to read the value of the key pressed and store it in a memory location.

References

Ian Somerville *Software Engineering* Addison-Wesley, 4th Edition, 1992.

A.C.Downton *Computers and Microprocessors - Components and systems* Chapman & Hall, 3rd Edn, 1992.

Motorola *MC6821 Data Sheet.*

13 Programming the 68020 & 8051

The previous chapter described in general terms the typical instructions and addressing modes provided on microprocessors. In this chapter the facilities provided for two specific microprocessors are considered, namely the 32-bit microprocessor, the 68020, and the single chip microprocessor, the 8051. These were chosen as they are two very different devices, and so give a good indication of the range of typical facilities.

These two microprocessors were introduced in chapter 8, where their registers and facilities were described. Here example programs are given for these microprocessors, and many of these are based on the systems which were outlined in chapter 10. The programming of these devices is only briefly introduced with the examples showing the use of some instructions. Fuller details are given in the appendices. First the 68020 is described.

13.1 Programming the 68020

The 68020 is a 32-bit microprocessor which has eight 32-bit data registers, D0..D7, and eight 32-bit address registers, A0..A7, with A7 being the stack pointer. It has a large instruction set with many addressing modes, and some of these facilities were designed to allow efficient coding of programs written in a high level language. This will be demonstrated in chapter 14.

Here only a brief overview of the 68020 is given, more details can be found in appendix 1. Much greater detail is to be found in specialist books on the 68020 and the data books produced by Motorola. The aim of the description here is to allow the reader to write some simple 68020 programs.

Format of 68020 instructions

The 68020 has many instructions, most of which have one or two operands; for example, the move instruction moves data from one location to another, so it requires operands specifying both locations; whereas the jump instruction causes the program to jump to the location specified in its one operand.

Instructions with two operands are of the form *INSTR src, dst*, where the particular instruction takes data from the location specified by the source address, *src*, and possibly the data from the destination address, dst, and puts the result in the location specified by *dst*.

Instructions with one operand are of the form *INSTR dst*, where the data at the location specified by the destination address dst are processed and the result put into that address.

The 68020 can process 8-bit, 16-bit or 32-bit data. The data size is specified by a command following the instruction. *INSTR.B* specifies a byte (8-bit) operation; *INSTR.W* specifies a word (16-bit) operation; and *INSTR.L* specifies a long (32-bit) word operation: if no size is specified, 16-bit operation is assumed. On the 68000, for branch instructions, a short (8-bit) relative address can be specified by *INSTR.S*. However, on the 68020, the .B, .W and .L specifications can be used to specify an 8-bit, 16-bit or 32-bit relative address. The above can be illustrated by some examples:

```
MOVE.B A5, D3   move least significant byte in A5 to that in D3
ADD.L D2, D6    add the 32-bit contents of D2 to those in D6
ASL.W D4        arithmetic shift left the lower word of D4
BCC $2000       branch if carry cleared to address $2000
```

Addressing modes

The 68020 has 14 addressing modes which can usually be applied to the source and destination operands of the instructions. Some of these modes are complicated and will be used rarely by the assembly language programmer; they were designed to allow efficient implementation of some high level language statements. The simpler addressing modes are listed below, where the name is given, followed by its syntax and then an example of its use.

Immediate   Syntax: #data   Example: MOVE #5, D0
The data in the mode are the data used by the instruction.
Absolute Address   Syntax: (xxx)   Example: MOVE (345), D2
The data are at the specified 16-bit or 32-bit address.
Data Register Direct   Syntax: Dn   Example: MOVE D1, D3
The data are in the specified register, where n is in the range 0..7.
Address Register Direct   Syntax: An   Example: MOVE A1, D5
The data are in the specified register, where n is in the range 0..7.
Address Register Indirect Syntax: (An)   Example: MOVE (A5), D7
The contents of the address register specify the address of the data.
Address Register Indirect with Postincrement
                 Syntax: (An)+   Example: MOVE (A1)+, D6
The data at the address stored in An are specified, then An is incremented by 1, 2 or 4, dependent on whether the instruction processes 8, 16 or 32-bit data.
Address Register Indirect with Predecrement
                 Syntax: -(An)   Example: MOVE -(A2), D0
The address register is decremented by 1, 2 or 4 and then the data at the address in the register are specified.
Address Register Indirect with Displacement
                 Syntax: (d16,An) Example: MOVE (100,A1),D2
The address of the data is the sum of the signed 16-bit data value d16 and the contents of the address register; in the example, if A1 contains 2000, the address of the data is 2100.

Address Register Indirect with Index   Syntax: (d8,An,Xn,SIZE)
                                    Example: MOVE ($FF, A1, D3.W), D6
The address is the sum of the signed 8-bit number d8, the contents
of the address register An and the contents of Xn, which is the nth
address register or data register; SIZE specifies the size of Xn, being
.W or .L. For the example, if A1 contains 2000 and D3 contains 100,
then the mode specifies the address 2099 (that is −1 + 2000 + 100).
Memory Indirect   Syntax: ([bd,An],od)
                                    Example: MOVE ([10,A5],45), D4
The address is the sum of the outer displacement od and the value
at the address found by adding the base displacement bd and the
contents of An. bd and od can be 16 or 32-bit values, and both may
be omitted. For the example, if A5 contains 2000, and the value at
address 2010 is 4000, then the mode specifies the address 4045.
   That is enough to be going on with! There are other modes, but the above
will allow some simple programs. Some other modes will be discussed in the
next chapter as they allow the efficient coding of some high level language
statements. The full list of addressing modes is in appendix 1.

68020 example programs

The 68020 has a large number of instructions, a full description of which is
given (in 170 pages) in the Motorola manual. The manual also provides a 2
page summary, which is too short to be of much use. Appendix 1 contains a
list of all instructions, including the ways in which the instructions affect the
flags. Here, rather than giving a list of instructions, some example subroutines
are provided showing how the examples given in the last chapter can be
implemented on the 68020. Some new examples are also given illustrating
some other instructions. Relevant instructions are described for each example.
   The first example is the keypad and display program which continually
waits for the user to press a key on the keypad, reads the key, converts the
value and displays it on a seven-segment display.
   The basic instructions, which require no comment, are *MOVE* for moving
data from one location to another, *JSR* for jumping to subroutine, *RTS* for
returning from subroutine, *BRA* the unconditional branch instruction, and *AND*
which performs the logical *and* on data. In addition there are some other
instructions which need explanation.
   LEA addr, An is load effective address, addr, into address register An. The
addressing mode, addr, specifies the address of the data and normally the data
at that address are used; addr is the effective address of the data. However, for
the LEA instruction it is the address specified by the mode, rather than the data
at that address, which is loaded into An.
   BTST.B #bnum, Dn tests bit number bnum in the register Dn, the state of
the bit determining the value in the zero flag. Thus *BTST.B #0,D1* will set the
zero flag if bit 0 of D1 is zero, but clear the flag otherwise.

MOVEM is the move multiple instruction; it allows many registers to be moved together. The registers are specified as various ranges of registers; for example *D0-D2/D6/A1-A5* specifies all the registers from D0 to D2, register D6, and the registers A1 to A5. This instruction is often used to push registers on to the stack and pull registers off the stack: the auto-increment and decrement indirect register modes being used. Thus *MOVEM D2/D6, –(A7)* pushes D2 and D6 on to the stack; *MOVEM (A7)+, D0-D5/A1* pulls D0,D1,D2,D3,D4,D5 and A1 from the stack.

Little else needs to be said about the program as it is very similar to that given for the imaginary processor. The remaining differences are associated with pseudo-operations and labels. *DS* and *DC* are pseudo-operations used to define space and constant data respectively; note the use of size commands to define constant bytes (*DC.B*) and to define space for long words (*DS.L*). Note also that in 68020 assembly language, the labels are words at the start of the line, with no following colon.

The 68020 program is as follows (excluding a heading and declarations of addresses), in which a * marks the start of a comment:

```
Start       LEA Stack, A7           * load stack pointer
Loop        JSR ReadKey             * read value input into D0
            JSR Convert             * convert D0 to 7-segment pattern
            JSR DisplayIt           * and put D0 in display
            BRA Loop

ReadKey     * subroutine which reads value of key pressed into D0
            MOVE.B KeyPadAddr, D0   * read key pad port
            BTST.B #7, D0           * test bit 7 (key pad status)
            BNE ReadKey             * loop if key not pressed
            AND.L #$F, D0           * mask off to leave bits 3..0
            RTS

Convert     * convert value in D0 into pattern for 7-segment display
            MOVEM A0, -(A7)         * push A0 onto stack
            LEA Table, A0           * load A0 with address of table
            MOVE.B (A0,D0), D0      * index by D0 into table
            MOVEM (A7)+, A0         * pull A0 from stack
            RTS

            * the following is the seven-segment look up table
Table       DC.B %11000000, %11111001, %10100100, %10110000
            DC.B %10011001, %10010010, %10000010, %11111000
            DC.B %10000000, %10010000, %10001000, %10000011
            DC.B %10100111, %10100001, %10000110, %10001110

DisplayIt   * put value in D0 into the seven-segment display
            MOVE.B D0, DisplayAddress
            RTS

            DS.L 10                 * define space for 10 long words for stack
Stack                               * label for initial top of stack
```

The routines to write to the 8-bit digital to analog converter and to read the 8-bit analog to digital converter are given below (with declarations of addresses omitted). These are straightforward and require no extra description.

```
DACOutput          * output value in D0 to DAC
          MOVE.B D0, DACAddress
          RTS

ADCInput           * use ADC to convert data, put result in D0
          MOVE.B D0, StartConvertAddress    * issue start convert
ADCWait   MOVE.B ADCStatus, D0       * read busy signal
          BTST.B #0, D0             * test bit 0 (busy signal)
          BNE ADCWait               * loop back if not ready
          MOVE.B ADCAddress, D0     * read actual data into D0
          RTS
```

The next subroutine implements another routine described earlier which uses the DAC and keypad. This outputs a square wave, with the period of the signal being determined by a value input at the keypad. Here this value is stored in a memory location called DelayValue.

Two new instructions are used here. *CLR* clears the specified data to zero. *NOT* inverts the data. *DBNE Dn, addr* is test condition and decrement register Dn and branch to addr, which is a special case of the *DBcc* instructions, where cc is one of the 16 condition codes listed in chapter 12. The operation of these instructions is as follows. If the condition specified by cc is false, Dn is decremented and the PC loaded with the addr if Dn now contains −1; otherwise the PC is unchanged. In the following example, the DBNE instruction is used to decrement a register until that register reaches −1.

The squarewave program is as follows, the heading and the instructions initialising the stack pointer being omitted.

```
SquareWave
          JSR ReadKey      * call subroutine to read value for delay
          MOVE.B D0, (DelayValue)    * save in DelayValue
          CLR D0           * load D0 with minimum value
SQLoop    JSR DACOutput    * output value in D0 to DAC
          JSR Delay        * delay for value depending on D1
          NOT D0           * invert value output to DAC
          BRA SQLoop

Delay     MOVE.L D0, -(A7) * push D0 on to stack
          MOVE.B (DelayValue), D0    * copy delay value into D0
DLoop     DBNE D0, DLoop   * dec D0, branch back if not zero
          MOVE.L (A7)+, D0 * restore D0
          RTS

DelayValue  DS.B 1         * define space for 1 byte
```

Next are two example subroutines which can be used to generate pseudo random numbers. For both methods, D0 contains the current random number and the subroutine processes that register to generate the next random number which is put in D0. The value in D0 is often termed the *seed*.

The first method is termed the linear congruential method, more details of which can be found in Knuth. The subroutine performs the following routine:

`seed := (seed * multiplier + constant) MOD modulus`

So in this case the value in D0 is replaced by the value found by multiplying D0 by the multiplier and adding a constant, and taking the modulus of the result: seed is in the range 0..modulus-1. The values multiplier, constant and modulus are crucial; ones that work are 58653, 13849 and 65536, which gives 16-bit positive only numbers. The modulus can thus be achieved by using 16-bit numbers.

The subroutine to achieve this uses one new instruction, *MULU*, which performs unsigned multiplication on the data. *MULU.W src,dst* multiplies the two 16-bit values in src and dst and puts the 32-bit result in dst. In the following, therefore, to ensure the result is a 16-bit number, it is important to AND the register by 65535. The complete subroutine is shown below.

```
LinConMethod      * D0 := D0 * 58553 + 13849
    MULU.W #58653, D0       * multiply D0 by 58653
    ADD.W #13849, D0        * add constant to result
    AND.L #$0000FFFF, D0    * ensure number is in range 0..65535
    RTS
```

A more general routine is shown below, in which 16-bit numbers are again used, but for which the values multiplier, constant and modulus are stored as 16-bit values in memory locations. This uses two new instructions *DIVU* and *SWAP*.

DIVU.W src,dst, divides the 16-bit number in dst by the 16-bit number in src; the quotient of the result is stored in the lower 16-bits of dst and the remainder (or modulus) is stored in the upper 16-bits of dst. For example, if 25 is divided by 7, the quotient is 3, the remainder is 4. SWAP is used to swap the upper and lower 16-bits of a register; when used after the divide instruction, SWAP can be used to move the remainder to the lower half of the register. The routine is as follows.

```
LinConMethod2     * D0 := (D0 * Multiplier + Constant) MOD Modulus
    MULU.W (Multiplier), D0 * multiply D0 by multiplier
    ADD.W (Constant) D0     * add constant to result
    DIVU.W (Modulus) D0     * add constant to result
    SWAP D0                 * put result into lower 16-bits of D0
    AND.L #$0000FFFF, D0    * ensure number is in range 0..65535
    RTS
```

The second method uses the feedback shift register technique introduced in chapter 6; this generates n-bit numbers which are processed here using 16-bit values, the lowest n-bits of which are relevant. Here the value in D0 is first anded with a given mask and the number of '1's in the result is counted; call this value r. D0 is then shifted to the left, with '1' being shifted into bit 0 if there was an odd number of '1's in the value r. Finally, D0 is anded with a given number to ensure that the result remains n bits long.

For example, consider a 4-bit shift register whose current value is in binary 1010, the mask is 1001, and the mask to ensure the number remains 4-bits long is 1111. When 1010 is anded with 1001, the result is 1000 which has only one 1 in it. Thus 1010 is shifted left and a 1 is shifted into bit 0; the result is 10101, which is then anded with 01111 so that the result is only 4-bits long.

The code to implement this uses some more new instructions. *TST dst* tests the specified data setting the zero flag if dst contained zero. *LSR #1, dst* shifts dst logically to the right by 1 bit, the bottom bit of dst being shifted into the extend flag. *ROLX #1, dst* is rotate left through extend once, that is, dst is shifted left, with the contents of the extend flag being shifted into bit 0, and the contents of the top bit of dst being shifted into the extend flag.

The action of the subroutine is to first and a copy of D0 with the bit mask; the result is put in D1; this is the value r mentioned above. Then the number of 1's in the result is found by shifting D1 to the left until D1 contains zero, and after each shift the carry flag is tested; if it is set then a 1 was shifted from D1, so the count of the number of 1's in r is incremented. Bit 0 of this count indicates if the number is odd or even, so the count is then shifted to the left so that the extend flag indicates whether the count was odd or even. D0 is then rotated left so that the extend flag is shifted into the result. Finally, the result is anded with the range mask so that the result is in the correct range. The bit mask and range masks are stored in memory locations The routine is:

```
        MOVEM D1/D2, -(A7)    * save D1 and D2
        MOVE D0, D1           * copy D0 into D1
        AND (BitMask), D1     * and to determine bits being fed back
        CLR D2                * clear count of number of 1's
loop    TST D1                * if D1 is zero, jump out of loop
        BEQ loopend
        LSR #1, D1            * shift D1 right, bottom bit into X
        BCC loop             * skip if 1 was not shifted out
        ADDQ #1, D2          * was 1 in D1, so increment D2
        BRA loop
loopend
        LSR #1, D2           * shift bottom bit of D2 into extend
        ROLX #1, D0          * rotate D0 left, shift in bit from D2
        AND (RangeMask), D0  * mask so answer in correct range
        MOVEM (A7)+, D1/D2   * reload registers from stack
        RTS
```

Exceptions on the 68020

Finally, the handling of interrupts is considered briefly. These are special cases of exceptions which are events that cause the current program to be aborted and the event to be serviced. For example, an exception occurs when an attempt is made to divide a number by zero; similarly a bus error exception occurs when a data transfer operation between the processor and a slave goes wrong. A full list of exceptions is given in appendix 1.

When an exception occurs, the 68020 saves its current state, enters supervisor mode and loads the PC and system SP from appropriate locations within an area of memory called the exception vector table. The 68020 then obeys the service routine at the given address.

For hardware interrupts, as was explained in chapter 11, there are seven levels of interrupt as determined by the three IPL lines on the 68020. At any time three bits in the 68020's status register specify the level above which it will respond to interrupts, lower priority interrupts will be ignored. If the 68020 responds to the interrupt it will automatically change the bits in the status register so that it will ignore all lower priority interrupts.

When an interrupt request at, say, level 2 occurs, then provided that such an interrupt is allowed, the 68020 must find the address of the service routine associated with that interrupt; this can be done with auto-vectoring or non-auto-vectoring. In the former, the level of interrupt specifies the address, so the address of the service routine is the second address in a particular part of the exception vector table. In the latter case, the 68020 requests the device which issued the interrupt to return a vector identifying itself, and this vector is used to index into another area of the exception vector table so as to find the address of the service routine. In the following auto-vectoring is assumed.

A program which uses interrupts needs two parts for handling the interrupts, the service routine and the code to load the address of the service routine and to set the interrupt priority level. The former is straightforward, the latter less so. These will be explained using the squarewave program given earlier. Here the frequency of the squarewave is determined by the value in the location DelayValue which was set at the start of the program by calling the ReadKey routine. Now the program should be modified so that the frequency of the squarewave can be changed dynamically; thus an interrupt should be generated each time a key is pressed, the value of the key should be read and this stored in DelayValue. The service routine for this is:

```
ReadKeyService  * service routine which reads value of key pressed
        MOVE.L D0, -(A7)      * save D0
        MOVE.B KeyPadAddr, D0 * read key pad port
        AND.L #$F, D0         * mask off to leave bits 3..0
        MOVE.B D0, DelayValue * store value in DelayValue
        MOVE.L (A7)+, D0      * restore D0
        RTE                   * return from exception
```

This is like a normal subroutine except that the RTE or return from exception instruction is used to terminate the action. Note that D0 is saved at the start of the service routine; a service routine should not return having changed a register as an interrupt could occur at any time.

At the start of the program, the address of the service routine should be specified and the interrupt priority level set. These both require access to facilities available only in system mode; the exception vector table is in system memory, the priority level is in three bits in the status register. A user program does not have access to these. Thus it is normal for the operating system of the 68020 to provide suitable routines which a user program can call.

Thus the following may be used to set up the interrupts for the program.

```
LEA ReadKeyService, A0     * load address of service routine
MOVE #2, D0                * specify interrupt level
JSR InstallServiceRoutine  * call relevant routine
```

This concludes for now the example programs for the 68020. These examples have given a flavour of the instruction set and addressing modes for the device. What has been omitted from the above is consideration of the algorithms required for these routines. This issue is deferred to the next chapter, in the course of which more examples of the 68020 are provided.

13.2   Programming the 8051

The 8051 is a different device. In general it is less powerful than the 68020, though it does have some in-built facilities, for example timers and a serial communications device. The basic device was introduced in chapter 8 and fuller details are given in appendix 2. Here, some simple 8051 subroutines are described showing how the device may be used for some simple programs.

As a reminder, the 8051 has an 8-bit accumulator called ACC, whose mnemonic in instructions is A; it has a second 8-bit register B; AB is the 16-bit register formed by concatenating registers A and B; the status register is called the program status word, PSW; C is the carry flag, which is sometimes considered to be a register; DPTR is a 16-bit address register, the upper and lower bytes of which being DPH and DPL; the PC is the 16-bit program counter and SP is the 8-bit stack pointer. Some of the internal RAM can be considered as four register banks, one of which is selected at any time, each bank containing eight 8-bit registers, R0..R7. Also, the 8051 has many special registers, such as those for controlling the timer and serial devices. The 8051 communicates with the outside world via its four ports, P0..P3. These can also be accessed as if they were registers. Note, sometimes the ports are used to provide address, data or control buses.

The device can access bytes of memory or individual bits in these bytes. Most instructions process the internal memory, but two special instructions are provided for accessing external ROM and external RAM. It should be remembered that the internal RAM is at maximum 256 bytes long, so 8-bit addresses can be used to specify locations in the RAM.

Instruction format

The format of two operand 8051 instructions is *INSTR dst,src*; the data from *dst* and *src* are processed, the result being put in *dst*: the reverse order is used for the 68020. The format for single operand instructions is *INSTR dst*. The operands can specify whole bytes like the contents of the registers such as A, R3 or DPH, or absolute internal RAM addresses, like 37. In addition, some instructions allow a specific bit in a byte to be specified; for example, A.6

means bit 6 of register A, and 37.3 means bit 3 of memory address 37. Single bit access is allowed only for certain registers and RAM between addresses 32 and 48. Fuller details are given in appendix 2.

Addressing modes

The 8051 has fewer addressing modes than the 68020, and the various modes can only be used with certain instructions. The 8051 does not have an ortho-gonal instruction set. The modes are outlined briefly below.

Register addressing   Syntax: Register   Example: MOV A,B
    The register could be A, B, C, AB and DPTR, or one of the 8 registers in the currently selected register bank, R0..R7.

Direct addressing   Syntax: Addr   Example: MOV A, 56
    Addr, an 8-bit value, specifies a location within the internal RAM; this thus includes all the registers in the 8051, and the other locations in the internal RAM.

Register indirect addressing Syntax: @Ri   Example: MOV A,@R0
    Here the data specified are at the address stored in R0 or R1 in the currently selected register bank.

Immediate addressing   Syntax: #data   Example: MOV A,#65
    The data are specified in the instruction.

Base register plus index register indirect addressing
            Syntax: BReg+A   Example: MOVC A, PC+A
    Here the base register (BReg) is the PC or DPTR. The data specified are at the address found by adding the contents of A to this base register. The data are in the ROM, either internal or external.

Example programs

These concepts will now be illustrated using various examples. The first example program reads the keypad and writes values to the seven-segment display. For this it is assumed that the keypad and display have been interfaced as two of only a few external memory locations, and that there is no external RAM. This means that they can be addressed using 8-bit addresses.

    Many of the instructions used in this program need little comment, like *MOV* which is to move data from the src operand to the dst operand, *PUSH* which pushes the register on to the stack, *POP*, which pops the register from the stack, *ANL* which performs the logical and operation, *INC* which increments the register, *ACALL* which is the call to a subroutine, *AJMP* which is jump to a location and *RET* which is return from subroutine.

    The A in front of ACALL and AJMP specify that it is a call or jump to an absolute address; in fact this is a jump to an address in the current 2K area of program memory. A jump to anywhere in the 64K address space is achieved using the LJMP or LCALL instructions: the L means long.

The instruction *MOVX A,@R0* moves into the A register the data from the external RAM (or any external memory mapped peripheral) whose address is found in R0. The instruction *MOVC A,@A+PC* moves into A the data from the location in the ROM whose address is found by adding the contents of A to the PC. External RAM or memory mapped I/O can be accessed only using MOVX and internal or external ROM can only be accessed using MOVC.

The MOVC instruction is here used to index into the series of bytes following the Convert subroutine. When the MOVC instruction has been fetched, the PC contains the address of the single byte RET instruction at the end of the Convert subroutine; thus the address of the pattern to display the number 0 is at address PC +1, the address of the pattern required to display 1 is at address PC+2, and so on. The A register contains the number to be displayed, in the range 0..15; thus the first instruction in the subroutine is to increment A, so that *MOVC A,@A+PC* causes the correct pattern to be loaded.

The other instruction to be mentioned is *JNB bit,addr* where the 8051 will jump to the given address if the specified bit is not set. In the program below, the bit is specified by A.7, that is, it is bit 7 of the accumulator. The program is shown below, though headings and some comments are omitted.

```
Start:     MOV SP, #Stack        ; load stack pointer suitably
Loop:      ACALL ReadKey         ; read value input into A
           ACALL Convert         ; convert A to 7-segment pattern
           ACALL DisplayIt       ; and put A in display
           AJMP Loop

ReadKey:   ; subroutine which reads value of key pressed into A
           PUSH R0
           MOV R0, #KeyPadAddr    ; R0 has address of key pad port
RKLp:      MOVX A, @R0           ; read data at keypad address
           JNB A.7, RKLp         ; loop if key not pressed
           ANL A, #$F            ; mask off to leave bits 3..0
           POP R0
           RET

Convert    ; convert value in A into pattern for 7-segment display
           INC A                 ; inc A to take account of RET
           MOVC A,@A+PC          ; index by A into table
           RET

           ; the following is the 7-segment look-up table
Table      DB %11000000, %11111001, %10100100, %10110000
           DB %10011001, %10010010, %10000010, %11111000
           DB %10000000, %10010000, %10001000, %10000011
           DB %10100111, %10100001, %10000110, %10001110

DisplayIt  ; put value in A into the 7-segment display
           PUSH R0
           MOV R0, #DisplayAddr  ; R0 has address of display
           MOVX @R0, A           ; write externally to display
           POP R0
           RET
```

The routines to access the ADC and DAC are shown below. These are relatively straightforward; it is assumed that the address of the status port for the ADC is one greater than the address from which the converted data can be read. The routines are:

```
DACOutput:      ; Output value in A register to the DAC
        PUSH R0
        MOV R0, #DACADC     ; load R0 with address of DAC
        MOVX @R0, A         ; output A to this address
        POP R0
        RET

ADCInput:      ; start ADC converting, wait for conversion
               ; then read converted data into A
        PUSH R0
        MOV R0, #ADCDAC+1  ; load R0 with address of start conv.
        MOVX @R0, A        ; issue start convert
ADCWait:                   ; loop waiting for conversion
        MOVX A, @R0        ; read ADC status (it is on bit 1)
        JNB A.1, ADCWait   ; branch back if not ready
        DEC R0             ; R0 now has address of ADC data
        MOVX A, @R0        ; read converted data
        POP R0
        RET
```

The next program is the square wave program with interrupts, that is, the user can at any time press a key on the keypad and the value entered is used to calculate the delay which determines the frequency of the squarewave.

This requires the use of interrupts, so their use on the 8051 is described here. It is assumed that the keypad issues an interrupt request signal which is connected to the $\overline{INT0}$ input, thus external interrupt 0 will be generated. If the interrupt is enabled, that is bits 1 and 7 of the interrupt enable register (IE) are set, when a key is pressed, the 8051 will stop its current action and jump to address 3 where there should be a jump to the relevant service routine. The service routine should read the value of the key pressed (an action which clears the interrupt request) and then return. The instruction at the end of the service routine is *RETI*.

Bit 0 of the register TCON needs to be set to a 0 so that an interrupt is generated when the signal on the $\overline{INT0}$ input is low; otherwise an interrupt would be generated on the falling edge of the signal.

The other new instructions in the program are *CPL A* which complements the contents of the A register, *CLRB bit* which clears the specified bit, and *DJNZ A,addr* which decrements the A register and jumps to the given address if the result is not zero.

The program is shown below. It uses one location in the internal RAM for storing the delay value: this location is defined by the name DelayValue. The first part of the program ensures that location 3 contains a jump to the service routine; this is followed by the code clearing the hardware and initialising interrupts; then there is the main part of the program.

```
ORG 3
        LJMP ServiceRoutine   ; have jump to service routine
ORG 100
        MOV R0, #KeyPad       ; load address of keypad
        MOVX A, @R0           ; dummy read to clear interrupt
        CLRB TCON.0           ; set level not edge interrupt
        ORL IE, #%10000010    ; enable interrupts
        MOV A, #15
        MOV DelayValue, A     ; initialise delay value
        CLR A
Mainloop:
        ACALL DACOutput       ; output value in A
        ACALL Delay           ; delay for specified time
        CPL A                 ; convert A from 0 to FF or v.v.
        AJMP MainLoop
DACOutput:      ; output value in A to DAC
        PUSH R0
        MOV R0, #DACADC       ; Load address of DAC
        MOVX @R0, A           ; output value to DAC
        POP R0
        RTS
Delay:      ; delay for value depending on DelayValue
        PUSH A
        MOV A, DelayValue     ; read in delay value
        INC A                 ; as next instruction decrements A
DLp:    DJNZ A, DLp           ; keep decrementing until A is 0
        POP A
        RET
ServiceRoutine:     ; read from keypad, store in DelayValue
        PUSH R0
        PUSH A
        LD R0, #KeyPad
        MOVX A, @R0           ; read value from keypad
        ANL A, #$F            ; mask so in range 0..15
        MOV DelayValue, A     ; store in delay value
        POP A
        POP R0
        RETI
```

The final two examples show the implementation of the two random number routines described earlier. First the linear congruential method is used, though here the numbers are 8-bit, as the 8051 has 8-bit unsigned multiply and divide instructions. *MUL AB* multiplies the numbers in A and B, leaving the 16-bit result in AB, A having the low byte. *DIV AB* divides the value in A by that in B, the remainder is put in B the quotient in A. The following routine performs the operation:

A := (A * Multiplier + Constant) MOD Modulus

where these values are in registers R0, R1 and R2 respectively.

```
LinearCongruential:   ; calculate next number in sequence in A
        PUSH B
        MOV B, R0       ; load Multiplier
        MUL AB          ; A now has low byte of (A * Multiplier)
        ADD A, R1       ; add constant
        MOV B, R2       ; load modulus
        DIV AB          ; so B has remainder, A has quotient
        MOV A,B         ; move remainder to A
        POP B
        RET
```

The final example is of the feedback shift register. Here the bit mask is in R0 and the range mask is in R1. Thus the routine ands A with R0, counts the number of 1's, and then shifts A left, shifting in a 1 if there were an odd number of 1's; finally the result is anded with the range mask.

This example uses the *JZ* instruction, which is jump if accumulator is zero, *JNC* which is jump if carry flag not set, *SJMP* which is short (8-bit offset) jump to the address, *RRC* which is rotate right through carry, *RR* which is rotate right, and *RLC* which is rotate left through carry. The subroutine is:

```
FeedBackShiftRegister:   ; this generates next random number in A
      ; A has current number, R0 the bit mask, R1 the range mask
        PUSH R2
        PUSH A          ; save A temporarily
        MOV R2, #0      ; count of 1's is set to zero
        ANL A, R0       ; and A with bit mask
FBSLoop:
        JZ FBSShift     ; exit loop when A contains zero
        CLR C           ; clear carry flag
        RRC A           ; rotate A right, shifting 0 in from carry
        JNC FBSLoop     ; jump back if 1 not shifted out
        INC R2          ; increment count of shifted 1's
        SJMP FBSLoop    ; jump to start of loop
FBSShift:
        MOV A, R2       ; count of number of 1's
        RR A            ; shift 'oddness' into carry
        POP A           ; reload register from A
        RLC A           ; shift left, shifting 'oddness'
        ANL A, R1       ; and with range mask
        POP R2
        RET
```

Summary

The above shows various example programs in which two very different microprocessors are used. Clearly the 68020 is a much more powerful processor than the 8051, even in these simple examples. The next chapter, however, provides examples of more complicated programs. It also describes a way in which high level and assembly language code can be combined.

Exercises

1. Write the software simulations of the ramp and successive approximation ADCs for a) the 68020 and b) the 8051.

2. An exercise in chapter 10 was to interface a 12-bit DAC and 12-bit ADC to systems with only an 8-bit data bus. Write subroutines which allow a) the 68020 and b) the 8051, to access these devices.

3. Write a subroutine which outputs a triangular wave using the DAC, that is, the program should first output 0, then 1, and so on until it has output 255, and then output 254, 253 and so on until it outputs 0, and then repeat.

4. A black/white graphics system has 256 lines each having 256 dots. The memory in which the image is stored is arranged as follows. The first byte contains the black/white values for the first eight dots of the first line, the next byte has the values of the next eight dots, and so on, so that the 257th byte has the values of the eight dots at the start of the second line. For each byte, bit 7 contains the value of the first of the eight dots; that bit is a 1 if a dot is shown at that position.

Each dot can be considered to be at position x,y, where x and y vary in the range 0 to 255. Thus if MemStart is the address of the first byte of graphics memory, then the byte in which position x,y can be found is at address MemStart + y × 32 + x / 8; x is divided by 8 as there are 8 bits per byte, and y is multiplied by 32 as the 256 dots of a line are stored in 256 / 8 (= 32) bytes. The bit required is bit 7 − x AND 7 of that byte.

Write the following subroutines which are passed x and y in registers:
   a) one to set a dot at position x,y (to set the appropriate bit in the byte),
   b) one to clear the dot at position x,y,
   c) one to return the state of the dot at position x,y.
Note, multiplying and dividing by 32 and 8 can achieved by shifting.

References

Motorola *MC68020 Microprocessor User's Manual MC68020 UM/AD* 1985.
Philips *Single-chip 8-bit Microcontrollers* User Manual, 1988.
D.E. Knuth *The Art of Computer Programming* Vol 2, Addison-Wesley, 1969.

14 High Level and Assembly Code

This chapter considers in detail the development of software in general and the use of high level and assembly languages in particular. In so doing, consideration is given to the use of high level prototyping, that is, the program is initially postulated in a high level language, or a pseudo high level language, and then converted to assembly language. Also described are the ways in which assembly language and high level languages are mixed. The first stage is to review high level languages.

14.1 Review of high level languages

A computer is a tool, a device to aid the solution of problems. To solve a problem, the programmer must generate the appropriate instructions which cause the computer to process data input to the system so as to generate the correct output data. What is required, therefore, is the correct algorithm, showing which instructions are needed, and the appropriate data structures, which allow the data being processed to be represented in the computer in the most appropriate manner.

The program, that is, the algorithm and the data structures, must then be converted into a form that the computer 'understands'. High level languages are the preferred form as, for example, they provide a better means of expressing the program in terms of the problem being solved than machine or assembly language. Thus, where possible, programs should be written in a high level language with, perhaps, some assembly language included where speed is required or where the high level language does not allow the particular action.

There are many books on the many high level languages. The aim of this section is to give an overview of the attributes of high level languages, thereby illustrating how assembly language programs can be modelled on high level program fragments, and how high level and assembly languages can be mixed. The overview considers two parts, the data structures and instructions.

Data structures

For the examples given in the two previous chapters, the data values are very simple, being numbers representing values input at a keypad and output to a seven-segment display, or numbers representing analog data being used by the analog-digital converters. Similarly, the algorithms used are simple. Possibly the most advanced feature of these examples is the use of a look-up table for converting a binary number in the range 0 to 15 into the equivalent pattern so that the number may be displayed on a seven-segment display. The look-up table is a series of bytes; in a high level language this is called an array.

215

However, for more complicated problems, greater care is required, both in generating the algorithms and in considering data structures. Simple high level programming languages, like BASIC, provide most of the facilities required which allow an algorithm to be implemented. Such languages, though, do not provide the facilities required to represent data appropriately. Data representation is as important as the algorithm; consider the following.

Suppose a program is required to store information about books in a library. The data required about each book would include the author(s), the title, the publisher, the ISBN number, the library catalogue code, whether the book is on loan, and if so the date when it was issued, to whom it was issued and the date it is due back. Ultimately, all such data are stored as binary values. However, it is convenient for the programmer to be able to define a structure in which all aspects of that book are stored.

In a language like Pascal or Modula-2, this is achieved by using a RECORD (in C it is called a struct), which might look like the following;

```
Book = RECORD
  Author : string;
  Title : string;
  Publisher : string;
  ISBNNumber : string;
  LibraryCode : string;
  BookOnLoan : BOOLEAN;
  DateIssued : Date;
  DateDue : Date;
  Borrower : string;
END;
```

where string is an array of characters and Date is another record defined by:

```
Date = RECORD
  Day : 1..31;
  Month : MonthType;
  Year : INTEGER;
END;
```

Here Day can take a value in the range 1 to 31 and MonthType can take one of the values defined by the following so-called enumeration type:

```
MonthType = (Jan, Feb, Mar, Apr, May, Jun,
             Jul, Aug, Sep, Oct, Nov, Dec);
```

In practice the value marked Jan will probably be interpreted by the computer as the value 0, with Feb being 1, and so on. However, the programmer does not need to know this; instead the programmer works in terms of the high level definitions.

Similarly all data about each book are stored in one area of memory; they can be manipulated together, passed around and processed together. By using such data structures, the programmer can seek to express the program in terms of the problem being solved, that is storing data about books, not in terms of binary numbers. A good high level language allows the programmer to define data in terms of the problem being solved.

The above definitions are used to indicate the types of data being processed. After that, the actual data are defined. These are called variables, as they are items whose value can change. In fact they are implemented as areas in the memory of the computer in which values of the variable can be stored and from which the values can be found.

Instructions

Algorithms can then be written to provide such facilities as a list of all overdue books, a search to find out all books by a particular author, or whether a particular book is on loan. These algorithms are implemented as a series of instructions. Such instructions could be simple statements or, when a task is complicated, the task is assigned to a part program, also called a procedure, function or subroutine. The essence of top down design is to divide the problem into part problems until the task is sufficiently simple. In the following description a pseudo high level language is used, which is similar to Pascal.

The simplest statements allow data variables to be given values and for various values to be processed. For example, if x and y are two integer numbers, then the following are possible:

```
x := 5;
y := x * 6 + 2;
```

The first loads the variable x with the value 5. The second loads y with the value found by multiplying the value of x by 6 and adding 2 to it.

Programs must be able to do different actions dependent upon circumstances. This is often achieved by an IF statement, some examples of which are given below:

```
IF x < 8 THEN x := 5;
IF (x > 1) AND (x < 5) THEN y := x - 1 ELSE y := 100;
```

The former statement assigns 5 to x if x is less than 8. The second loads y with x − 1 if x is in the range 2 to 4, and loads y with 100 otherwise.

Another facility required is for a particular action to be done many times; this is achieved by looping constructs. The simplest is the WHILE loop. The statement can be expressed as:

```
WHILE condition DO action
```

This tests the condition and if it is true the action is obeyed, and then the program goes back and tests the condition again. The statement ends when the condition is false.

This loop is illustrated by the following algorithm which finds the greatest common denominator (GCD) of two positive integers, that is, the largest number which divides exactly into the two integers. This can be found using Euler's algorithm, working on two integers x and y and using one other temporary integer, as follows:

```
WHILE y <> 0 DO
  temp := x MOD y;      (* MOD calculates the remainder *)
  x := y;
  y := temp;
```

The value left in x is the answer.

The three assignment statements are obeyed while y is non zero. The function MOD is the remainder when x and y are divided. Suppose x and y have the values 24 and 18, the largest integer which divides into both exactly is 6, and this is found by the above. The following table shows the variables changing; the program stops when y is 0, so the answer is 6:

temp	x	y	comment
	24	18	initial values for x and y
6	18	6	24 divided by 18 is 1, with remainder 6
0	6	0	18 divided by 6 is 3, remainder 0

Another loop is the REPEAT UNTIL loop.

```
REPEAT
  do action
UNTIL endcondition
```

This keeps obeying the action until the end condition is true.

It might be thought that Euler's algorithm could be implemented as a REPEAT UNTIL loop:

```
REPEAT
  temp := x MOD y;
  x := y;
  y := temp;
UNTIL y <> 0
```

However, if x and y contained 6 and 0 initially, the first assignment to temp would require 6 to be divided by 0; this would cause an error.

The other main loop is one which allows a loop to be obeyed many times. This is the FOR loop which in its simplest form is:

```
FOR x := startvalue TO endvalue DO action
```

Here x is assigned the startvalue. Then, while x does not exceed the endvalue the action is obeyed and x is assigned the next integer value. The following program outputs all integers and their squares from 0 to 10:

```
FOR x := 0 TO 10 DO
  OutputInt (x);
  OutputInt (x * x)
```

where OutputInt is a procedure which outputs the value sent to it.

The above are examples of the simple statements. However, anything but the simplest of programs is too complicated to be achieved merely by such simple statements. Therefore, using the top down approach, the program is divided into various part programs, or procedures.

One such procedure could be the OutputInt procedure alluded to above. This procedure is assigned a value which it then outputs on to the appropriate display. It is important for procedures to have values passed to them: these are called the parameters to the procedure, and they allow the procedure to process different data. Procedure OutputInt may be as follows:

```
PROCEDURE OutputInt (value : INTEGER);
   << then action to output the given value >>
END;
```

The first line of the above declares that OutputInt is a procedure which has an integer parameter passed to it.

Procedures can also return results. For example, the following procedure evaluates the GCD of two integers:

```
PROCEDURE GCD (x, y : INTEGER) : INTEGER;
VAR temp : INTEGER;
   WHILE y <> 0 DO
      temp := x MOD y;
      x := y;
      y := temp;
   RETURN x
END;
```

The first line declares the procedure GCD to be one which is passed two integer parameters and which returns an integer result. The second line declares temp to be an integer variable. The following lines show Euler's algorithm at work. Then the statement RETURN x is saying that the result returned by the procedure is the value in the variable x.

This procedure could be used by the following statement:

```
OutputInt (GCD (24, 18) );
```

which would output the greatest common denominator of x and y.

One point worth stressing is the declaration of the variable *temp* which is a temporary variable used only in the procedure GCD; it is not needed elsewhere and it should not be affected by any other part of the program. Therefore it is declared inside the procedure; it is said to be a *local* variable and it can only be used in procedure GCD. If a variable were declared outside the procedures, that variable would be *global* and so could be accessed by and changed by all of the program.

The top down approach to programming aims to allow the programmer to concentrate on one part of the program, ignoring all others. Local variables help in this, as a local variable cannot be changed by other parts of the program.

The above illustrates procedures, with parameters passed to them, and with a result returned by them. In the above, the parameters and results have been integers, but all types of data, even records, can be passed as parameters.

One other point to consider is the use of variable parameters. The above procedures had value parameters, these being values passed to the procedure, which cannot be changed. A variable parameter is one which can be changed, and so a result can be returned in that parameter. This could be used to input an integer. Consider the following procedure:

```
PROCEDURE InputInt (VAR data : INTEGER);
  << read characters entered at keypad >>
  << convert these to integer number >>
  data := << this number >>
END;
```

Here the parameter data is declared, by the word VAR, to be a variable parameter, one whose value can be changed by the procedure; this is required as the InputInt procedure should return the value entered at the keypad.

This could be used by the following program which continually reads two values from the keyboard and calculates their greatest common denominator (GCD). The program halts when the two values entered are 0. The program is shown below, although the procedures InputInt and OutputInt are omitted, as is the procedure WriteString, which outputs the string passed to it.

```
PROGRAM GCDTest;
(* Tests GCD algorithm  R.J.Mitchell    25/9/93 *)

VAR int1, int2 : INTEGER;    (* declares two variables *)

  PROCEDURE GCD (x, y : INTEGER) : INTEGER;
  (* uses Euler's algorithm to find GCD of x and y *)
  VAR temp : INTEGER;    (* local variable *)
    WHILE y <> 0 DO    (* loop until y is 0 *)
      temp := x MOD y;
      x := y;
      y := temp
    RETURN x;              (* result is in x *)
  END;

  REPEAT
    WriteString ('Input two integers  ');  (* prompt user *)
    InputInt (int1);    (* inputs two integers *)
    InputInt (int2);
    WriteString ('Their GCD is ');
    OutputInt ( GCD (int1, int2) );
  UNTIL (int1 = 0 ) AND (int2 = 0);
  END
```

The GCD procedure above is interesting; it is passed two parameters x and y, and these are processed by the procedure, and apparently changed by the procedure. In fact, the changes to x and y are local, that is, the parameters are changed only in the procedure. Thus, when int1 and int2 are passed as the parameters to GCD, and are hence the parameters x and y as seen by the procedure, x and y are given the values of int1 and int2, but they are not the variables int1 and int2. Thus the procedure changes x and y, not int1 and int2. However, when int1 is passed as a parameter to InputInt, as InputInt is passed a variable parameter, then int1 is passed to the procedure and is changed by that procedure.

Thus a value passed as a parameter is not changed by the procedure, but a variable parameter can be changed by the procedure. A procedure may have any number of value and/or variable parameters, and it may return a result.

The above illustrates the pertinent parts of high level languages, namely data types, variables, assignment statements, the IF and loop statements and procedures. The next section then considers how they can be put together to form a program.

14.2 Software development

A program requires algorithms, implemented using the above techniques, and appropriate data structures. But how should they be chosen? Often the decisions as to what are required are made on the basis of experience, the program being developed is similar to one written already. Thus a similar technique is used, or part of an existing program is used directly. But how should the program be developed?

The basic approach, even when adapting existing programs, is the top down approach. Essentially this is the process whereby the problem being solved is divided into sub-problems. These sub-problems are themselves then divided. This process continues until a particular sub-program is sufficiently simple that it can be implemented. The advantage of this approach is simple; it is possible to concentrate on part of the problem (the sub-problem) and ignore, to a certain extent, the rest of the problem.

It is during this top down design process that it is likely that the applicability of existing software becomes apparent, as it is possible that a part of one program may be required in another. For example, consider the code required for handling the hex keypad; this was used in the simple echo program where keys pressed on the keypad were shown in the display, but it was also used for setting the delay for the squarewave generator using the digital to analog converter.

This is why many high level languages are provided with, and allow the user to develop, libraries containing useful code which can be used in many programs. The program therefore consists of some code written specifically for the particular program as well as the code found in various useful libraries.

Developing libraries is important and occurs as a natural consequence of the top down approach. The problem being solved is divided into parts which are implemented separately. The implementation is achieved by creating subprograms, the procedures, functions or subroutines mentioned earlier, and these can be implemented in one file, or they can be implemented in separate files. It is best to use separate files for those parts of the program which may be useful in other programs; these would become libraries. Thus it would be appropriate to create library files containing routines which handle the keypad, the seven-segment display and the analog-digital converters.

Once the program is designed it must be encoded into a form that the computer 'understands'; in machine code, assembly language or a high level language. Ideally, programs should be written in a high level language (for the reasons discussed in chapter 2), but it is sometimes necessary to write part of the program in assembly language. The parts of the program are then compiled or assembled and then linked together. To be considered, therefore, are the means whereby high level and assembly languages may be mixed, and how the assembly language algorithms are developed. These are discussed below.

The next section considers high level prototyping, the process whereby the assembly language program is initially expressed in a real or pseudo high level language and then converted to assembly language. Simple rules are discussed allowing high level constructs to be implemented directly. During the process short-cuts may be identified, providing a more efficient implementation. In the description of these prototypes, examples will be given demonstrating features of the 68020 which allow for efficient implementation of these constructs.

The following section considers how the data structures of high level languages are implemented in assembly language. This is required both for the implementation of complex techniques in assembly language, and when high level and assembly languages are mixed. This then leads on to the next stage, which describes the actual interface of the two languages, specifically how information is passed between high level and assembly language routines.

14.3 High level prototyping

This section considers the assembly language implementation of constructs used in high level languages. To an extent some of the ideas have been met already. The top down approach and the associated dividing of the program into procedures or subroutines has already been used. Also, the philosophy that a subroutine does not terminate having changed a register unless a result is returned in that register is an embodiment of the top down approach, as it implies the use of local variables not seen from outside.

This section considers other high level constructs, namely the implementation of the IF-THEN statement, the WHILE, REPEAT-UNTIL and FOR loops and the CASE statement. For each of these, example high level language statements are given, followed by their implementation in 68020 assembly language. First the IF-THEN statement is considered.

IF-THEN statement

The simplest form of the IF-THEN statement is illustrated by the following:

```
IF X >= 0 THEN X := 8;
```

The implementation of this requires that the value of the variable X be tested; only if X >= 0 should the statement loading the variable X with 8 be obeyed. In other words, X should be tested, and if X < 0 then the program should jump past the instructions which load X with 8. An implementation of this is shown below where X is stored in a memory address declared as X.

```
        TST X           * test X
        BLT xless0      * branch if X < 0
        MOVE #8, X      * load X with 8
xless0                  * this label shows the address to jump to
```

A more complicated version of the IF statement is given next:

```
IF X > 6 THEN X := X + 1 ELSE X := X - 10;
```

The implementation of this is as follows:

```
        MOVE X, D0      * load D0 with X
        CMPI #6, D0     * compare X with 6
        BLE sub10       * if false, branch to where 10 subtracted
        ADDQ #1, D0     * increment X
        MOVE D0, X      * store X + 1 in X
        BRA endexpr     * now branch to the end of the statement
sub10                   * reached here if X <= 6
        SUBQ #10, D0    * decrement 10 from X
        MOVE D0, X      * store result in X
endexpr                 * at end of the statement, program is here
```

If the condition is false, the program skips the THEN part to obey the ELSE clause; otherwise the THEN clause is obeyed with a jump past the ELSE part.

An even more complicated IF statement and its implementation are:

```
IF X = 'A' THEN X := 'Z'
ELSIF X = 'Z' THEN X := 'a'
ELSE X := X+1;
```

```
        MOVE.B X, D0     * load D0 with X
        CMPI.B #'A', D0  * compare X with 'A'
        BNE notA         * jump if not A
        MOVE.B #'Z', X   * load X with 'Z'
        BRA endexpr      * jump to end of the statement
notA                     * reached here of X is not 'A'
        CMPI.B #'Z', D0  * now test X with 'Z'
        BNE notZ         * jump if not 'Z'
        MOVE.B #'a', X   * load X with 'a'
        BRA endexpr      * jump to end of expression
notZ                     * reached here if not 'A' and not 'Z'
        ADDQ #1, D0      * increment X
        MOVE D0, X       * store in memory
endexpr
```

The above is straightforward, since it just extends the previous examples. Note, suitable names should be given to the labels used to indicate places to which the program should jump; there cannot be two labels both called *endexpr*.

The next stage is to consider more complicated conditions, for example:

    IF X >= 0 AND X <= 5 THEN X := X - 1

The action decrementing X can only be performed if both conditions are true. The first is tested and if it is false there is no point in testing the second. Thus the assembly language implementation of the above is:

```
          MOVE X, D0       * load X into D0
          TST D0           * test X
        · BLT endexpr      * branch to end of expression if test false
          CMPI #5, D0      * now test second condition
          BGT endexpr      * branch if false
          SUBQ #1, D0
          MOVE D0, X       * load X-1 into X
    endexpr
```

Similarly, for an OR expression like

    IF X < 3 OR X > 7 THEN X := X + 1

there is no need to test X > 7 if X < 3 is true. Thus the above can be implemented by:

```
          MOVE X, D0
          CMPI #3, D0      * test X for 3
          BLT doincr       * if X < 3, then jump to X := X + 1
          CMPI #7, D0      * test X for 7
          BLE endexpr      * branch if condition false
    doincr
          ADDQ #1, D0
          MOVE D0, X       * store X+1 into X
    endexpr
```

WHILE Loop

The format of a while loop is simple:

    WHILE condition is true DO action

Its implementation in assembly language should be achieved by the following:

    wloop
        IF condition FALSE jump to instruction after loop
        do action
        branch to wloop

So, the high level instruction

    WHILE X < 8 DO X := X + 2

can be implemented by:

```
wloop                  * label at start of loop
       MOVE X, D0
       CMP #8, D0
       BGE wend        * branch if X >= 8
       ADDQ #2, D0     * X := X + 2
       MOVE D0, X      * copy value back into memory
       BRA wloop       * jump back to do it again
wend                   * label at end of loop
```

The while loop has the test at the beginning of the loop; hence if the condition is false the first time then the program will not obey the main part of the loop at all. The next loop however has the test at the end.

REPEAT-UNTIL loop

The general form of the REPEAT-UNTIL loop is

REPEAT action UNTIL condition is true

As the test is at the end of the loop, the action in the loop is obeyed at least once. The assembly language implementation of this uses the following

```
rloop
    do action
    test condition and branch if false to rloop
```

So, the high level instruction

REPEAT X := X - 4 UNTIL X < 0

can be implemented by

```
rloop
       MOVE X, D0    * move X into D0
       SUBQ #4, D0   * subtract 4
       MOVE D0, X    * put into X
       TST D0        * test X
       BGE rloop     * branch back if X >= 0
```

FOR loop

The FOR loop is typically used for obeying various statements many times. The general form of the FOR loop is

FOR ct := startvalue TO endvalue BY step value DO action

This is in fact shorthand for

```
ct := startvalue
WHILE ct <= endvalue DO
    action
    ct := ct + stepvalue
```

If stepvalue is negative, then the test for the end condition in the while statement is $ct >= endvalue$.

The implementation of a while loop has already been given, so the for loop can be implemented easily. Consider the example:

```
FOR ct := 0 TO 255 BY 16 DO DACOutput (ct)
```

where DACOutput is the subroutine given in chapter 13, outputting the value in D0 to the digital-to-analog converter. The implementation of this is as follows. Note in this case the variable ct is stored in D0.

```
        CLR D0          * load D0 (that is ct) with 0
floop
        CMPI #255, D0   * is D0 < = 255
        BGT fend
        JSR DACOutput   * output ct to DACOutput
        ADDQ #16, D0    * increment count
        BRA floop       * jump back to start of loop
fend                    * label at end of loop
```

However, often the for loop is required to do some action so many times and the action does not need to know how many times the loop has been obeyed so far. In which case,

```
FOR ct := 1 TO n DO action
```

can be achieved by

```
ct := n
REPEAT
   do action
   ct := ct - 1
UNTIL ct = 0
```

So the statement

```
FOR ct := 1 TO 4 DO ReadKey
```

which calls the ReadKey subroutine of chapter 13, can be implemented as follows, note the use of the DBF instruction (decrement and branch instruction)

```
        MOVEQ #3, D1    * loaded with 3 as DBF stops when reg is -1
rloop   JSR ReadKey     * it is assumed D1 is not changed by ReadKey
        DBF D1, rloop   * decrement D1, jump if not reached -1
```

CASE statement

The CASE statement in Pascal (or switch statement in C) is a multiway if statement. Its general form is shown by the following;

```
CASE option OF
   opt1 : action1;
   opt2 : action2;
   optn : actionn;
   ELSE actione;
END
```

This can be implemented in a straightforward manner by turning the above into an IF statement;

```
IF option = opt1 THEN action1
ELSIF option = opt2 THEN action2
ELSIF option = optn THEN actionn
ELSE actione
```

However, if the options are very similar, a look-up table method can be used, and the address of the appropriate action is found by indexing into that table. Consider the following example.

Suppose subroutines have been written which output a squarewave, a sinewave or a triangular wave using the DAC. A program to use these might well ask the user to enter a value at a keyboard, Q for squarewave, S for sinewave and T for triangular wave, and the program would call the appropriate subroutine dependent upon the value entered at the keyboard. If the user typed a character other than Q, S or T then the program would report that the user should enter Q, S or T. In a high level language, this could be encoded as:

```
ch := ReadKey;      (* read character from keyboard *)
CASE ch OF
    'Q' : DrawSquarewave;
    'S' : DrawSinewave;
    'T' : DrawTriangularwave
    ELSE ReportError
END
```

The codes that the program accepts are three of four consecutive letters, so a look-up table for characters Q, R, S and T would be appropriate containing, respectively, the addresses of the subroutines for DrawSquareWave, ReportError, DrawSinewave and DrawTriangularWave. The program would also check that the character was in the range Q..T, and if not call ReportError.

The assembly language implementation of this works as follows. If the character entered is not in the range Q..T, then address register A0 is loaded with the address of the subroutine ReportError, otherwise A0 is loaded suitably from the look-up table. Then the appropriate subroutine is called. This is implemented as follows:

```
          JSR ReadKeyboard      * read into D0 char from keyboard
          CMPI.B #'Q', D0
          BLT LoadElse          * less than Q, so load else
          CMPI.B #'T', D0
          BGT LoadElse          * greater than T, so load else
          LEA [Table - 'Q' * 4,,D0.B*4], A0
          BRA GoDoIt
Table     DC.L DrawSquareWave, ReportError,
          DC.L DrawSinewave, DrawTriangularWave
LoadElse  LEA ReportError, A0 * load A0 with error subroutine
GoDoIt    JSR A0                * call subroutine: (address in A0)
```

Most of the above is straightforward. Once it is established that the character is in the range Q..T, the value in D0 is used to index into the table. The value required is at the address found by Table + (D0 − Q) * 4; the *4 is needed as addresses are 4 bytes long. This address is found using an advanced 68020 addressing mode, memory indirect pre-indexed, whose general form is:

[bd, An, Xn.SIZE*SCALE], od

where bd and od are 32-bit displacements, An an address register, Xn a data or address register, SIZE is B, W or L, specifying the size of Xn, and SCALE is 1,2,4 or 8. All operands in the mode are optional. The address returned by the addressing mode is:

(Value at address bd + An + Xn*SIZE) + od

In this case, the mode does not use An or od, the mode being:

[Table − 'Q'*4,,D0.B*4]

which is the value found at address Table − 'Q' * 4 + D0 * 4, that is, the address of the addressing mode is the D0th element in the table. That value is the address of the required subroutine, so it is loaded into A0 using the LEA, load effective address, instruction. (Remember LEA src,An loads the address generated by the addressing mode src into An; MOVEA src,An would load An with the value at the address returned by src.)

The above illustrates how a look-up table can be used for implementing a CASE statement. It is a matter of judgement as to whether a look-up table or IF-THEN-ELSE statement is the best method; it depends on how similar are the values of the options. For example, the following is best achieved using an IF-THEN-ELSE statement as a look-up table would be too large:

```
CASE int OF
    0 : action0;
    100 : action100;
    2067 : action2067
END
```

Example

The above gives some ideas; the next stage is to reinforce them by giving an example. The following subroutine has proved useful in various programs that the author has written. This routine allows the user to enter a 32-bit value as a series of hexadecimal characters entered using a full ASCII keyboard; the value is returned in D2. The routine terminates when the character entered is not hexadecimal, and this terminating character is returned in D0. If more than 8 hex characters are entered, the last 8 are remembered, and the number of characters entered (in the range 0..8) is returned in D1. In practice, the algorithm would normally be implemented in a high level language as there is no need for fast code, for example. The following is used therefore only as an example of high level prototyping.

The algorithm is:

```
D2 := 0;
D1 := 0;
WHILE Key Read from Keyboard into D0 is a hex character DO
   D2 := D2 * 16 + D0
   IF D1 <= 8 THEN D1 := D1 + 1
```

The implementation of this is given below. Here it is assumed that bit 7 at address called KeyStatus is 1 if a key has been pressed and that the value of the key can be read from the address KeyData. Note the extensive use of subroutines, breaking the problem down into suitable parts. The main part of the subroutine is as follows.

```
IN32       * read 32-value entered as a series of hex characters
       CLR D2          * answer := 0
       CLR D1          * count of valid hex characters := 0
IN32Loop               * WHILE Read Key that is Hex DO
       JSR ReadKeyAndCheckHex
       BCS IN32End     *    (Carry flag set if char not hex)
       JSR D2Times16PlusD0  * D2 := D2 * 16 + D0
       CMPI #8, D1     *    IF D1 < 8 THEN
       BEQ IN32Loop
       ADDQ #1, D1     *          D1 := D1 + 1
       BRA IN32Loop
IN32End
       RTS
```

ReadKeyAndCheckHex reads a value from the keyboard into D0, and then checks to see if that character is hexadecimal, that is, whether the character is '0'..'9', 'A'..'F' or 'a'..'f'. The carry flag is cleared if the character is hexadecimal and the character is converted to the appropriate value in the range 0..15; that is, a character in the range '0'..'9' is converted to a value in the range 0..9, and one in the range 'A'..'F' or 'a'..'f' is converted to a number in the range 10..15. The subroutine has two parts, so it is conveniently encoded as calls to both parts, as follows:

```
ReadKeyAndCheckHex     * read keypad, check answer is hex character
       JSR ReadKey     * read char into D0
       JSR CheckHex    * if it is hex, convert to 0..15
       RTS
```

First ReadKey is implemented. This is straightforward, first looping until a key is pressed, and then reading the data.

```
ReadKey  * read character entered at keyboard: store it in D0
       MOVE.B KeyStatus, D0
       BPL ReadKey          * branch back if bit 7 is 0
       MOVE.B KeyData, D0    * read value of key into D0
       RTS
```

CheckHex is given below: it returns having set the carry flag if the character entered is not hex, but clears the carry flag and converts the character to a number in the range 0..15 if the character is hex.

```
CheckHex   * if character '0'..'9', 'A'..'F', convert to 0..15
           CMPI.B #'0', D0
           BCS CHEnd            * return carry set, not hex
           CMPI.B #'9'+1, D0
           BCC CHLetter         * branch if > 9: it might be a letter
           SUBI.B #'0', D0      * convert '0'..'9' to 0..9
           RTS
CHLetter
           CMPI.B #'A', D0
           BCS CHEnd            * return carry set, not hex
           CMPI.B #'F'+1, D0
           BCC CHLowerCase      * branch if > F, lower case letter ?
           SUBI.B #'A'-10, D0   * convert 'A'..'F' to 10..15
           RTS
CHLowerCase
           CMPI.B #'a', D0
           BCS CHEnd            * return carry set, not hex
           CMPI.B #'f'+1, D0
           BCC CHEnd            * branch if > f, not hex character
           SUBI.B #'a'-10, D0   * convert 'a'..'f' to 10..15
           RTS
CHEnd      ORI #1, CCR          * set carry flag (bit 0 of CCR)
           RTS
```

The above is simple, though long-winded. For each possible range ('0'..'9', 'A'..'F', 'a'..'f'), D0 is tested to see if it is in range. If so, then D0 has a suitable value subtracted from it to convert it to the appropriate value in the range 0..15. Note the use of ORI to set the carry flag.

The final routine D2Times16PlusD0 shifts D2 to the left 4 times and adds in the value in D0. Thus, for example, if D2 had the (hex) value 0000129A and the user typed 'B', D2 would become 000129AB.

```
D2Times16PlusD0    * D2 := D2 * 16 + D0
           LSL #4, D2           * shift D2 left four times
           ADD.B D0, D2         * add in latest character in D0
           RTS
```

This completes the example, showing how a relatively complex routine can be developed using the prototypes.

The corresponding output routine, OUT32, works as follows. The top 4 bits of the register are rotated left into the bottom 4 bits, which are then converted to the appropriate character, '0'..'9','A'..'F' and output. The process is then repeated, for the remaining 7 nibbles. Thus the algorithm is:

```
FOR ct := 0 TO 7 DO
    Rotate D2 left 4 times
    Convert and output NIBL at bottom of D2
```

The implementation of this is given below. Here it is assumed that bit 0 at address called OutStatus is 1 if a value can be output and that the value is output by writing to the address OutData. The routine is thus:

```
OUT32             * output value in D2 as 8 hex digits
        MOVEM D0-D2, -(A7)    * push D0, D1, D2
        MOVEI #7, D1          * doing 8 times
O32Loop
        ROL #4, D2            * shift top nibble to bottom
        MOVE.B D2, D0
        AND.B #15, D0         * mask off bottom NIBL
        JSR HexToASCII        * convert 0..15 to ASCII char
        JSR OutChar           * and output it
        DBF D1, D32Loop
        MOVEM (A7)+, D0-D2
        RTS
```

This is straightforward, using a FOR loop to do the action 8 times. The next subroutine converts the 0..15 value in D0 to the equivalent ASCII character:

```
HexToASCII    * convert 0..15 in D0 to '0'..'9', 'A'..'F'
        CMP.B #10, D0         * IF < 10
        BCC HToALetter
        ADDQ.B #'0', D0       *    THEN add '0'
        RTS
HtoALetter
        ADDQ.B #'A'-10, D0    *    ELSE add 'A' - 10
        RTS
```

The above adds the appropriate value to D0. The final subroutine, OutChar, outputs the ASCII value in D0.

```
OutChar    * output character in D0 to display
        BTST.B #0, OutStatus  * keep testing bit 0 at OutStatus
        BEQ OutChar           * until is 1
        MOVE.B D0, OutData     * now output character in D0
        RTS
```

14.4 Representation of structured data types

The structured data types provided are arrays, which contain many data of the same type, and records, which contain data which can have different types. Arrays will be considered first.

An array is a list of data which is usually stored in order, the first element, then the second, and so on. The address of the first element is thus that of the whole array, the address of the second element is the address of the first plus the size of one element. Thus, as characters are single byte, an array of characters are stored in successive bytes, and the address of the nth character is the address of the array plus n−1. In an array of 32-bit integers, the address of the nth integer is offset from the start by 4*(n−1).

One use of an array has been given, in the look-up table for patterns to be shown on a seven-segment display. In a high level language, the table could be defined as:

```
Table : ARRAY [0..15] OF BYTE;
```

If A0 contains the address of the table and D0 is the index for the table, then D0 can be loaded with the appropriate element in the table by:

```
MOVE.B (A0, D0), D0
```

Another use of arrays is in the look-up table for the CASE statement. Indexing into an array is easily achieved using the advanced 68020 addressing modes.

A record (or struct in C) is also a list of data, though different data can be mixed in a record. An example of a record is shown below:

```
ARec = RECORD
   x : INTEGER;
   ch : CHAR;
   arr : ARRAY [0..11] OF INTEGER;
END
```

This will be stored in memory in order; the first four bytes for the 32-bit integer x, the one byte for the character ch, then the 12 32-bit integers for the array arr. Thus if the address of the record is at 100, say, then that for ch is at 104, and that for arr[6] is at $100 + 5 + 6 * 4$. In the following it is assumed that A0 contains the address of the record:

```
MOVE.L (A0), D1            * D1 is loaded with element x
MOVE.B (4, A0), D2         * D2 is loaded with the element ch
MOVE.L (13, A0), D3        * D3 is loaded with element arr[3]
MOVE.L (5, A0, D0,.L*4), D4  * D4 is loaded with element arr[D0]
```

The last one is of particular note, it generates the 'D0th' element of the array. The address is found by adding 5, A0 and four times the contents of D0.

Note, it is possible to have an array of records, and these will also be stored in order. Thus, if the variable ARecArray is defined as follows:

```
ARecArray : ARRAY [0..35] OF ARec
```

the address of ARecArray[11].arr[7], that is, of element 7 in the arr part of element 11 of the array, is the address of ARecArray plus:

$$12 * (\text{size of ARec} = 37) + 5 + 7 * 4$$

and the addressing modes of the 68020 can be used to find this address.

Another data type encountered in high level languages is the pointer. A pointer variable contains the address of another variable. In fact, these have been met already: when a procedure is called with a variable parameter, it is a pointer to that parameter which is passed. Handling pointers is easy in the 68020; an address register can be used to contain the pointer variable and hence to address the location of the variable referenced by the pointer.

One use of pointers is to produce a linked list. More details of these can be found in Wirth or in Mitchell, for example. A linked list consists of a number of record elements each of which contains a pointer to the next one in the list;

the element at the end has a pointer containing 0. A record for one such element can be defined as follows:

```
LinkedListElement = RECORD
    Value : INTEGER;
    NextOne : ^LinkedListElement;
        (* this is a pointer to such a RECORD *)
END
```

If P is a pointer to one such element, then P^ is the element pointed to by P; thus the Value part of the element is P^.Value. If A0 contains the address of the element, the long word at that address is the Value; (4,A0) specifies the address of the NextOne field.

An algorithm to add up all the values in such a list is as follows:

```
P := Address of First Element;
Sum := 0;
WHILE P <> 0 DO
  Sum := Sum + P^.Value
  P := P^.NextOne
```

The following is a 68020 implementation of the above. It assumes that A0 contains the address of the first element, and it stores the sum in D0.

```
        CLR.L  D0           * D0 (Sum) := 0
loop    TST.L  A0           * WHILE A0 <> 0 DO
        BEQ loopend
        ADD.L  (A0), D0     *    D0 := D0 + A0^.Value
        MOVEA  (4,A0), A0   *    A0 := A0^.NextOne
        BRA loop
loopend
```

More details of other data structures can be found in other books on high level languages. These can also be implemented in assembly language.

14.5   Mixing high level and assembly languages

The main factor when mixing high level and assembly language is the means whereby information is passed between the high level and assembly language code. Various methods are used, the one given here is used by the author.

When a procedure is called, the following occurs. First, if the procedure returns a result, space is created on the stack for the result. Next the procedure parameters are pushed on to the stack in the order that they are declared in the procedure heading. Then the procedure is called.

Inside the procedure, the parameters are processed and any result stored in the allocated space at the top of the stack. At the end of the procedure, the subroutine should return and remove any parameters pushed on the stack; the result should be left on the stack.

Note, the procedure should not return having changed any register. Thus, any registers used should be pushed on to the stack at the start of the procedure, and pulled from the stack near the end.

When pushing parameters, the following rules are used. The value of each value parameter is pushed on the stack. The address of each variable parameter is pushed on the stack. 8 and 16-bit values are stored in 16-bit memory, 32-bit values (including addresses) are stored in 32 bits. Larger parameters, like arrays and records, have their contents pushed on to the stack in order. Note, it is more efficient to pass arrays and records as variable parameters, even if there is no intention to change their value, as then only the address of the parameter is put on the stack, not the whole parameter. Care is needed, though, to ensure that their values are not changed.

These concepts are now illustrated by example. Consider the following procedure declaration.

```
PROCEDURE Fred (c : CHAR; i : INTEGER; VAR ca : INTEGER) : BYTE;
```

When this is called, two bytes are allocated for the result, then c is pushed on the stack (in two bytes), then i, then the address of ca, and then procedure Fred is called. Figure 14.1a shows the state of the stack before the parameters are put on the stack, and figure 14.1b shows its state after the call to Fred. After the procedure ends, the stack pointer A7 will be pointing to the location where the result is stored, as shown in figure 14.1c.

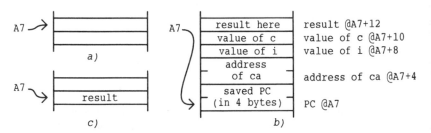

Figure 14.1 The stack before and after calling the procedure

This sounds complicated. However, the 68020 has some useful instructions for processing the stack in this manner. Consider the following example. Remember the procedure to calculate the greatest common denominator (GCD) of two integers:

```
PROCEDURE GCD (large, small : INTEGER) : INTEGER;
VAR remainder : INTEGER;
    WHILE small <> 0 DO
        remainder := large MOD small;
        large := small;
        small := remainder
    RETURN large
END;
```

The assembly language implementation of this is shown below (it was produced by a compiler), an explanation of which follows.

```
GCD             * calculate GCD (large, small) - parameters on stack
        LINK A6, #%FFFE         * load A6 with stack frame
        MOVE.L D2, -(A7)        * push D2 on to stack
        MOVE.L D1, -(A7)
loop    TST.W (8,A6)            * is small zero?
        BEQ loopend             * end loop if so
        MOVE.W (10, A6), D1     * load large
        EXT.L D1                * sign extend to 32 bits
        MOVE.W (8, A6), D2      * load small
        DIVS D2, D1        ·    * large DIV small
                           * upper word of d1 has large MOD small
        SWAP D1                * large MOD small in lower byte
        MOVE.W D1, ($FFFE, A6)    * store this in remainder
        MOVE.W (8,A6), (10,A6)    * large := small
        MOVE.W ($FFFE, A6), (8, A6)  * small := remainder
        BRA loop                 * go to start of while loop
loopend
        MOVE.W (10,A6), (12,A6)  * RETURN large
        MOVE.L (A7)+, D1         * pop D1
        MOVE.L (A7)+, D2
        UNLK A6                  * reset A6
        RTD #4                   * return removing parameters
```

The first instruction in the assembly language procedure, *LINK A6, #data*, pushes A6 on to the stack, loads A6 with the contents of the stack pointer (A7) + data, and adds data to A7. This means that A6 points to an area of memory where parameters are stored, and if *data* is non zero then space is allocated below A6 where local variables can be stored. In this case, the value of data is $FFFE (−2) so 2 bytes are allocated below A6 in which the local variable remainder is stored. A7 now points below these values, so any push instruction will load data in free memory. Figure 14.2a shows the state of the stack when the procedure has been called (that is, the parameters are on the stack), and figure 14.2b shows the state of the stack after the link instruction has been obeyed. The first push instruction saves data in the memory marked 'free'.

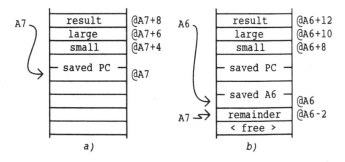

Figure 14.2 Stack before and after the link instruction

This area of memory is called a *stack frame*, and all relevant data in the stack frame can be accessed by using the addressing mode (offset,A6). The next instructions push D1 and D2 on to the stack. This, of course, adjusts A7; however, A6 is unchanged so, for example, the value for large is still at address A6+10.

Then there is the main body of the procedure, the while loop calculating remainder, large and small. At the end of the loop, the result (large) is copied into the space for the result in the stack frame (at A6+12).

Then D1 and D2 are pulled from the stack. Next, the *UNLK* instruction is used which is the opposite of link (it reloads A6 from the stack); hence the return address is now at the top of the stack. Then the *RTD #4* instruction is used. This reloads the program counter from the top of the stack, and then adds (in this case) 4 to the stack pointer. In this one instruction, the program correctly returns from the procedure and removes the (4 bytes of) parameters from the stack; the result is left at the top of stack. If there are no parameters to remove, then the *RTS* instruction can be used instead of *RTD*.

The above example maintains all its local variables and parameters in the stack frame. As only three values are needed, these can conveniently be kept in registers. Thus a more efficient implementation of the above is shown below. This version also uses the movem instruction to push two registers on to the stack in one instruction, rather than the two instructions used above.

```
GCD        * calculate GCD of two numbers passed on stack
           LINK A6, #0          * Set A6 to point to stack area
           MOVEM.L D1-D2, -(A7) * push D1,D2 onto stack
           MOVE.W (10,A6), D1   * large into D1
           MOVE.W (8,A6), D2    * small into D2
GCD1p      TST.W D2             * is small 0 ?
           BEQ GCDAend
           EXT.L D1             * sign extend large
           DIVS D2,D1           * D1 := D1 DIV D2,
           SWAP D1              * remainder in bottom 16-bits of D1
           EXG D1,D2            * exchange rem and small
           BRA GCD1p
GCDend     MOVE.W D1, (12,A6)   * put larger (D1) into result
           MOVEM.L (A7)+,D1-D2  * pull D1 and D2 from stack
           UNLK A6              * unlink A6 (opposite of link)
           RTD #4               * return, removing 4 bytes of
                                * parameters from stack
```

Here, the link instruction is used, this time with zero offset as no space is needed for a local variable (registers are used not memory). Then D1 and D2 are pushed on to the stack. Next D1 and D2 are loaded with large and small, found using the addressing mode (8,A6) and (10,A6). Then the main while loop operates, keeping all variables in registers. At the end of the procedure, the result is stored suitably and then another *movem* instruction is used to pull D1 and D2 from the stack. Then the *unlk* instruction is used to reload A6, and the subroutine is ended by the *RTD #4*.

The following give examples of two assembly language procedures in which the 68020 can access the DAC and ADC from a high level language.

```
PROCEDURE DACOutput (value : BYTE);

DACOutput          * output value at top of stack to DAC
      LINK A6, #0
      MOVE.L D0, -(A7)        * push D0 on to stack
      MOVE.B (8, A6), D0      * load D0 with value
      MOVE.B D0, DACAddress   * write to DAC
      MOVE.L (A7)+, D0        * pull D0
      UNLK A6
      RTD #2

PROCEDURE ADCInput () : BYTE;

ADCInput           * use ADC to convert data, put result on stack
      LINK A6, #0
      MOVE.L D0, -(A7)        * push D0 onto stack
      MOVE.B D0, StartConvertAddress * issue start convert
ADCWait
      MOVE.B ADCStatus, D0    * read ADC status
      BTST.B #0, D0
      BNE ADCWait             * loop back until bit 1 is zero
      MOVE.B ADCAddress, D0
      MOVE.B D0, (8,A6)       * load D0 into result
      MOVE.L (A7)+, D0        * pull D0
      UNLK A6
      RTS                     * RTS used not RTD as no parameters
```

The above can be used as the basis of other procedures which access the hardware, like writing to a seven-segment display, or reading from a keypad.

An alternative version of the ADCInput procedure is shown below in which a variable parameter is passed (that is, the address of the parameter is put on the stack) and the result is stored at the address of the variable parameter, rather than the procedure returning the result at the top of the stack. The procedure declaration and implementation are shown below.

```
PROCEDURE ADCInput (VAR answer : BYTE);

ADCInput      * use ADC, put result at address passed on stack
      LINK A6, #0
      MOVEM.L D0/A0, -(A7)    * push D0 and A0 onto stack
      MOVE.B D0, StartConvertAddress   * issue start convert
ADCWait
      MOVE.B ADCStatus, D0    * loop to wait until ADC is ready
      BTST.B #0, D0
      BNE ADCWait             * is ready when bit 0 is 1
      MOVE.L (8; A6), A0      * load A0 with addr of answer
      MOVE.B ADCAddress, (A0) * load result into answer
      MOVE.L (A7)+, D0/A0     * pull D0 and A0
      UNLK A6
      RTD #4                  * remove 4 byte address parameter
```

Note, as answer is a variable parameter, its 32-bit address is on the stack. Thus, A0 is loaded with this address, and the result is read from ADCAddress and loaded at the address contained in A0, thereby storing the result in answer.

The above illustrate assembly language procedures called from a high level language. In these, the stack is set up before the assembly language procedure is called. The following illustrates how the stack is set up by describing a recursive version of the GCD procedure.

The greatest common denominator (GCD) of x and 0 is x, whereas the GCD of x and y (where y > 0) is the GCD of y and x MOD y. For example

$$GCD \ (24, \ 18) \ = \ GCD \ (18, \ 24 \ MOD \ 18) \ = \ GCD \ (18, \ 6)$$
$$= \ GCD \ (6, \ 18 \ MOD \ 6) \ = \ GCD \ (6, \ 0) \ = \ 6.$$

Thus, a high level recursive procedure for calculating GCD is:

```
PROCEDURE GCD (large, small : INTEGER) : INTEGER;
    IF small = 0 THEN RETURN large
                    ELSE RETURN GCD (small, large MOD small)
END;
```

The assembly language equivalent of this is an extension of the earlier versions, first setting up the stack frame and saving registers, then doing the calculations. If small is not zero, then GCD is called, so the stack must be set up and GCD called, and afterwards the result popped from the stack and stored suitably in the stack frame. The procedure is as follows:

```
gcd        * calculates GCD (large, small) recursively
       LINK A6, #0
       MOVEM.L D1-D2, -(A7)
       TST.W (8, A6)             * if small = 0
       BNE reccall
       MOVE.W (10,A6), (12,A6)   * result := large
       BRA gcdend
reccall
       SUBQ.L #2, A7            * make space on stack for answer
       MOVE.W (8, A6), -(A7)    * push small on to stack
       MOVE.W (10, A6), D1      * load large
       EXT.L D1
       MOVE.W (8, A6), D2       * load small
       DIVS D2, D1             * compute large MOD small
       SWAP D1                * and move it to lower word in D1
       MOVE.W D1, -(A7)       * push large MOD small on to stack
       BSR GCD                * call GCD
       MOVE.W (A7)+, (12, A6)  * pop result off stack into result
gcdend
       MOVEM.L (A7)+, D1-D2    * pop D1 and D2
       UNLK A6
       RTD #4
```

The following explains the instructions after the label reccall which set up the stack: first space for two bytes is allocated on the stack by the subq instruction; then small is pushed on the stack; then large MOD small is calculated and pushed on the stack; and then gcd is called. After the call to gcd, the result of the recursive call is pulled from the top of the stack and then put at (12,A6) the position in the stack frame for the result.

Figure 14.3 shows the state of the stack at various stages when the procedure is called with the values 18 and 6. Figure 14.3a shows the stack when gcd is first called (after D1 and D2 have been pushed on to the stack). Figure 14.3b shows the stack after the recursive call, here processing 6 and 0, again after D1 and D2 have been put on the stack. Figure 14.3c shows the stack after the return from the recursive call; the result is on the stack below the saved value of D2. Figure 14.3d shows the stack after the return from the first call to gcd, the final result is on the top of the stack.

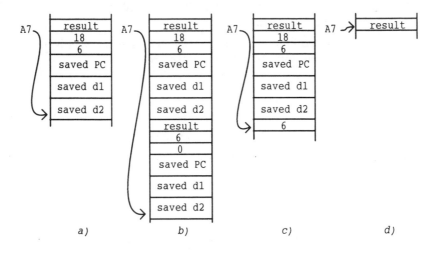

Figure 14.3 State of stack when evaluating GCD (18,6)

Summary

This chapter has reviewed high level languages; it has considered how high level language constructs can be used to program in assembly language and how high level and assembly languages may be mixed.

Exercises

1. A sinewave can be produced by outputting appropriate data to a DAC. Such data can be stored as a series of data in a look-up table. Assuming that a table of 360 entries exist for the value of the sinusoid for each degree, the code to output a sinusoid once is *FOR ct := 0 TO 359 DO DACOutput (Table[ct])*. Write an assembly language procedure which outputs a sinusoid continually.

2. Modify the exercises of earlier chapters to produce assembly language procedures to output to a 12-bit DAC and to read from a 12-bit ADC.

3. A string is an array of characters, where a byte with 0 is at the end of the string. Write algorithms to find the length of a string, to copy one string to another and to compare two strings lexicographically, that is, to return −1 if the first string would come before the second in a dictionary, to return 0 if the strings are equal and to return +1 otherwise. Implement these as 68020 assembly language procedures.

4. An exercise in chapter 13 required the writing of subroutines to use the graphics memory. Modify these to produce two assembly language procedures defined as follows:

> PROCEDURE DrawDot (x, y, colour : INTEGER);
> (* colour is 0 or 1; the dot at position x, y is set or cleared accordingly *)
> PROCEDURE FindDot (x, y : INTEGER) : INTEGER;
> (* This returns the colour (0 or 1) at position x, y *)

5. BubbleSort is an algorithm for sorting data values in an array; it is described in Wirth. The following sorts 10 integers in the array Data;

```
FOR i := 1 TO 9 DO
 FOR j := 10 TO i + 1 BY -1 DO
  IF Data[j-1] > Data [j] THEN Swap Data[j-1] and Data [j]
```

Write an assembly language procedure to sort such data.

6. The following is used to store the name and mark attained by a student:

```
StudentRecord = RECORD
   Mark : INTEGER;
   Name : STRING;   (* a string is an array of chars *)
END;
```

Write one assembly language procedure which sorts an array of 20 such records in order of marks, and one which sorts them lexicographically by name (using the string compare procedure written as answer to question 3).

References

Niklaus Wirth *Algorithms and Data Structures* Prentice Hall, 1986.
Ian Somerville *Software Engineering* Addison-Wesley, 4th Edn 1993.
R.J. Mitchell *Modula-2 Applied* Macmillan Press, 1991.

Also, see appropriate books on suitable high level languages; for example:
B.A.E. Meekings, T.P. Kudryci and M.D. Soren *A Book on C* Macmillan Press, 3rd Edn. 1993.
I.R. Wilson and A.M. Addyman *A Practical Introduction to Pascal* 2nd Edn, Macmillan Press, 1988.

15 System Development and Testing

For a computer system to work correctly, both the hardware and the software must be right. Good design methodologies should produce correct systems; however humans are fallible and make mistakes, so it is impossible to guarantee that a system will be correct; the hardware may be at fault, or the software. Certainly the software can be in error; a computer does exactly what it is told and not necessarily what you thought you told it to do; the algorithm may be at fault, or its implementation. Similarly, the hardware may have been designed incorrectly, or an error may have occurred during construction, or one of the components may be damaged. Thus, when a system is first configured and it does not work, is it the software that is wrong, or is the hardware faulty, or both? This chapter considers various methods which can be used in testing a microprocessor system.

15.1 Top down approach

Building a complete system and expecting it to work first time is a mistake. It is far better to develop and test the system in stages. This is true of software; in the recommended top down method of programming, the program is divided into suitable parts with parts written and tested separately, and then the parts are brought together and tested gradually. This process is greatly enhanced by the use of libraries of useful routines which, hopefully, are known to work.

The same top down approach applies to hardware; it should be divided into many modules and each module tested separately. A microprocessor bus system like STE inherently contains modules, so it is relatively easy to adopt this philosophy, although the approach can also be applied to dedicated computer systems; the system is developed in stages with the next part tested before it is added. There is the problem that the complete testing of a slave module requires that the microprocessor is working and running suitable test software to exercise the slave. Thus the microprocessor must work as well as the memory which contains the program in order that the other slaves can be tested. One potential solution to this is problem to buy a microprocessor board (and many are available) which will have been tested by the manufacturer, and use that to test the other modules. Testing microprocessor modules is more complicated than testing slave devices.

Computer aided development

Computer aided design (CAD) systems allow the user to enter a circuit diagram from which a printed circuit board (PCB) layout can be produced. In such an integrated system checks can be made that the PCB connections match those of the original circuit. Advanced CAD systems also allow the user to run a simulation of the circuit to verify that it will work correctly (at least in those instances which are tested by the simulation). However, even when this has indicated that the design is correct, the circuit must be built and then tested. In this chapter, therefore, the strategies for testing such circuits are described.

Similarly, special programs have been produced to help the design of software. These are called Computer Aided Software Engineering (CASE) tools. They allow the user to present specifications for programs, to develop algorithms for their implementation, and help testing, documentation and maintenance of the program. More details about these tools are provided in books on software engineering; see for example the book by Sommerville.

Problems in testing

Testing is not easy, whether on hardware or software. There are certain rules which should be followed, and these help to sort out most of the problems. If the system is still at fault, testing can be tricky. Then it involves the acquisition of information about the system by injecting suitable stimuli and then processing that information, removing those parts which are irrelevant and using the rest to deduce the problem or to suggest further tests. The following anecdotes illustrate how trivial mistakes can cause baffling problems, thus making testing difficult.

The first system being tested consisted of a 6809 based circuit connected to a microcomputer via a serial link. The microcomputer was running a program such that it appeared to be a terminal, thereby providing a keyboard and a VDU for the 6809 board. When the board was turned on a suitable 20-character message should have appeared on the VDU; it did not. However, the complete message did appear if the 6809 was reset; the system worked, but then it stopped again. The program on the board was known to work as it had been tested on another copy of the board, so that was not the problem. Eventually it was discovered that the reset button was wired upside-down; the system worked only when the button was pressed!

The second system was a 68000 board which again used a microcomputer as a terminal. Here the software for the board was tested in an EPROM simulator (see section 15.3), that is, the program was in the memory of another computer connected to the board under test by a cable which plugged into the socket for the EPROM; this memory appeared to be the EPROM of the microprocessor board. The software worked, so it was decided to replace the simulator with a real EPROM. Then the system stopped working. Checks were made regarding the speed of the memory (if anything the simulator was slower!), but to no avail. Then it was discovered that the system worked when an oscilloscope (CRO) was connected to the reset line. This suggested that the capacitance of the CRO was having a significant effect (this has been observed in the past, the CRO acts as an expensive capacitor! The problem is that the CRO cannot then be used to help find the fault). However, the 'capacitor theory' seemed dubious as there was no reason why the system should have worked when the EPROM simulator was used. Then it was discovered that the CRO could be connected anywhere on the board to make it work! Then it was noticed that the important point was that the earth of the CRO had to be connected to make the board work; without it there was no earth link between the board and the microcomputer. Such a link was provided by the simulator, hence the board worked then, but there was no earth link when the EPROM was installed. In this case the CRO was acting as an expensive piece of wire!

Testing software can also have problems. Recently the author was working on a problem which involved considerable amounts of arithmetic including some matrix routines. Approximate values for the final results were known, but not the intermediate values, so it was hoped that the program would be correct, as debugging would be a problem. Unfortunately the answers were wrong. As usual, by default, the compiler does not put any checks on (to ensure data are in range or indexes are not outside arrays) as this ensures that the program runs slightly faster and is shorter, which gives good performance in the standard tests, the 'benchmarks'. So, in response to the error, checks were put on to try to find the error, but then the program worked correctly. The program also worked when statements were added to the program printing out suitable values. Eventually the problem was diagnosed as an uninitialised variable. In the original program the contents of memory where the variable was stored contained a value which caused the program to be in error. When the checks were on or the printing statements added, the address of the data variable changed, to where the memory contained zeros, and the program worked.

15.2 Software testing

This section outlines ways in which software can be tested, including the use of print statements alluded to above and the use of 'debuggers'. One problem in testing is that a program can be demonstrated to work under certain circumstances, that is, with particular data, but may not work when other data are input. Care is required, therefore, to ensure that a suitably representative set of test data is used. One area where this can be a problem is in a program in which the user can enter data. If a program has been designed in which it is expected that the user will enter data in a particular way, often that program will do unexpected things when the user enters data differently. The solution to these problems is to be able to verify that the program will work under all circumstances, by having an adequate analysis of the program. This, unfortunately, is frequently not possible except on simple programs. Again, refer to Sommerville for more details on program verification.

Simple debugging statements

One way in which correct program operation can be detected is to view the results of the program for particular data; these are displayed on the VDU or saved in a file for later perusal. If the results are incorrect, then the programmer must find the 'bug'; the program must be 'debugged'.

If the final data are wrong, a simple debugging process is to print out the intermediate data values. Thus the programmer edits the program and adds suitable statements at appropriate places, recompiles the program and runs it again. The program operation can thus be observed by viewing the results as they are displayed.

One problem with this is to decide at which points in the program to add these debugging statements. If too many results are displayed, there is too much information and it is difficult to extract the appropriate data. Hopefully, the program is structured in a top down fashion. In which case, the debugging can be achieved in a similar manner, with the results after each of the top level actions being examined first to determine the area where the program went wrong, and then for that area to be investigated in more depth.

The main disadvantage of this method, however, is that the program may need to be changed and recompiled often, which can be a slow process. Nonetheless, the technique can be used to advantage, and if there are no other facilities, this is the best way of testing software.

Nowadays, various systems are provided to help debugging. For high level languages, high level debuggers are provided, which allow the programmer to view the operation and values of data in terms of the high level code. For assembly languages, debuggers are provided which allow the operation of the microprocessor and the values in its registers to be viewed.

Using a high level debugger

Many software development systems provide a high level debugger. These allow the user to see the program in operation, obeying the high level statements, and view the value of the variables in the program.

The user can specify *breakpoints*, that is, positions in the code where the program will stop; the user can then run the program until it reaches that point. Then the user can examine the state of the program and can view and possibly change the values of the program variables. Then the user can create another breakpoint and set the program to run again until it reaches that point.

In addition, the user can 'single step' through the program; here the next high level instruction is obeyed and then the program stops, allowing the user to view the program. Variants of the single stepping process allow the user to 'step over' calls to procedures, where the program stops after the procedure has been executed, or to 'step into' the procedure, where the program stops before the first instruction in that procedure, thereby allowing the user to watch the program obeying each statement in the procedure.

In a microcomputer system, the debugger is another program running on the system. Some microcontrollers have their programs developed on a micro-computer; the editor, compiler and linker run on the microcomputer, and then the compiled program is loaded into the microcontroller. Debugging of the controller can then be achieved using a cross-debugger, that is, the debugger runs on the microcomputer, and it communicates with the microcontroller, specifying which code is to be run. If no suitable communication is possible, then debugging is still possible, using a program on the microcomputer which simulates the microcontroller.

Using a monitor program

Another useful program to assist in the testing of microprocessor systems is a machine-code monitor. This program, which runs on the processor being tested, allows the user to examine the memory and peripheral devices in the system and to load, run and debug programs.

The debugging here is similar to that for high level debuggers, in that breakpoints can be set, single-stepping through the program is allowed and data can be examined and modified. The main difference, however, is that the operation is at machine instruction level, not high level instruction. So when single stepping, the next machine instruction is obeyed (for a high level debugger, the next instruction may be implemented by many machine instructions). Similarly, the data in machine terms are the registers and the memory locations, so the monitor allows these to be examined and modified.

When a program contains both high level and assembly language code, ideally the debugger should allow high level debugging of the former and machine debugging of the latter. The author uses one such system; it is a cross-debugger running on an IBM-PC microcomputer. Modula-2 and 68020 programs are written on the PC, the object code is then loaded into a 68020-based STE system which communicates with the PC via a serial link. When debugging, the PC runs the debugger, which commands the 68020 to set breakpoints, run the code and show values of variables. The user of the program can debug the program in both high level and low level modes, the latter being used primarily for those parts of the program written in assembly language.

Other uses of a monitor

Another use of the monitor is to help test hardware. Often such tests are achieved by short programs, reading or writing to particular slave devices. As the monitor allows the user to examine and change memory, it can let the user write such a short program into the memory and then run it. Alternatively, the program can be written in assembly language, assembled and then the monitor is used to load the assembled code into the memory.

In the course of its operation, the monitor must be able to accept commands from the user and to display suitable messages. Thus it must have its own routines for reading the keyboard and writing to the VDU, and these routines (called traps) are often accessible by the user program. Thus, if the program is to read from the keyboard, it can call the associated trap.

15.3   Testing hardware

This section considers the ways in which hardware should be tested. First the available test equipment is described, then the testing of slave devices is considered and then the testing of microprocessor circuits. More details can be found in Wilkins.

Test equipment

Various pieces of equipment are available to help in the testing of micro-processor systems. Some allow static testing, in which the level of signals that are not changing can be seen; others allow dynamic testing, where the variation of signals can be seen. The latter is usually more useful.

A simple *test probe* typically has a small LED which is on if the logic signal being touched by the probe is a logic 1, off if the signal is a logic 0, and dim if the signal is open circuit. Also available are logic clips which are connected to an integrated circuit, making contact with each pin on the device, and associated with each is a small LED indicating the state of the pin.

An *oscilloscope* (CRO) is a device which can display the variation of one or more signals with time. The device is like that used for television and CRT based displays; the main difference is that the movement of the electron beam follows that of the signal, rather than using the raster scan mode. The CRO can be set to start drawing a waveform (it is said to be triggered) when a certain signal goes high or low. As with the CRT type visual display unit, the signal must be continually redrawn if it is to be seen. Thus the CRO is best used when the signals being examined keep repeating. By examining the two or more signals on the display, the tester can see how signals are changing and the relationships between them; a typical display is shown in figure 15.1. Note, the signals there are not pure logic 1 or 0, they take time to change; there is also a slight overshoot, that is, the signal goes further than its final value, but then settles back. When analysing microprocessor systems it is important to see, for example, that the data being written are still valid after the write strobe signal goes inactive; this can be seen on a CRO.

Figure 15.1 Two typical signals on a CRO

For a CRO to show useful information, it must show the data repeatedly. However, if regular signals do not occur, for example with the interrupt handler in the keypad interface, a *storage CRO* can be useful in testing. Such a device is capable of storing information for a short period before and after a trigger event, and this information is then displayed continuously. For the keypad interface, the trigger could be the assertion of the status line from the keypad, and the values recorded being the data being read during the service routine.

Another test device which can be useful is a *logic analyser* or *bus analyser*. This is capable of recording signals which travel along a bus over a particular period before and after some trigger event occurs. During this time all transfers along the bus are recorded and these are then presented to the user to help in debugging. Some analysers can recognise the signals from different microprocessors and so can tell that an instruction is being fetched and thus deduce the type of instruction; on some systems it is then possible to list these instructions in assembly language mnemonics. Such a device seems ideal, the only problem is that it provides a great deal of information, sometimes too much, which the user has then to process in order to extract the relevant data. Another problem is that these devices can be programmed to do a great variety of functions and working out which is the most appropriate, and how to program the device to do it, can be difficult.

An *in-circuit emulator*, or ICE, is a device which plugs into the socket of the microprocessor and simulates the action of the processor. The ICE drives all the address, data and control signals of the processor, and so reads and obeys the program thereby accessing memory and peripherals. In addition the action of the program and the associated data are stored within the ICE so that the user can see what has happened over a period of time. The program can be run in parts, stopped at suitable moments, and memory examined. Unfortunately, ICEs are expensive pieces of test equipment. Also, separate emulators or adapters for 'universal' emulators are required for the different microprocessors, thereby increasing the cost of the device. However, they can be very useful.

An *EPROM simulator*, also called a *pseudo-EPROM*, is a memory whose contents can be set by one computer, but which appears to be an EPROM to the microprocessor under test. The advantage of the simulator is that programs can be easily loaded into the 'EPROM' for the microprocessor to test. Without such a device, the various programs to be tested would each have to be separately programmed into the EPROM, the EPROM would be inserted into its socket in the microprocessor system, the test made, and then the EPROM erased again. As erasing and programming can take time, this can be slow. Also, the socket can be damaged if devices are inserted into it too many times.

A block diagram of an EPROM simulator is shown in figure 15.2. Essentially the simulator is a piece of RAM in a computer which is connected by a suitable cable to a header which plugs into the socket of the EPROM in the system being tested. To the circuit under test it appears that there is an EPROM in the socket, but in fact the memory is RAM whose contents can be set by the other computer. Thus changes to the contents of the 'EPROM' require only that the contents of the RAM be changed, and this can be done quickly. Such a device is very useful when developing the initial software for a system, as it allows the user to try out a series of simple test programs very rapidly.

Referring to figure 15.2, the central part of the circuit is the RAM which can either be accessed as RAM by the computer or as EPROM by the board under test. Therefore, the address, data and control lines to the memory must

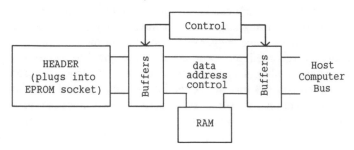

Figure 15.2 Block diagram of EPROM simulator

be buffered so that only one set of signals controls the memory at any time; a switch selects one of the two signal sets. Care is required with the simulator that the characteristics of the RAM (like the access time) are sufficiently similar to those of the EPROM, that the wires from the EPROM header are not so long that they significantly affect the circuit under test, and that the address lines of the RAM are in the correct order. For the second point, it is a good idea if there are buffers sufficiently close to the header.

Testing a peripheral slave

To illustrate the strategies, the testing of the STE peripheral interface of figure 11.20 will be considered. For convenience this circuit is redrawn here as figure 15.3. It is assumed that a working microprocessor board is available and that suitable test software can be written. It is a good idea to have an 'extender board' which allows the board under test to protrude out of the bus so that CROs and other test equipment can be connected.

The board should be tested in stages. The first test should be made before inserting the board; a check that the system still works. Then there should be a check that there is no short-circuit between the power rails on the board. Then, with no chips connected, the board should be plugged in and a check made that the system still works; if it does not then there is probably a short-circuit between some lines on the bus. If the board now works it is time to start inserting chips.

The first part of the circuit to be tested is that which verifies the address is correct and which generates DATACK*. Thus the two comparators at the top of the circuit, the shift register and the NAND gate chip should be inserted and the board plugged in. Static tests could be employed by driving the appropriate lines from switches and measuring other points using a test probe, but these tests do not show any hazards or glitches, so it is better to exercise the board repetitively and watch the signals on a CRO. This requires a simple program of the form:

```
loop:       read from an address allocated to board
            jump back to loop
```

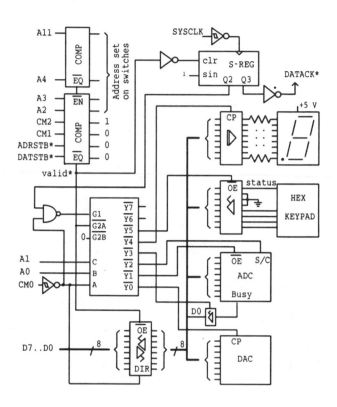

Figure 15.3 Peripheral interface on STE

On a CRO the signals that should be seen are like the somewhat idealised signals shown in figure 15.4a: first the comparator output should go low, and then a little time later DATACK* should be generated, then all signals should be turned off for a period longer than they were on (enough time for the jump instruction to be fetched and executed and the read instruction to be fetched) before the process is repeated. This assumes that the program is read from memory on the same board as the processor, and so the accesses to the memory do not appear on the STE bus; hence the dotted lines shown in figure 15.4a will not be there. If, however, the program instructions are transferred along the STE bus, it will be possible to see those extra DATSTB* and DATACK* strobes.

The DATSTB* signal could be used as the trigger for the CRO as it provides regular timings; alternatively SYSCLK could be used. If the DATACK* circuit is not working, the cycle should be ended by the circuit which detects when a cycle has been on too long, so there will be a longer delay before the pattern repeats, or the program might abort because of the

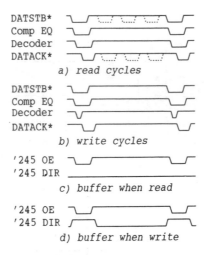

Figure 15.4 Expected signals on STE interface

error so the regular pattern will not be visible on the CRO. If the comparator circuit does not work, the switch settings may be incorrect.

When this part of the circuit works, connect the 3-to-8 decoder. Now check that the same program still works. If it does then one output of the decoder should go low just after the comparator output (this is also shown in figure 15.4a). If this does not happen then the decoder chip is probably wired incorrectly; check connections to it. Next modify the program so that it writes continually to one address. Now a different decoder output should go low, but for a shorter time: it should go high before DATACK* is generated (see figure 15.4b). Then try accessing different addresses.

Now check the output enable and direction pins on the bidirectional data buffer; for a read cycle they should be like those in figure 15.4c and for a write cycle like those in figure 15.4d. If they are correct then insert the buffer. Note that the whole system may stop working if the buffer is wired incorrectly, as the buffer may drive the data lines at wrong times and thus corrupt all data transfers on the bus.

Then the latch for the display should be added and a test program written which sends different data to the display. When this works, the keypad buffer should be connected and a program written which reads the keypad. The DAC and ADC should then be added and suitable test software written. Thus, the board is gradually built up with each part tested in the process.

Testing a memory slave

The testing of a memory module follows much the same strategy as that described above; the circuit is tested gradually. However, there are a few extra problems associated with memories because one memory chip contains a number of different locations; a circuit which appears to work, in that data are transferred to or from some locations, can be found to be in error when other addresses are accessed.

The first problem is that the address lines to the memory may be in the wrong order. This is significant for EPROMs, because instructions will be read in the wrong sequence. For RAMs there is no problem; although the wrong location will be read, data will have been written to that same wrong location.

Another problem with memory devices occurs when there is a short-circuit between two address lines, or an address line is not connected. The effect of either of these is that two different addresses are decoded as the same memory location. Testing for this requires some thought.

A simple program of writing a value to a location and then reading back immediately to verify that data were written correctly is not a good test, because capacitance in the wires may help to preserve the data for a short time. Also, this test does not check for short-circuited address lines. A better test is to write to the whole of memory and then read back from each location. There should be no correlation between the address and the data written there. This can be achieved by writing a particular sequence of data to successive locations. The test then uses the following algorithm:

```
initialise sequence
for each memory location
   write next number to memory
reinitialise sequence
for each memory location
   if value at location <> next number
      then report error
```

Testing a microprocessor

The testing of a microprocessor module is more difficult because for the device to operate correctly both the microprocessor and the memory circuits should be working. If there is another master device, the system can be configured with the other master as the default master, the master under test as a potential master, and any necessary slaves. The system is then switched on and the default master used to set up all necessary devices (including loading a suitable program into memory). Then the test master requests and is given control of the bus, and then runs the test program in the memory. If, on the other hand, the memory is on the same board as the master, much more of the circuit must be tested initially. An EPROM simulator is very useful in such circuits.

The first tests on a master module are to check the power supply, then the clock circuit, as this provides a good signal for triggering the CRO. After checking that the signals are correct around the socket for the microprocessor, the chip itself can be inserted. Without other circuits in place the processor will try to instigate data cycles, and these can be observed. For a processor with an asynchronous bus, a suitable acknowledge signal should be generated. If the processor seems to be working correctly, the memory circuit should be connected with a suitable simple program in it, one which loops continuously for example, or one which lights a LED and halts. Then the rest of the circuit can be added and tested.

The main problem with testing a master device is starting. Once the system is working programs can be written to help testing and debugging. Although a simple CRO can be used to get a system going, more advanced pieces of equipment can also be used to make testing easier.

Summary

For testing and developing microprocessor systems suitable test equipment and software are required. Much development can be done using only a CRO and a simple monitor program, but bus analysers and in-circuit emulators are also useful. Then the software must be considered. Again suitable software is needed for producing the code and for testing. The key for both hardware and software is to ensure that the system is well designed and that the system can be tested by gradually adding more parts to the system.

Exercises

1. Describe how you would test the 8051 microcontroller described in section 11.1. Outline the programs you would write to test the hardware and draw the timing diagrams you would expect to see.

2. Repeat the above for the 68020 microcontroller.

References

Ian Sommerville *Software Engineering* 4th Edition, Addison-Wesley 1993.
B.R.Wilkins *Testing Digital Circuits - an introduction* Chapman & Hall, 1990.

Afterword

This book has described various aspects of microprocessor systems, using a top down approach in which the concepts are introduced and then the topics are examined in more detail. The three topics covered are logic, hardware and software.

In logic, simple combinational logic circuits were considered first, together with techniques for their design. Then sequential circuits were described. Finally, it was shown how logical operations are used to perform arithmetic operations.

The hardware section considered the structure and operation of a system and the principles by which information is transferred between the components of the system. Specific circuits were then developed showing how slave devices may be connected to a simple system and then to three practical systems, the 8051, the 68020 and the STE bus.

The software section considered the ways in which software can be developed, the typical instructions provided on microprocessors, and then programs were written for the 8051 and the 68020; for the latter it was also shown how assembly language and high level language code can be mixed.

In the final chapter, the means were described whereby a microprocessor system is developed and tested, both the hardware and the software.

The appendices describe the 68020, 8051 and the STE bus in more detail, as well as describing some practical details of logic devices and the new standard for logic symbols, which may be adopted in practice, and providing answers to the exercises.

The author hopes that the reader finds the book useful by showing how microprocessor systems may be designed and developed and providing insight into the ways in which these systems operate.

P.S. In the preface, the author expressed the hope that all the acronyms in the book were explained. The reader, however, might be wondering what STE stood for (even though STE is not an acronym). In fact, STE was originally developed as an improvement on the STD bus (STD standing for standard). Thus the E in STE is the next letter on from the D of STD. Subsequently, it has been said that STE stands for standard on Eurocard. It has also been claimed that the E comes from the name of the person who first proposed STE.

253

Appendix 1 - The MC68020

This appendix contains fuller details of the instructions, addressing modes and hardware of the 68020, providing the extra details omitted from chapters 8, 11, 13 and 14, in which the 68020 microprocessor was introduced.

68020 structure

The 68020 can operate in user mode or supervisor mode. User mode is where the processor is running an application program typically written by a user of the computer. Supervisor mode is where the processor is running 'system software', for example the operating system. In supervisor mode the processor can access all resources of the device, both hardware and software. In user mode, certain facilities are inaccessible. This allows some protection of the computer system; making it more difficult for the user program to crash the computer. Figure A1.1 shows the registers available in the different modes.

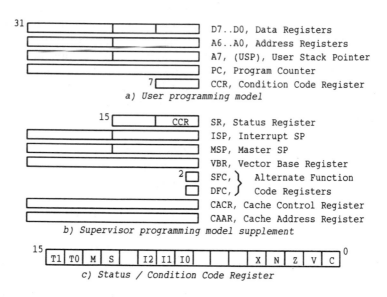

a) User programming model

b) Supervisor programming model supplement

c) Status / Condition Code Register

Figure A1.1 Registers in the 68020

In user mode, the 68020 has eight 32-bit data registers, D7..D0; seven 32-bit address registers, A6..A0; the user stack pointer, USP, also called A7; a 32-bit program counter, PC; and an 8-bit condition code register, CCR. The flags in the CCR are shown in figure A1.1c and described in chapter 8.

The 68020 has extra registers accessible in supervisor mode, as shown in figure A1.1b. These are the master stack pointer, MSP, the stack pointer used in supervisor mode; the interrupt stack pointer, ISP, which is used when an interrupt occurs; the vector base register, VBR, which contains the address of memory in which the addresses of routines for exceptions are stored; two alternative function registers, SFC and DFC; and two cache memory registers, CACR and CAAR, for controlling the cache memory which is used to speed operation of the processor by acquiring information in preparation for the time when the 68020 is ready to use it. In addition there is the 16-bit status register, SR, the lower byte of which is the condition code register, and the upper byte specifies various aspects; this is shown in figure A1.1c. Bits I2, I1 and I0 are the interrupt mask; an interrupt is requested when an external 3-bit number is specified, and this request will be serviced only of the number exceeds that on the interrupt mask. The bits S and M specify the mode of the 68020; S = 0 for user mode; S = 1, M = 1 for supervisor master mode; and S = 1, M = 0 for supervisor interrupt mode. Bits T1-T0 indicate the trace mode, in which part of the user program is obeyed and then the program stops, by calling an exception which typically allows the state of the machine to be examined. If T1 = 1 and T0 = 0, then only one instruction of the user program is obeyed before the 68020 stops. If T1 = 0 and T0 = 0, then the processor obeys a sequence of instructions; a typical end of sequence is a branch to subroutine instruction. The 68000 has only the first trace mode and thus one trace bit in the status register.

Format of 68020 instructions

Instructions on the 68020 are of the form:
    INSTR SIZE OPERANDS
where
    INSTR is the mnemonic for the instructions
    SIZE is the optional field indicating that byte (.B), word (.W) or longword (.L) data are to be processed; if SIZE is omited, then word data is assumed.
    OPERANDS are the zero, one or two addressing modes.

Addressing modes

The 68020 has 14 addressing modes which can be applied in general to both the source and destination operands. Some of these modes are complicated and will be used rarely by the assembly language programmer. However, these complicated modes were designed to allow efficient implementation of some high level language statements.

The addressing modes are listed below, where the name is given, followed by its syntax and then an explanation with appropriate examples. (68020) next to a mode means that the mode is available on the 68020 and subsequent processors, but not the 68000.

Immediate

Syntax: #data

The addressing mode contains the data, the size of which is determined by the size associated with the instruction.

Absolute Address

Syntax: (xxx)

The address of the data is the value given by xxx. If xxx is a 16-bit value then the assembler generates for the instruction a 16-bit value, which the processor 'sign extends' to a 32-bit value; that is, bits 31..16 have the same value as bit 15; so xxx is in the range $8000..$7FFF which will be extended to a value in the range $FFFF8000..$00007FFF. If xxx is a 32-bit value, then that 32-bit value is encoded in full into the instruction.

Absolute Short Address

Syntax: (xxx).W

Here the .W is forcing the assembler to generate a 16-bit value for the address. The assembler also checks to see that xxx is in the correct range.

Absolute Long Address

Syntax: (xxx).L

Here the .L forces the assembler to generate a 32-bit address.

Data Register Direct

Syntax: Dn

This specifies the nth data register, n is in the range 0..7.

Address Register Direct

Syntax: An

This specifies the nth address register, n is in the range 0..7.

Address Register Indirect

Syntax: (An)

The contents of the address register specify the address.

Address Register Indirect with Postincrement

Syntax: (An)+

The data at the address stored in An are specified, then An is incremented. The amount by which the register is incremented is 1, 2 or 4 bytes, depending on whether the instruction was processing 8, 16 or 32 bits of data, except if the address register is the stack pointer (A7) and 1 byte is specified, the register is incremented by 2, so that the stack pointer remains on an even boundary.

Address Register Indirect with Predecrement

Syntax: −(An)

The address register is decremented, then the data at the address specified by the register are specified. The amount by which the register is decremented is determined by the rules given above.

Address Register Indirect with Displacement
Syntax: (d16,An) or d16(An)
> where d16 is a 16-bit signed number. Here the address is that found in the address register to which d16 is added; if A1 contains 2000, then (100,A1) specifies address 2100.

Address Register Indirect with Index
Syntax: (d8,An,Xn,SIZE) or d8(An,Xn,SIZE)
> where d8 is a signed 8-bit number, Xn is the nth address register or data register, and SIZE specifies the size of Xn, being .W or .L (.W is assumed if it is omitted). The address is found by d8 + An + Xn. Both d8 and Xn are sign extended to 32-bit numbers. If A1 contains 2000 and D3 contains 100, then ($FF,A1,D3.W) specifies address 2099 (that is −1 + 2000 + 100).

Address Register Indirect with Scaled Index
Syntax: (d8,An,Xn,SIZE*SCALE) or d8(An,Xn,SIZE*SCALE)
> This is the same as the previous mode, except the value SCALE, which can be 1, 2, 4 or 8, and this is the value by which the contents of the register Xn is multiplied after being sign extended. If A1 contains 2000, and D2 contains 100 and A0 contains $FFFF then (10,A1,D2,.L*2) specifies address 10 + 2000 + 100*2 = 2210; and (10,A1,A0,.W*4) is address 10 + 2000 + ($FFFFFFFF)*4 = 2006.

Address Register Indirect with Base Displacement (68020)
Syntax: (bd,An,Xn,SIZE*SCALE)
> where bd is the 16- or 32-bit signed base displacement whose size and scale are specified by the last parameter. The address is found by bd + An + Xn. Note, in this mode, bd, An, Xn and size and scale are all optional. If A5 contains 4000, A1 contains 255 and D4 contains 200, then (100,A5,A1,.W*2) specifies address 100*2 + 4000 + 255 = 4455; (D4) specifies address 200.

Memory Indirect (68020)
Syntax: ([bd,An],od)
> where bd and od are the 16-bit or 32-bit base and outer displacements, both of which may be omitted. The address is (value found at bd + An) + od. If A5 contains 2000, and 4000 is at address 2010, then ([10,A5],45) is address 4045.

Memory Indirect PostIndexed (68020)
Syntax ([bd,An],Xn,SIZE*SCALE,od)
> Address is (value found at bd + An) + Xn*SCALE + od
> Again, SIZE and SCALE specify the size of the index register Xn and its scale factor, which can be 1, 2 or 4. bd, An and od are optional. If A5 contains 2000, the value at address 2010 is 4000 and D6 contains 100, then ([10,A5],D6,.W*4,50) specifies the address 4000 + 100*4 + 50 = 4450

Memory Indirect Preindexed (68020)
Syntax ([bd,An,Xn,SIZE*SCALE],od)
  Address is (value at bd + An + Xn * SCALE) + od
  bd and od are optional. This is like the previous mode except the
  index register is used to calculate the address prior to the indirection.
  The modes 'Address Register Indirect with Displacement' onwards can also
be used with the program counter instead of an address register. Thus the
following are allowed (no further explanation is needed).
Program Counter Indirect with Displacement
Syntax: (d16,PC) or d16(PC)
Program Counter Indirect with Index
Syntax: (d8,PC,Xn,SIZE) or d8(PC,Xn,SIZE)
Program Counter Indirect with Scaled Index
Syntax: (d8,PC,Xn,SIZE*SCALE) or d8(PC,Xn,SIZE*SCALE)
Program Counter Indirect with Base Displacement (68020)
Syntax: (bd,PC,Xn,SIZE*SCALE)
Program Counter Memory Indirect Postindexed (68020)
Syntax: ([bd,PC],Xn,SIZE*SCALE,od)
Program Counter Memory Indirect Preindexed (68020)
Syntax: ([bd,PC,Xn,SIZE*SCALE],od)

Instructions

The 68020 has a large number of instructions a full description of which is
given in 170 pages in the Motorola manuals. The following is an attempt to
describe the instructions briefly but with sufficient detail. This expands the
information given in chapter 12, giving a complete list of 68020 instructions.
  The instructions are defined in tables which give the instruction mnemonic,
its addressing modes, the sizes of data transfer allowed, how the flags are
affected, whether it is a supervisor mode instruction, and a brief description.
  For these tables, assume the following unless specifically contradicted:
src is any addressing mode and **dst** is any addressing mode except
immediate and PC indirect with displacement or index. **An** is an address
register, **Dn** is a data register, **Xn** is An or Dn, **PC** is the program counter,
CCR is condition code register and **USP** is user stack pointer. **data** is data
value of any size, **d8** is 8-bit data, **d16** is 16 bit data. For the flags, **0** is set to
0, **1** is set to 1, - is unchanged, **@** is set or reset according to the result of the
operation, and **?** is undefined. The allowable sizes are byte (**B**), word (**W**) or
longword (**L**). An S following the mnemonic means that it is a supervisor mode
instruction.

Data transfer instructions

The main data transfer instructions with relevant comments are as follows:

Mnemonic		Operands	Size	XNZVC	Operation
MOVE		src,dst	B,W,L	-@@00	move data from src to dest
MOVE		src,CCR	W	@@@@@	move from src to CCR
MOVE		CCR,dst	W	-----	move CCR to dest
MOVE	S	src,SR	W	@@@@@	move from src to SR
MOVE	S	SR,dst	W	-----	move SR to dest
MOVEA		src,An	W,L	-----	move src to An
MOVEQ		#data,Dn	L	-@@00	move data to Dn
MOVEP		Dn,dst	W,L	-----	move Dn to dst
MOVEP		src,Dn	W,L	-----	move from src to Dn
MOVEM		regs,dst	W,L	-----	move registers to dst
MOVEM		src,regs	W,L	-----	move from src to registers
MOVEC	S	Rc, Rc	L	-----	move control register
MOVES	S	src, Xn	B,W,L	-----	move address space
MOVES	S	Xn, dst	B,W,L	-----	move address space
LEA		src,An	L	-----	load effective address into An
PEA		src	L	-----	push effective address
SWAP		Dn	L	-@@00	swap bits 15..0 and bits 31..16
EXG		Xn,Xm	L	-----	exchange two registers

The dst for MOVE may not be an address register, so MOVEA is used instead. MOVEQ is move quick as it can be encoded as a one word instruction if the data value is 8 bit. MOVEP is designed for moving between registers and peripherals; dst and src may only be the address register indirect with displacement or index addressing modes.

MOVEM, move mulitple, allows many registers to be moved at one time; it is often used for pushing and pulling off the stack. The registers to be moved are specified as various ranges of registers, as is explained in chapter 13. For the MOVEM instructions there are restrictions on the dst and src addressing modes; src may not be Dn, An, or −(An) or #data; dst may only use the (address), (An), −(An), d16(An) or d8(An,Xn).

MOVEC allows data to be moved between a control register (e.g VBR) and a general purpose register. MOVES moves data between a register and the address space specified by the DFC or SFC registers.

LEA is load effective address; the address specified by the addressing mode is loaded into the specified address register. The addressing mode may not be immediate or address or data register direct. PEA is push effective address; the address is pushed on to the stack. The same restrictions on addressing modes apply here as for LEA. SWAP swaps the upper and lower words of the specified data register. EXG swaps the two specified registers.

Arithmetic instructions

The main arithmetic instructions are shown below. For those with two operands, the data from the src and dst locations are processed and the result (in general) put in dst; for those with one operand, the result is put in dst.

Mnemonic	Operands	Size	XNZVC	Operation
ADD	src,dst	B,W,L	@@@@@	dst := dst + src
ADDA	src,An	W,L	-----	An := An + dst
ADDI	#data,dst	B,W,L	@@@@@	dst := dst + data
ADDQ	#data,dst	B,W,L	@@@@@	add quick (data in range 1..8)
ADDX	src,dst	B,W,L	@@@@@	dst := dst + src + X flag
CHK	src,Dn	W,L	-@uuu	check Dn, trap if out of range
CHK2	src,Xn	B,W,L	-u@u@	check Xn, trap if out of range
CLR	dst	B,W,L	-0100	dst := 0
CMP	src,Dn	B,W,L	-@@@@	Dn - src, just compare
CMPA	src,An	W,L	-@@@@	An - src
CMPI	#data,dst	B,W,L	-@@@@	dst - data
CMPM	src,dst	B,W,L	-@@@@	dst - src, both must be (An)+
CMP2	src,Xn	B,W,L	-u@u@	- is Xn within bounds
DIVS	src,Dn	W	-@@@0	Dn := Dn / src (signed divide)
DIVSL	src,Dn	L	-@@@0	Dn := Dn / src (signed divide)
DIVU	src,Dn	W	-@@@0	Dn := Dn / src (unsigned divide)
DIVUL	src,Dn	L	-@@@0	Dn := Dn / src (unsigned divide)
EXT	Dn	W,L	-@@00	sign extend Dn to W or L size
EXTB	Dn	L	-@@00	sign extend byte in Dn to L size
MULS	src,Dn	W	-@@@0	Dn := Dn * src (signed multiply)
MULSL	src,Dn	L	-@@@0	Dn := Dn * src (signed multiply)
MULU	src,Dn	W	-@@@0	Dn := Dn * src (unsigned mult.)
MULUL	src,Dn	L	-@@@0	Dn := Dn * src (unsigned mult.)
NEG	dst	B,W,L	@@@@@	dst := 0 - dst (negate)
NEGX	dst	B,W,L	@@@@@	dst := 0 - dst - X flag
SUB	src,dst	B,W,L	@@@@@	dst := dst - src
SUBA	src,An	W,L	-----	An := An - src
SUBI	#data,dst	B,W,L	@@@@@	dst := dst - data
SUBQ	#data,dst	B,W,L	@@@@@	sub. quick (data in range 1..8)
SUBX	src,dst	B,W,L	@@@@@	dst := dst - src - X flag
TST	dst	B,W,L	-@@00	dst - 0 (test dst)

With the ADD and SUB instructions src or dst must be a data register. With the ADDI instruction, if the data are in the range 1..8, the assembler encodes the instruction as ADDQ, add quick; the instruction is quick as one 32-bit word encodes the instruction with data, so it is fetched more rapidly than one requiring two long words. ADDQ forces the assembler to generate the single long word instruction. The same applies to SUBI and SUBQ. There are 14 variants of multiply and divide; 7 each for signed and unsigned numbers:

```
MULS.W src,Dn ; src & Dn are 16-bit values. 32-bit result in Dn
MULS.L src,Dn ; src & Dn are 32-bit. lower 32-bits of result in Dn
MULS.L src,Dh:Dl; src and Dl are 32-bit. 64 bit result in Dh & Dl
DIVS.W src,Dn ; divide 32 bit value in Dn by 16-bit value in src;
        quotient in lower part of Dn, remainder in upper part of Dn
DIVS.L src,Dn; src & Dn 32-bit, 32-bit quotient in Dn
DIVS.L src,Dr:Dq ; Dr:Dq is 64-bit, src is 32 bit
        quotient put in Dq, remainder put in Dq
DIVSL.L src,Dr:Dq; Dr:Dq and src have 32-bit data
        quotient put in Dq, remainder put in Dr
```

Most of the CMP instructions are straightforward, subtracting src from dst, setting the flags, but leaving dst unchanged. CMPM is used to compare sequences of data; the modes are (An)+. CMP2 compares the register with the bounds found at the src address; @src is the lower bound and @src+n is the upper bound, where n is 1, 2 or 4 depending on byte, word or long operation. The CHK instruction causes the 68020 to execute a TRAP if the register is less than 0 or greater than the value at src. CHK2 executes the TRAP if the register is outside the bounds found at the src address (c.f. CMP2).

BCD arithmetic

For BCD arithmetic the 68020 has the following instructions.

Mnemonic	Operands	Size	XNZVC	Operation
ABCD	src,dst	B	@?@?@	BCD add: dst := dst + src
NBCD	dst	B	@?@?@	dst := 0 - dst (negate BCD)
PACK	src,dst,#data		@?@?@	pack into BCD format (see below)
SBCD	src,dst	B	@?@?@	dst := dst - src (BCD)
UNPACK	src,dst,#data		@?@?@	unpack into BCD

With these instructions, src and dst must both be data registers or both use auto-decrement mode. The 68000 provided ABCD, NBCD and SBCD, all of which processed bytes containing two BCD nibbles. The 68020 has the PACK and UNPACK instructions which convert between such two nibble BCD numbers and BCD digits stored as two bytes in ASCII. *PACK src,dst,#data* processes src which contains the ASCII codes for two decimal characters and stores in dst the decimal values of the characters + data; if src has $3835, the codes for '8' and '5', *PACK src,dst,#1* would put $86 in dst. UNPACK does the opposite; if src contains $43, *UNPACK src,dst,#$3030* would put $3433 in dst.

Logical instructions

The 68020 has the following logical instructions.

Mnemonic		Operands	Size	XNZVC	Operation
AND		src,dst	B,W,L	-@@00	dst := dst AND src
ANDI		#data,dst	B,W,L	-@@00	dst := dst AND data
ANDI		#data,CCR	B	@@@@@	CCR := CCR AND data
ANDI	S	#data,SR	W	@@@@@	SR := SR AND data
EOR		src,dst	B,W,L	-@@00	dst := dst EOR src
EORI		#data,dst	B,W,L	-@@00	dst := dst EOR data
EORI		#data,CCR	B	@@@@@	CCR := CCR EOR data
EORI	S	#data,SR	W	@@@@@	SR := SR EOR data
NOT		dst	B,W,L	-@@00	dst := NOT dst
OR		src,dst	B,W,L	-@@00	dst := dst OR src
ORI		#data,dst	B,W,L	-@@00	dst := dst OR data
ORI		#data,CCR	B	@@@@@	CCR := CCR OR data
ORI	S	#data,SR	W	@@@@@	SR := SR OR data

For the AND and OR instructions, either src or dst must be a data register. For all of them, src and dst may not be an address register. The instructions processing the condition code register CCR are used to set, clear or invert the flags. The instructions processing the status register SR can only be used in supervisor mode; in user mode an exception occurs if the instruction is obeyed.

Shift and rotate instructions

The 68020 has the following shift and rotate instructions.

Mnemonic	Operands	Size	XNZVC	Operation
ASL	cntdst	B,W,L	@@@@@	shift left; lsb := 0; X,C := msb
ASR	cntdst	B,W,L	@@@@@	shift right; X,C := lsb
LSL	cntdst	B,W,L	@@@0@	shift left; lsb := 0; X,C := msb
LSR	cntdst	B,W,L	@@@0@	shift right; msb := 0; X,C := lsb
ROL	cntdst	B,W,L	-@@0@	rotate left; lsb,C := msb
ROR	cntdst	B,W,L	-@@0@	rotate right; msb,C := lsb
ROLX	cntdst	B,W,L	@@@0@	rotate; X,C := msb; lsb := X
RORX	cntdst	B,W,L	@@@0@	rotate; X,C := lsb, msb := X

cntdst has three forms: Dm,Dn where Dn is shifted Dm times (the lowest 6 bits of Dm are used); #cnt,Dn where Dn is shifted cnt times, and 1<=cnt<=8; and dst where dst is shifted once and the operation size is W. In the above X and C are flags and msb and lsb are the most and least significant bits of the data.

Bit instructions

The 68020 has the following bit test instructions.

Mnemonic	Operands	Size	XNZVC	Operation
BCHG	bnum,dst	B,L	--@--	test bit bnum, then invert it
BCLR	bnum,dst	B,L	--@--	test bit bnum, then clear it
BSET	bnum,dst	B,L	--@--	test bit bnum, then set it
BTST	bnum,dst	B,L	--@--	test bit bnum
Scc	dst	B	-----	if cc, dst := $FF else dst := 0

bnum may be immediate data in the range 0..7, or a data register whose contents are in the range 0..31. dst may not be an address register. Scc, the set condition instruction, tests the condition specified by cc, and sets or clears the register; cc is defined in the section on program control instructions.

Read-modify-write instructions

Three instructions are provided in this category.

Mnemonic	Operands	Size	XNZVC	Operation
CAS	Dc,Du,dst	B,W,L	-@@@@	Compare and swap
CAS2	Dc1:Dc2,Du1:Du2,(Xn1):(Xn2)			Compare and swap
TAS	dst	B,L	-@@00	test dst and set msb of dst

TAS tests the data at the specified address and then sets the data. CAS fetches the data at dst and compares them with the Dc register; if they are equal, Du is written into dst. CAS2 is similar except pairs of registers are processed. With TAS, CAS and CAS2 read-modify-write cycles are generated.

Bit field instructions

The 68020 has bit field instructions which allow the processing of many bits in a register; a bit field is specified by offset:width, which specify the first bit and the number of bits. The instructions are shown below.

Mnemonic	Operands	Size	XNZVC	Operation
BFCHG	bf,dst	B,L	-@@00	test bitfield bf, then invert it
BFCLR	bf,dst	B,L	-@@00	test bitfield bf, then clear it
BFEXTS	src bf,Dn		-@@00	sign extend the bit field into Dn
BFEXTU	src bf,Dn		-@@00	extract bit field and put in Dn
BFFFO	src bf,Dn		-@@00	Dn given position of first 1 in bf
BFINS	Dn,dst bf		-@@00	insert Dn into the bitfield
BFSET	bf,dst	B,L	-@@00	test bitfield bf, then set it
BFTST	bf,dst	B,L	-@@00	test bitfield bf

In the above, bf is specified by[offset:width]. The simpler instructions, like BFTST, just test the bits specified by bf in dst; so *BFTST[3:2],D1* tests bits 3 and 4 in D1. *BFINS Dn, dst bf* copies the data in Dn into the bit field in dst. BFEXTS and BFEXTU copy the bitfield into Dn, the former sign extending the data; thus *BFEXTS 100[5:8], D1* copies bits 5 to 12 in address 100 into the lower 8 bits of D1, with the remaining bits in D1 being given the value of bit 12 from address 100. BFFFO finds the first 1 in the specified bit field and puts its position in the Dn register.

Program control and stack instructions

The 68020 has the following instructions for branch, calling and stack handling.

Mnemonic	Operands	Size	XNZVC	Operation
Bcc	addr		-----	Branch if condition cc true
BRA	addr		-----	Branch
BSR	addr		-----	Branch to subroutine
CALLM	#data,dst		-----	Call module
DBcc	Dn,addr	W	-----	Decrement, test and branch
JMP	addr		-----	Jump to addr
JSR	addr		-----	Jump to subroutine
LINK	An,#data		-----	Link: see description below
NOP			-----	No operation
RTD	#data		-----	return then add data to SP
RTM			@@@@@	return from module
RTR			@@@@@	return, with CCR restored
RTS			-----	return from subroutine
UNLK	An		-----	unlink An

The DBcc instruction operates in the following manner. If the condition specified by cc is false, then Dn is decremented and, if Dn <> −1, then the program branches by the displacement. The displacement for DBcc and Bcc is, as normal, specified in the instruction by specifying a branch to a given location, and the assembler calculates the relative offset and encodes that in the instruction. For Bcc and DBcc, cc denotes one of the 16 conditions. These conditions, the mnemonic and the flags which are tested, are shown below.

mnemonic	meaning	flags tested
CC	carry clear	NOT (C)
CS	carry set	C
EQ	equal	Z
F	false	
GE	greater or equal	NOT (N EOR V)
GT	greater than	NOT Z AND NOT (N EOR V)
HI	high	NOT (C) AND NOT (Z)
LE	less than or equal	Z OR (N EOR V)
LS	low or same	C or Z
LT	less than	N EOR V
MI	minus	N
NE	not equal	NOT (Z)
PL	plus	NOT (N)
T	true	
VC	overflow clear	NOT (V)
VS	overflow set	V

The link instruction pushes the address register An on to the stack, then loads An with the value of the stack pointer SP and then adds the displacement to SP. This basically allocates so many bytes of the stack for use, and is typically used to provide a stack frame for local variables and parameters; this is described in detail in chapter 14. The unlink instruction loads SP with An and then pulls the value for An off the stack; it is the opposite of link.

The 68020 supports modules where code and data on a stack frame are associated. The CALLM instruction calls a module, RTM returns from a module. More details of this can be found in the 68020 technical manual.

The return instructions are RTS, which needs no comment; RTR which pulls the value from the top of the stack into the CCR and then pulls the next value at the top of the stack into the PC; and RTD which pulls the top of the stack into the PC and then adds the displacement to SP.

Exceptions

An exception or a trap is a name given to an occurrence which causes the program to break from its current program sequence. Typically these are caused by a hardware trigger, such as an interrupt, or a particular software instruction, like a divide by zero or a deliberate break instruction.

When an exception occurs, the 68020 stops its current action, the PC and SR are saved on the stack, the SR is loaded suitably, such that, for example, the processor enters supervisor mode, and the PC is loaded with the address of the associated service routine. The address is found by indexing into a table of exception vectors. The following table lists the exception vectors (those in bold are for 68020):

Vector	Address	Assignment
0	000	Reset: initial value for ISP
1	004	Reset: initial value for PC
2	008	Bus Error (see chapter on interfacing)
3	00C	Address Error
4	010	Illegal Instruction
5	014	Zero divide
6	018	CHK, **CHK2** instructions
7	01C	TRAPV, **Tcc** and **TPcc** instructions
8	020	Privilege Violation
9	024	Trace
10	028	Line 1010 emulator
11	02C	Line 1111 emulator
12	030	Unassigned, reserved
13	**034**	**Coprocessor Protocol Violation**
14	**038**	**Format error**
15	03C	Uninitialised interrupt
16-23	040-5C	Unassigned, reserved
24	060	Spurious interrupt
25-31	064-7C	Level 1-7 Interrupt auto vector
32-47	080-BC	Trap 0..15 interrupt vectors
48-54	**0C0-D8**	**Floating point coprocessor errors**
55	0DC	Unassigned, reserved
56-58	**0E0-E8**	**Memory management unit errors**
59-63	0EC-FC	Unassigned, reserved
64-255	100-3FF	Interrupt vectors

A full description of the above includes material beyond the scope of this book. The following, however, gives enough relevant information to be able to use and appreciate the exception vectors.

When the 68020 starts, it loads its stack pointer and program counter from the first addresses in memory. In fact, the 68020 can separate memory into different areas, including user data, user program, supervisor data and supervisor program; user memory is accessible in user mode, supervisor memory in supervisor mode; data memory is used for storing general data, program memory is used for storing instructions. The initial values for stack pointer and program counter are in supervisor program memory, the rest of the exception vectors are in supervisor data memory.

A bus error occurs when the 68020 attempts to access memory but the attempt fails; reasons for this occuring are given in chapter 11. An address error is when the 68020 issues an illegal address. An illegal instruction occurs when the processor reads an instruction which it does not recognise. Zero divide occurs when the 68020 attempts to divide a number by zero. Privilege violation occurs when the processor tries to execute a supervisor resource in user mode.

The trace exception is the service routine obeyed when the processor is operating in trace mode, that is, when it is obeying one or a sequence of instructions and then stopping. The service routine will typically allow the user to examine the state of the processor. This is useful in debugging a program.

The 68020 has some instructions for calling exceptions.

```
Mnemonic   Operands   Size    XNZVC   Operation

BKPT       #data              -----   Execute breakpoint instruction
ILLEGAL                       -----   Cause illegal trap exception
RESET                         -----   Reset other devices in system
RTE                           @@@@@   return from exception
STOP     S #data              -----   load SR with data and stop
TRAP       #vector            -----   call trap number vector (0..15)
TRAPcc     #data      W,L     -----   If cc then call trap
TRAPV                         -----   If V set then call trapv
```

When, for example, TRAPV is obeyed, exception number 7 is called if the overflow flag is set. The instruction TRAP #data, where 0<=data<=15, causes exception number 32+data to be obeyed.

The floating point coprocessor (FPCP) is a special chip which is designed to perform floating point operations. The 68020 and FPCP communicate with each other, for example, the 68020 is used to provide the data for the FPCP. There can be errors in the operation of the FPCP, for example a divide by zero, or an overflow. Traps 48-54 provide routines for handling such errors. There are instructions for processing the FPCP: see the data books.

Another device associated with the 68020 is the memory management unit (MMU). As its name suggests, this is used to manage the memory of the computer; exactly what this does is beyond the scope of the book. Again, there are exception traps for handling errors associated with the use of the MMU.

Pin out for the 68020

The 68020 comes in a pin grid array package; the pins are arranged in a 13×13 matrix. Figure A1.2 shows the layout of the pins, when viewed from below, and below that are the pin assignments for the signals on the device.

References

Motorola *MC68020 Microprocessor User's Manual* MC68020UM/AD, 1985.
Motorola MC68881 *Floating Point Coprocessor Manual* MC68881UM/AD, 1985.

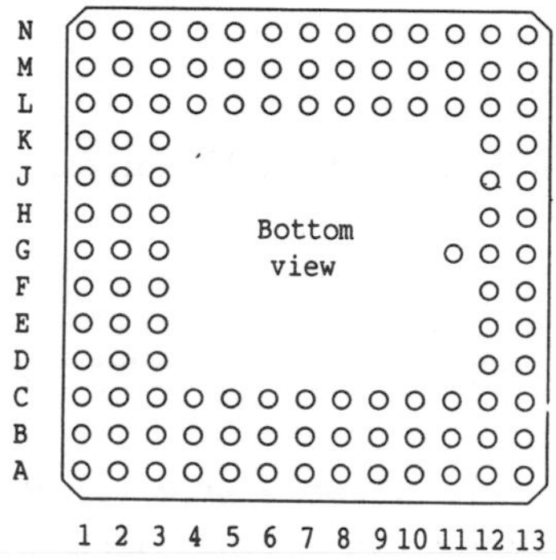

Figure A1.2 Pin layout for the 68020

Pin	Signal	Pin	Signal	Pin	Signal	Pin	Signal	Pin	Signal
A1	$\overline{\text{BGACK}}$	C1	$\overline{\text{RESET}}$	F1	SIZ0	J1	$\overline{\text{DSACK1}}$	M1	$\overline{\text{DS}}$
A2	A1	C2	CLOCK	F2	FC2	J2	$\overline{\text{BERR}}$	M2	D29
A3	A31	C3	GND	F3	FC1	J3	GND	M3	D26
A4	A28	C4	A0	F12	GND	J12	$\overline{\text{IPL0}}$	M4	D24
A5	A26	C5	A29	F13	$\overline{\text{IPEND}}$	J13	$\overline{\text{IPL1}}$	M5	D21
A6	A23	C6	A25					M6	D18
A7	A22	C7	A21					M7	D16
A8	A19	C8	A17	G1	$\overline{\text{ECS}}$	K1	GND	M8	Vcc
A9	Vcc	C9	A16	G2	SIZ1	K2	$\overline{\text{HALT}}$	M9	D13
A10	GND	C10	A12	G3	$\overline{\text{DBEN}}$	K3	GND	M10	D10
A11	A14	C11	A9	G11	Vcc	K12	D1	M11	D6
A12	A11	C12	A7	G12	GND	K13	D0	M12	D5
A13	A8	C13	A5	G13	Vcc			M13	D4
B1	CND	D1	Vcc	H1	$\overline{\text{CDIS}}$	L1	$\overline{\text{AS}}$	N1	D31
B2	$\overline{\text{BR}}$	D2	Vcc	H2	$\overline{\text{AVEC}}$	L2	R/W	N2	D28
B3	$\overline{\text{BG}}$	D3	Vcc	H3	$\overline{\text{DSACK0}}$	L3	D30	N3	D25
B4	A30	D12	A4	H12	$\overline{\text{IPL2}}$	L4	D27	N4	D22
B5	A27	D13	A3	H13	GND	L5	D23	N5	D20
B6	A24					L6	D19	N6	D17
B7	A20					L7	GND	N7	GND
B8	A18	E1	FC0			L8	D15	N8	Vcc
B9	GND	E2	$\overline{\text{RMC}}$			L9	D11	N9	D14
B10	A15	E3	Vcc			L10	D7	N10	D12
B11	A13	E12	A2			L11	GND	N11	D9
B12	A10	E13	$\overline{\text{OCS}}$			L12	D3	N12	D8
B13	A6					L13	D2	N13	Vcc

Appendix 2 - The 8051

This appendix gives more details of the 8051 microcontroller than are given in chapters 8, 11 and 13. Extra information can be found in the various data books on the 8051.

8051 family

The 8051 is one of a family of microcontrollers, the MCS-51 series. Each device contains the microprocessor, some memory, some peripherals and facilities whereby the processor may be connected to external devices. The following table lists some of the series with the facilities provided on each chip.

Device	on-board ROM	on-board RAM	other notable facilities
8051	4K bytes	128 bytes	
8052	8k bytes	256 bytes	1 extra counter
8031	0	128 bytes	ROM-less 8051
8032	0	256 bytes	ROM-less 8052
8751	4K bytes	128 bytes	EPROM version of 8051

The devices also have the following facilities and attributes:
- 8-bit microprocessor
- The RAM contains the registers, the stack and user memory
- 21 special function registers (26 on 8052/8032)
- 32 input/output lines (some of which can be dedicated for certain purposes) arranged as four 8-bit ports
- On chip oscillator
- Two 16-bit counters (three on 8052/8032)
- Five interrupt sources (six on 8052/8032)
- Fully duplex serial I/O channel
- Bit addressability for processing of boolean variables
- The CMOS versions of the devices have low power consumption.

In the following description the name 8051 will be used generically to refer to any of the MCS-51 family.

Memory and registers in the 8051

The memory of the 8051 is separated into program memory, external data memory and internal data memory. The program memory, which can be up to 64K bytes, is used to store the programs the 8051 executes; the first 4K of this memory (or 8K for the 8052) is the internal ROM. The external data memory, which can also be up to 64K bytes, can be used for storing data. Different instructions are used to access the external data memory and program memory;

268

however, suitable interfacing (as described in chapter 11) allows the external memory to be used both as external program memory and external data memory; the external memory is connected via the ports of the 8051. The internal data memory contains the registers as well as extra RAM some of which can be used as the stack.

Figure A2.1 shows the memory layout and registers of the 8051. The addresses of these are given in hexadecimal. Note, those registers marked with a * can be addressed either as bytes or each bit of the bytes can be addressed separately, in which case the address of the register is the address of bit 0 of the byte, the next address is that of bit 1, and so on. For example, the address of the SCON register is 98H and the bit-address of bit 4 of SCON is 9CH. Locations 20H to 2FH of the RAM are also bit-addressable, at bit-addresses 0 to 127. The lower 32 bytes of the RAM are divided into four 8-register banks: certain instructions allow access to the currently selected bank; they are referred to as R0..R7. The rest of the RAM can be used for any purpose, though it is usual to use some of the RAM as the stack. The stack cannot exceed 256 bytes, so an 8-bit stack pointer is sufficient.

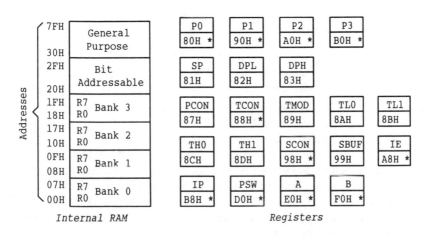

Figure A2.1 Memory and Registers in the 8051

The addresses of the registers are given above, but it should be noted that any assembly language program which uses the registers should refer to them by name not number, like SCON rather than 98H, or SCON.4, to mean bit 4 of register SCON. The special function registers in the 8051 are:

- ACC, the 8-bit accumulator, sometimes referred to as A
- B, a general purpose 8-bit register
- AB, the 16-bit register formed by concatenating A and B
- DPTR, the 16-bit data pointer register; it can be loaded with the address of external ROM or RAM. The high and low bytes of this can be accessed as DPH and DPL
- SP, the 8-bit stack pointer

- PSW - program status word - the flag register
    - bit 7 = C - carry (this is also referred to as register C)
    - bit 6 = AC - auxiliary carry (used in BCD arithmetic)
    - bit 5 = F0 - user flag testable and controllable by user program
    - bit 4,3 = RS1, RS0 - register select 1 and register select 0
        these specify which of the four register banks is selected
    - bit 2 = OV - overflow flag set if the result overflowed
    - bit 1 - reserved
    - bit 0 = P - parity (set if A has an even number of 1s)

  Note instructions may affect the carry, auxiliary carry and overflow flags depending upon the result of the last operation. The parity flag is determined by the value in the A register.
- P0..P3, the four 8-bit ports (these are described later)
- PC, the 16-bit program counter: not addressable directly.

The other registers are used for controlling the serial communications link, interrupts, timers and power control. These registers are described in detail later when these facilities are described.

8051 addressing modes

Instructions for the 8051 are of the form *INSTR dst,src* or *INSTR dst*, where *dst* and *src* refer to the addressing modes. The 8051 has only five addressing modes, and these modes cannot be used with all instructions. The modes are:

Register   Syntax: Register   Example: MOV A,B
    The register is one of A, B, C, AB, DPTR or R0..R7 (being one of the eight registers in the currently selected register bank).
Direct   Syntax: Addr   Example: MOV A,56
    Addr is an 8-bit value specifying a location within the internal RAM: it can also be used to refer to any of the registers.
Register indirect   Syntax: @Ri   Example: MOV A,@R0
    Here the data specified are at the address which is in R1 or R0 in the current register bank.
Immediate   Syntax: #data   Example: MOVE A,#65
    The data are specified in the instruction.
Base register plus register indirect
                        Syntax: Basereg+A Example: MOVC A,PC+A
    Here the base register (either PC or DPTR) and the contents of the A register are added to form the required address.

8051 instructions

The instructions of the 8051 are described below. These are categorised as data transfer instructions, arithmetic instructions, logic instructions, boolean variable instructions and control transfer instructions. For each instruction, the addressing modes, how the C, AC and OV flags are affected and a description are given. The following abbreviations are used in these descriptions.

Rn   Register R7..R0 of the currently selected bank.
dir   8-bit internal memory location (RAM or register)
@Ri   8-bit internal memory location whose address is in R1 or R0
#data   8-bit immediate data
#data16   16-bit immediate data
addr16   16-bit destination address (used in some jumps and calls)
addr11   11-bit destination address (used in other jumps and calls)
rel   signed 8-bit offset (used in relative jumps)
bit   directly addressed bit of byte in internal memory location

In addition, the names of registers (A, B, AB, C, DPTR and PC) are used. As regards affecting the flags: u is unchanged, 0 is cleared to '0', 1 is set to '1' and @ is set according to the result of the instruction. The flags will also be affected if the destination operand is the PSW register or a bit in the PSW.

Data transfer instructions

Instruction	C	OV	AC	Description
MOV A,Rn	u	u	u	Move register into accumulator
MOV A,dir	u	u	u	Move direct byte into accumulator
MOV A,@Ri	u	u	u	Move indirect byte into accumulator
MOV A,#data	u	u	u	Move immediate data into accumulator
MOV Rn,A	u	u	u	Move accumulator into register
MOV Rn,dir	u	u	u	Move direct byte into register
MOV Rn,#data	u	u	u	Move data into register
MOV dir,A	u	u	u	Move accumulator into direct byte
MOV dir,Rn	u	u	u	Move register into direct byte
MOV dir,dir	u	u	u	Move direct byte into direct byte
MOV dir,@Ri	u	u	u	Move indirect byte into direct byte
MOV dir,#data	u	u	u	Move data into direct byte
MOV @Ri,A	u	u	u	Move accumulator into indirect RAM
MOV @Ri,dir	u	u	u	Move direct byte into indirect RAM
MOV @Ri,#data	u	u	u	Move data into indirect RAM
MOV DPTR,#data16	u	u	u	Move accumulator into register
MOVC A,@A+DPTR	u	u	u	Move data from ROM into accumulator
MOVC A,@A+PC	u	u	u	Move data from ROM into accumulator
MOVX A,@Ri	u	u	u	Move from RAM (8-bit addr) to acc.
MOVX A,@DPTR	u	u	u	Move from RAM (16-bit addr) to acc.
MOVX @Ri,A	u	u	u	Move from acc. to RAM (8-bit addr)
MOVX @DPTR,A	u	u	u	Move from acc. to RAM (16-bit addr)
PUSH dir	u	u	u	Push register onto stack
POP dir	u	u	u	Pop register from stack
SWAP A	u	u	u	Swaps the two nibbles in the accumulator
XCH A,Rn	u	u	u	Exchange register with accumulator
XCH A,dir	u	u	u	Exchange direct byte with accumulator
XCH A,@Ri	u	u	u	Exchange indirect byte with acc.
XCHD A,@Ri	u	u	u	Exch. indirect lower digit with acc.

The above need little comment. MOV instructions move data from source to destination. MOVC instructions move data from ROM (internal or external) into the accumulator. MOVX instructions move data between the accumulator and RAM (internal locations are specified by 8-bit addresses; external locations are specified by 16-bit addresses). PUSH and POP need no comment. SWAP exchanges the upper and lower nibbles of the accumulator. The XCH instructions swap the contents of the source and destination operands. The XCHD instruction exchanges the low order nibble of the accumulator with that of the specified byte in the RAM. None of these instructions affects the flags unless the destination location is the PSW register.

Arithmetic instructions

Instruction	C	OV	AC	Description
ADD A,Rn	@	@	@	Add register to accumulator
ADD A,dir	@	@	@	Add direct byte to accumulator
ADD A,@Ri	@	@	@	Add indirect byte to accumulator
ADD A,#data	@	@	@	Add data to accumulator
ADDC A,Rn	@	@	@	Add with carry register to accumulator
ADDC A,dir	@	@	@	Add with carry direct byte to acc.
ADDC A,@Ri	@	@	@	Add with carry indirect byte to acc.
ADDC A,#data	@	@	@	Add with carry data to accumulator
SUBB A,Rn	@	@	@	Subtract with borrow register from acc.
SUBB A,dir	@	@	@	Sub. with borrow direct byte from acc.
SUBB A,@Ri	@	@	@	Sub. with borrow indirect byte from acc.
SUBB A,#data	@	@	@	Subtract with borrow data from acc.
INC A	u	u	u	Increment A
INC Rn	u	u	u	Increment register
INC dir	u	u	u	Increment direct byte
INC @Ri	u	u	u	Increment indirect byte
INC DPTR	u	u	u	Increment DPTR
DEC A	u	u	u	Decrement A
DEC Rn	u	u	u	Decrement register
DEC dir	u	u	u	Decrement direct byte
DEC @Ri	u	u	u	Increment indirect byte
MUL AB	0	@	u	Multiply A and B, result in AB
DIV AB	0	@	u	Divide A and B, quot. & rem. in A & B
DA A	@	u	u	Decimal adjust A

Again little comment is needed. ADD is add the data; ADDC adds the data and the state of the carry flag; SUBB subtracts the data and borrow (the carry flag); INC, DEC and DA are self explanatory; MUL multiplies the 8-bit unsigned values in A and B putting the 16-bit result in AB; and DIV divides the 8-bit unsigned value in A by that in B, the integer quotient of this is put in A, the remainder put in B (if B contained 0, the results in A and B are undefined but the overflow flag is set).

Logical and rotate instructions

Instruction	C	OV	AC	Description
ANL A,Rn	u	u	u	And register to accumulator
ANL A,dir	u	u	u	And direct byte to accumulator
ANL A,@Ri	u	u	u	And indirect byte to accumulator
ANL A,#data	u	u	u	And data to accumulator
ANL dir,A	u	u	u	And accumulator to direct byte
ANL dir,#data	u	u	u	And data to direct byte
ORL A,Rn	u	u	u	Or register to accumulator
ORL A,dir	u	u	u	Or direct byte to accumulator
ORL A,@Ri	u	u	u	Or indirect byte to accumulator
ORL A,#data	u	u	u	Or data to accumulator
ORL dir,A	u	u	u	Or accumulator to direct byte
ORL dir,#data	u	u	u	Or data to direct byte
XRL A,Rn	u	u	u	Exclusive-Or register to accumulator
XRL A,dir	u	u	u	Exclusive-Or direct byte to accumulator
XRL A,@Ri	u	u	u	Exclusive-Or indirect byte to acc.
XRL A,#data	u	u	u	Exclusive-Or data to accumulator
XRL dir,A	u	u	u	Exclusive-Or accumulator to direct byte
XRL dir,#data	u	u	u	Exclusive-Or data to direct byte
CLR A	u	u	u	Clear accumulator
CPL A	u	u	u	Complement accumulator
RL A	u	u	u	Rotate left accumulator
RLC A	@	u	u	Rotate left accumulator through carry
RR A	u	u	u	Rotate right accumulator
RRC A	u	u	u	Rotate right accumulator through carry

These require no extra comment.

Boolean variable instructions

Instruction	C	OV	AC	Description
CLR C	0	u	u	Clear the C register (carry flag)
CLR bit	u	u	u	Clear the specified bit
SETB C	1	u	u	Set the C register (carry flag)
SETB bit	u	u	u	Set the specified bit
CPL C	@	u	u	Complement the C register (carry flag)
CPL bit	u	u	u	Complement the specified bit
ANL C,bit	@	u	u	And C with specified bit
ANL C,/bit	@	u	u	And C with inverse of specified bit
ORL C,bit	@	u	u	OR C with specified bit
ORL C,/bit	@	u	u	OR C with inverse of specified bit
MOV C,bit	@	u	u	Move specified bit into C
MOV bit,C	u	u	u	Move C into specified bit

These instructions process single bits, which could be the carry flag (the C register) or a bit in those registers and RAM locations which are bit addressable; the latter being addressed by their address or, for example, A.7 meaning bit 7 of the A register. The instructions require no further comment.

Program branching instructions

Instruction	C	OV	AC	Description
ACALL addr11	u	u	u	Call subroutine at the given address
LCALL addr16	u	u	u	Call subroutine at the given address
AJMP addr11	u	u	u	Jump to the given address
LJMP addr16	u	u	u	Jump to the given address
SJMP rel	u	u	u	Relative jump to the given address
JMP @A+DPTR	u	u	u	Jump indirect relative
RET	u	u	u	Return from subroutine
RETI	u	u	u	Return from interrupt
JZ rel	u	u	u	Jump relative if acc. contains zero
JNZ rel	u	u	u	Jump relative if acc. contains non-zero
JC rel	u	u	u	Jump relative if C is set
JNC rel	u	u	u	Jump relative if C is reset
JB bit,rel	u	u	u	Jump relative if bit is set
JNB bit,rel	u	u	u	Jump relative if bit is reset
JBC bit,rel	u	u	u	Jump rel. if bit set, then clear bit
CJNE A,dir,rel	@	u	u	Compare byte and acc; jump if not equal
CJNE A,#data,rel	@	u	u	Compare data and acc; jump if not equal
CJNE Rn,#data,rel	@	u	u	Compare byte and Rn; jump if not equal
CJNE @Ri,#data,rel	@	u	u	Compare byte and @Ri; jump if not equal
DJNZ Rn,rel	u	u	u	Decrement Rn, then jump if not zero
DJNZ dir,rel	u	u	u	Decrement byte, then jump if not zero
NOP	u	u	u	No operation

The ACALL and AJMP instructions load the lower 11 bits of the PC from the addr11 operand; the upper 5 bits are unchanged from the value they have *after* the instruction has been fetched. LCALL and LJMP load the PC with the 16-bit value in the operand. All the conditional and unconditional relative jump instructions add the signed offset rel to the PC.

The ports

Ports 0 to 3 are 8-bit input/output lines where each individual bit can be accessed separately, or the ports can be allocated for special purposes, for example, for connecting external memory. This section describes how they are configured and the special purposes of the ports.

Associated with each port is a register (P0..P3). If a bit on the port is to be an input, then '1' must be written into the associated location in the register; then the value of the input bit of the port can be found by testing that bit in the P0..P3 register. If that bit is to be used as an output, then the appropriate value can be set by writing '0' or '1' to the bit in the port. It should be noted that ports 1..3 have internal pull-up resistors, but port 0 does not; therefore if an open collector circuit is providing the input to a bit on port 0 then an external pull-up resistor is required. An output bit from ports 1..3 can drive about four LS-TTL gates, a bit from port 0 can drive eight such gates; a bit from port 0 must have a pull-up resistor if it is driving a MOS circuit.

When external memory is connected to the 8051, ports 0 and 2 are used to provide the address and data bus. Port 0 provides the lower half of the address bus and the data bus multiplexed (when the ALE signal is asserted the port is the address bus). Port 2 provides the upper half of the address bus if the external memory requires a 16-bit address. The 8051 assumes these ports will provide the address and data buses if external memory is accessed; this occurs if it reads an instruction whose address is above that of the highest byte in the internal ROM, or if its $\overline{EA}$ pin is '0', or if the address of the RAM is above that of the highest address of the internal RAM.

The bits on port 3 also have special uses; bit 0 is the receiver bit of serial data, RXD, and bit 1 is the transmitter bit of serial data, TXD; bits 2 and 3 are the sources of the interrupts $\overline{INT0}$ and $\overline{INT1}$; bits 4 and 5 are the input bits of the timers T0 and T1; and bits 6 and 7 provide the write and read strobes which are used to access external RAM. These are described in more detail in the relevant sections below and in chapter 11.

Timers

The 8051 has two timer/counters, timer 0 and timer 1, which are controlled by the TMOD and TCON registers; the counters can be configured to be 8-bits, 13-bits or 16-bits long, and they count up from a preloaded initial value. The values of the counters can be found in the four 8-bit registers TL0, TH0, TL1 and TH1, which provide the upper and lower bytes of the two counters. (The 8052 has an extra counter, which is not described here.) These devices can provide various timing functions by counting internal clock pulses (which occur at 1/12th of the processor clock frequency) or external pulses on the T0 or T1 pin on port 3. It is generally better to use such hardware for these functions than to do the same in software: they provide more accurate timings and do not miss events, which a microprocessor may do as it has various other functions to perform.

The timers are also associated with interrupts: the timers can be set to generate an interrupt when they overflow, that is, when the counter exceeds its maximum value (for example, an 8-bit counter goes from 255 to 0).

The timer control register, TCON, is shown below:

```
Bit  Name       Purpose
 7   TF1    Timer 1 overflow: set when timer overflows
                    cleared when interrupt service routine run
 6   TR1    Timer 1 run/stops when software sets this to 1/0
 5   TF0    Timer 0 overflow
 4   TR0    Timer 0 run/stop
 3   IE1    External interrupt 1: set by external interrupt
                    cleared when service routine called
 2   IT1    Interrupt control 1: 1/0 to specify edge/level
                    triggering of interrupt
 1   IE0    External interrupt 0
 0   IT0    Interrupt control 0
```

The mode register, TMOD, determines the mode of the counters.

Bit	Name	Purpose
7	Gate1	If 1, then timer 1 will not count if INT1 is 0
6	C/T̄1	Timer/Counter select: if 0, timer 1 will count using internal clock; if 1, using T1 input pin
5	M1	Mode selector bit 1 for T1
4	M0	Mode selector bit 0 for T1
3	Gate0	The enable for counter 0
2	C/T̄0	Timer/Counter select for counter 0
1	M1	Mode selector bit 1 for T0
0	M0	Mode selector bit 0 for T0

The mode bits for the two counters define the following four modes:

M1	M0	Mode	Comment
0	0	0	13-bit timer
0	1	1	16-bit timer/counter
1	0	2	8-bit auto-reload timer/counter
1	1	3	TL0 and TH0 controlled by timer modes of timer 0 and timer 1 control bits.

In mode 0, the timer is a 13-bit counter, the upper 8 bits being in THx, the lower 5 bits being the upper 5 bits of TLx (where x is 0 or 1). The clock for the counter is the normal internal clock (processor clock divided by 12). The timer flag is set when the counter goes from 8191 to 0.

In mode 1, the timer is a 16-bit counter whose values are in THx and TLx.

In mode 2, TLx acts an 8-bit counter which is automatically reloaded from THx when TLx reaches 0.

In mode 3, timer 1 is stopped and the two halves of timer 0, in registers TH0 and TL0, are controlled respectively by the mode control bits for timer 1 and timer 0.

One use of these counters is to provide accurate regular timings, and one application of such is in serial communication, and this is described next.

Serial I/O interface

The 8051 has a full duplex serial communications port, using bit 0 of port 3, RXD, and bit 1 of port 3, TXD. Data can be transmitted and received at the same time. The receiver is also buffered, the next byte can be sent to the 8051 immediately after one byte has been sent, although the microprocessor should read the first byte before the last bit of the next byte is received; otherwise the first byte is lost. The SBUF register is used for storing data transmitted or received. The PCON register and timer 1 control the rate at which data are sent. The serial port can operate in four modes, as follows, the mode being determined by bits in the SCON register.

In mode 0, synchronous operation, the data are transmitted and received through RXD, the least significant bit being sent first, and the clock for the communication is output on TXD.

In mode 1, asynchronous operation, data are received through RXD and transmitted from TXD. The data are sent as one start bit, eight data bits and then one stop bit. The baud rate is variable.

In mode 2, asynchronous operation, the data are sent as one start bit, eight data bits, an optional ninth bit (which could be parity) and then a stop bit. The baud rate is either 1/32 or 1/64 of the processor clock frequency.

Mode 3 is just like mode 2 except the baud rate is variable.

The SCON register controls the operation, its bits being as follows:

```
Bit     Name    Function
7       SM0       Serial mode specifier
6       SM1       Serial mode specifier - these act as follows:
                    SM0   SM1
                    0     0       Mode 0 operation
                    0     1       Mode 1 operation
                    1     0       Mode 2 operation
                    1     1       Mode 3 operation
5       SM2     Multiprocessor communication mode
4       REN     Enable/disable reception (1 is enable)
3       TB8     9th data bit sent in modes 2 and 3
2       RB8     9th bit received in modes 2 and 3
1       T1      Transmit interrupt flag
0       R1      Receive interrupt flag
```

The T1 and R1 flags are set when a byte has been transmitted or received; this is detectable by software, which should then clear the flag. In modes 2 and 3, if SM2 is set, then an interrupt is generated when RB8 is '1'; this is used in multimicroprocessor mode, where information is sent at once to many microprocessors; more details of which can be found in the data book. To send data in any mode, a suitable value is written to SBUF; the T1 bit can then be tested to determine when the byte has been sent, that is, when the next byte can be output to SBUF. An incoming data byte is loaded into SBUF when the whole byte has been received, its presence being detectable by testing R1; this byte can then be read. The assertion of T1 and R1 can generate an interrupt.

The baud rate for mode 0 is fixed at 1/12 of the microprocessor's clock. For mode 2, the baud rate is either 1/64 or 1/32 of the clock: if the SMOD bit of the PCON register is '0', the former clock frequency is used. For modes 1 and 3, the baud rate is determined by the overflow rate of timer 1 (timer 2 for the 8052). When using timer 1, the baud rate is the overflow rate divided by n, where n is 32 if the SMOD bit in PCON is '0', and n is 16 otherwise. Timer 1 should be set to auto-reload mode, and interrupts on timer 1 should be disabled (as an interrupt is not required each time the timer overflows). The value of TH1 required, that is, the value the counter is reloaded with each time, is as follows, where fosc is the frequency of the microprocessor clock:

$$TH1 = 256 - 2^{SMOD} * fosc / (384 * baudrate)$$

For example, if fosc is 11.059MHz, and 9600 baud is required, SMOD should be set to 0, and TH1 loaded with 253.

Interrupts

The 8051 has five sources of interrupt, three of which are generated internally
(by the flags for the two timers and the serial port, where an interrupt can be
generated when a byte has been sent or received) and two externally, by signals
input into the $\overline{INT0}$ and $\overline{INT1}$ pins on port 3. These interrupts are enabled or
disabled by the interrupt enable register, IE, whose bits are as follows:

Bit	Name	Function
7	EA	Enables/disables all ints when EA is 1/0
6,5		not used
4	ES	Enables/disables serial port interrupt
3	ET1	Enables/disables timer 1 interrupt
2	EX1	Enables/disables $\overline{INT1}$ interrupt
1	ET0	Enables/disables timer 0 interrupt
0	EX0	Enables/disables $\overline{INT0}$ interrupt

Note an interrupt is enabled only if its associated bit and bit 7 are both set.

Priority of interrupts can be specified using the interrupt priority register,
IP. A low priority interrupt can be interrupted by a higher priority interrupt.
Normally the priority of interrupts is as follows $\overline{INT0}$ (highest), Timer 0, $\overline{INT1}$,
Timer 1 and Serial (lowest). However, an interrupt source can be made the
highest priority by setting the appropriate bit in IP. The following table
indicates the bit in IP associated with each interrupt and the address of the
service routine for that interrupt.

Interrupt	Bit in IP	Address of Service Routine
Serial Port	4	0003H
Timer 1	3	000BH
$\overline{INT1}$	2	0013H
Timer 0	1	001BH
$\overline{INT0}$	0	0023H

An interrupt is generated when the appropriate bit in a register is set: for
example, when timer 1 overflows, the TF1 bit in the TCON register is set and
an interrupt is generated (if it is enabled); similarly, when an interrupt request
occurs on $\overline{INT0}$, the IE0 bit of TCON is set; also, when a byte has been
received serially, the R1 bit of SCON is set. Note, an interrupt can be generated
by software: the microprocessor itself sets the appropriate flag. When an
interrupt occurs, the 8051 saves the PC onto the stack and loads the PC with
the appropriate address. Note, the PSW is not saved; so a service routine should
save it and any other register used. A RETI, return from interrupt, instruction
is at the end of the service routine; when this is obeyed, the interrupt bit in the
appropriate register is cleared thereby removing the interrupt request.

Power-down, idle mode and the PCON register

The 8051 has a power-down mode, and the CMOS versions of the device also
have an idle mode. When power-down mode is invoked, the clock to the device
is frozen so everything stops, but the contents of the RAM are saved; the

device then consumes much less power. A hardware reset is the only way to end this mode. When idle mode is invoked the clock to the 8051 microprocessor is stopped, so the microprocessor ceases to obey instructions, but the interrupt, timer and serial communications parts of the 8051 continue to operate. Idle mode can be terminated by an interrupt or a hardware reset.

For non-CMOS versions of the 8051, power-down is used to maintain the contents of the RAM when the power supply of the device fails, in which case a battery may be used to supply the RAM via the RST pin. See the data book for more details of this mode.

For CMOS versions of the 8051 these modes (and other functions) are controlled by the PCON register, whose contents are as follows:

Bit	Name	Function
7	SMOD	Used for baud rate generation (see earlier)
6,5,4	not used	
3	GF1	General purpose flag 1
2	GF0	General purpose flag 0
1	PD	Power-down mode is activated if this is set
0	IDL	Idle mode is activated if this is set

Reset conditions of registers

The 8051 can be reset by forcing its RST pin high for at least 24 clock cycles. When the RST pin is released the 8051 begins operation by reading its first instruction from address 0. The contents of the internal RAM are not affected by reset, and the values of the RAM are undefined when the device is first powered up. However, the registers are assigned definite values, as shown by the table below, where the initial values are shown in hexadecimal or binary, which ever is appropriate (where x means undefined).

Register	Reset to	Register	Reset to	Register	Reset to
A	00H	P2	FFH	SCON	00H
B	00H	P3	FFH	TCON	00H
DPTR	00H	PCON	0xxxxxxxB	TMOD	00H
IE	0xx00000B		or 0xxx0000B	TH0	00H
IP	xxx00000B	PSW	00B	TH1	00H
P0	FFH	SP	07H	TL0	00H
P1	FFH	SBUF	xxH	TL1	00H

Note, the CMOS versions of the 8051 have the second initial value for PCON; for them idle and power down modes are cleared initially.

External connections to the 8051

The 8051 comes in various packages: figure A2.2 shows the connections to the 40 pin package versions; here the pins are named and alternative uses of some pins shown; for example, bit 0 of port 3 (P3.0) is also RXD, the received data serial input. Most of the pins need little comment, but more details are given of other pins, where appropriate.

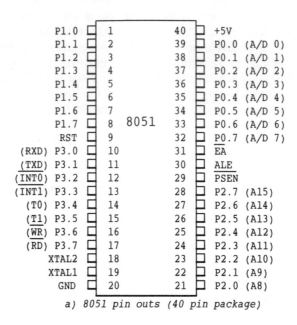

a) 8051 pin outs (40 pin package)

Figure A2.2 Pin outs of 40 pin package 8051

P0.0..P0.7 are the 8 lines for port 0, bits 0..7, with similar names for ports 1, 2 and 3. RST is the active high reset line. ALE, address latch enable, is used by external circuitry to latch the lower half of the address bus when external memory is accessed. $\overline{PSEN}$, program store enable, is the read strobe for accessing external ROM. $\overline{EA}$ is pulled low if the 8051 is to be forced to read from external ROM rather than internal ROM. XTAL1 and XTAL2 are used to provide the clock to the 8051. More details on the clock and the use of the ports for connecting external memory are given in chapter 11.

Reference

Philips *Single-Chip 8-bit Microcontrollers* User Manual 1988, Philips.

Appendix 3 - STE Bus Details

This appendix discusses a few practical points concerning the STE bus. Full details are given in the IEEE specification for the bus. Chapter 11 gives some examples of the use of the bus and it includes timing diagrams for the signals. See also appendix 5 where details on different logic families are given.

Logic signals on STE

This section considers aspects of logic signals as they apply to the STE bus. First the types of gates which drive the bus need to be considered, whether they are tristate, open collector or the standard totem pole output. The types of output of the STE bus signals are as follows:

tristate:	A19..A0, D7..D0, CM2..CM0, ADRSTB*, DATSTB*
open collector:	DATACK*, TFRERR*, SYSRST*, BUSRQ1*, BUSRQ0*, ATNRQ7*..ATNRQ0*
totem pole:	SYSCLK, BUSAK1*, BUSAK0*

The signal voltage levels on STE are shown in figure A3.1. To summarise, a receiving device will accept a voltage greater than or equal to 2.0 V as a logic '1', and a voltage less than or equal to 0.8 V as a logic '0'. A device which drives the bus should output at least 2.4 V for a logic '1' and at most 0.5 V for a logic '0'. Thus there is a small noise margin between the levels for driving and receiving signals. These logic levels are compatible with most TTL gates, but not with HC TTL or CMOS devices which therefore cannot be used directly on the bus. ECL devices cannot be used for a similar reason.

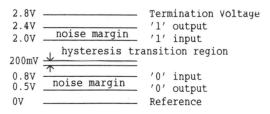

Figure A3.1 Logic levels on STE

Between these voltages receivers should exhibit Schmitt trigger character-istics with a hysteresis of at least 200 mV. This requirement is mandatory for the synchronisation signals ADRSTB*, DATSTB*, DATACK*, TFRERR* and SYSCLK, and it is recommended for other devices to minimise the effects of noise.

The minimum sink capability of a driver must be 24 mA at 0.5 V, and the source capability should be 24 mA at 2.4 V. The minimum rise and fall transition times of any line driver should be 5 ns when driving a capacitive load of 45 pF. When inactive no board should exhibit a load leakage on to a line greater than 50 µA at 2.4 V or greater than 200 µA at 0.5 V. Also, no board shall present a capacitance greater than 20 pF for any signal line. The length of track from the bus connector to any on board device should be less than 50 mm on a double sided board and less than 25 mm on a multilayer board.

The STE specification does not state which form of digital technology should be used, instead it requires that the above criteria should be met. The LS logic family can be used, for example, but for new designs the high speed CMOS families are recommended because they consume less power. Devices from the HC or AC families cannot be connected to the bus directly, but they can be used on STE boards if HCT or ACT components are used to provide an interface between the bus and the HC or AC devices. The HCT family can be used for receiving signals from the bus, but these cannot drive the bus directly as they do not have the necessary current drive capability, so the ACT family should be used instead.

Power supplies on STE

It is essential that the power supply of a system should be capable of supplying the necessary power. It should be remembered that a large current flows when the system is first switched on, so the supply should be able to handle this as well as the requirements during normal operation. The power supplies required are 5 V, +/−12 V and a 5 V standby. The following table summarises the requirements for these.

Supply	Nominal	Variation	pk-pk ripple (Below 10 MHz)	Maximum Current (Per board/Per system)
+Vcc	+5 V	+5%, -2.5%	50 mV	4 A / 50 A
+AUX	+12 V	+/- 5%	50 mV	1 A / 4 A
-AUX	-12 V	+/- 5%	50 mV	1 A / 4
+VSTBY	+5 V	+/- 5%	50 mV	1 A / 4 A
GND	0 V	ref	ref	- / -

The STE specification also provides guidelines for handling power failure. If the system has an early indication of failure in the primary power supply and can do something appropriate, the attention request line ATNRQ0* should be used to signal imminent power failure and the following protocol adopted.

For power down, the DC output of the 5 V supply should remain within its specified tolerance for at least 4 ms after ATNRQ0* is asserted, the system controller should assert SYSRST* at least 2 ms after ATNRQ0* is asserted, and SYSRST* should be asserted at least 50 µs before the 5 V supply falls below its minimum specified tolerance.

For power up, SYSRST* should remain asserted for at least 200 ms after the 5 V supply reaches its minimum specified tolerance, and at least 200 ms after ATNRQ0* is released.

Bus connections

Figure A3.2 shows the pin numbers used on STE. Note, two rows of the three provided on the reliable DIN41612 connector are used (defined by standard IEC 603-2-1980). Also, there are many 0 V lines positioned at various points along the bus. These help to reduce the effects of crosstalk and noise.

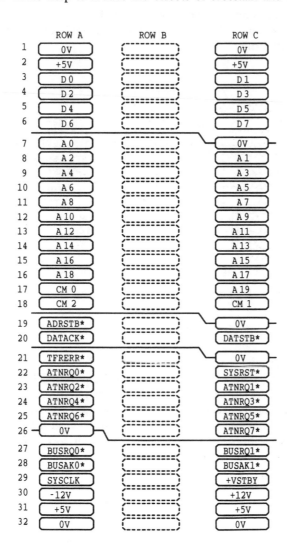

Figure A3.2 Bus connections on STE

One problem with buses is that a signal passing along the bus can reach the end of the bus and then be reflected back again (for reasons explained in books on transmission lines like that by Davidson).

This problem can be prevented by the use of termination in which a load is connected at the end of a wire whose impedance matches that of the wire and so absorbs the energy of the signal as it reaches the end of the bus. Figure A3.3 shows some termination networks for STE, details of which can be found in Mitchell (1989) and the IEEE STE specification. Termination networks are required at both ends of the bus unless the number of connectors is less than 6. The maximum number of slots on an STE bus is 21, the maximum length of any signal line on the bus is 500 mm and the minimum separation between connectors is 20.3 mm.

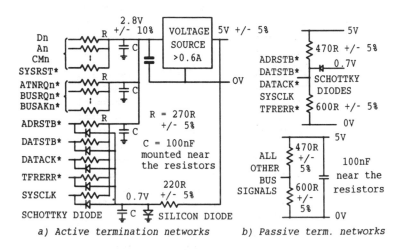

Figure A3.3 Bus termination networks

Another requirement of the specification is that there should be a ground plane for the bus, thus a printed circuit board bus for STE has the tracks on one side and a complete earth plane on the other interrupted only for the holes through which the connector passes. This plane provides 'a well defined transmission line environment'. The easiest way to meet these specifications is to buy in the relevant backplane and termination networks. These are available from various sources, like RS components or specialist STE suppliers, like ARCOM or ProActive.

References

C.W. Davidson *Transmission Lines for Communications* 2nd Edn, Macmillan Press, 1989.

IEEE *Standard for an 8-bit backplane interface: STE bus* ANSI/IEEE Std 1000-1987.

R.J. Mitchell *Microcomputer Systems Using the STE Bus* Macmillan Press, 1989.

Appendix 4 - Logic Symbols

This appendix introduces the logic symbols specified in the standards BS3939 section 21 in the UK, and ANSI/IEEE Std 91-1984 in the USA. Although it is recommended that these standards should be used, instead of the symbols used in this book, the standard has not been widely accepted in industry, yet. This is partly because the symbols used here easily distinguish between AND and OR gates, whereas the newer standard requires more careful scrutiny.

Figure A4.1 shows the symbols used to represent the standard logic gates; both the earlier symbols and the equivalent new symbols. These new symbols represent all circuits by a rectangular shapes, whose size is not specified. The reason for these symbols, it is said, is that it is easier for CAD systems to draw them than the 'rounded' symbols. This may have been true in the early 1980s, but these days microprocesor systems can easily draw both shapes.

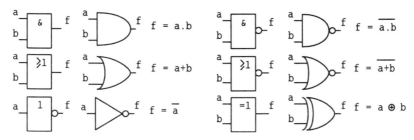

Figure A4.1 Logic symbols for simple gates

The newer symbols, however, progress further than the representation of simple gates. All shapes have three primary characteristics; *outline shape*, *qualifying symbols* and *dependency notation*. These are shown in figure A4.2.

The outline shape is usually rectangular. If the circuit has n sub-circuits, this is represented by n rectangles stacked above each other. If these n sub-circuits are controlled by a common circuit, this control block is represented by a rectange with notched corners above the n rectangles (such a control block is shown in figure A4.3a).

The qualifying symbols are used to identify the basic function performed by the component. The general qualifying symbol is put at the top of the rectangular shape, as shown in figure A4.2a; this indicates the element function, like & for AND or MUX for multiplexer; a list of such symbols is given in figure A4.2b. In addition, the inputs and outputs can be qualified, indicating if an output is active low or open-collector, for example, or that an input is negated or an edge-triggered signal. Some input/output qualifying signals are shown in figure A4.2c.

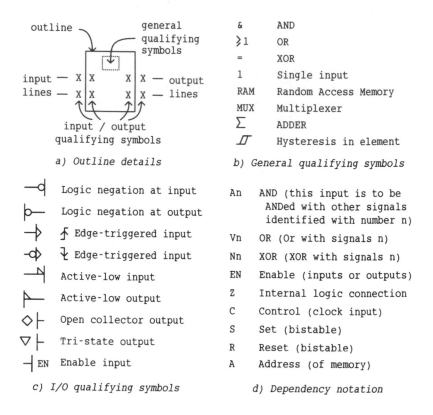

a) *Outline details*

b) *General qualifying symbols*

c) *I/O qualifying symbols*

d) *Dependency notation*

Figure A4.2 Outline and qualifying symbols

Dependency notation is used to describe functions which affect only some elements in a component. For example, an input marked G2 means that all inputs marked with the number 2 are anded with this input; an input marked R3 means that all sub-circuits marked 3 are reset by this input.

Figure A4.3a shows the symbol used to represent four 2 to 1 multiplexers, for which the enable signal G and select signal SEL are common; the equivalent circuit is shown in figure A4.3b. The control block is the rectangle with notched corner at the top of the figure into which G and SEL are input, thus G and SEL are common to the four multiplexers; the multiplexers are shown as the four rectangles below the control block. Note, the circle on the G input indicates that the signal is active low.

It can be seen that these symbols must be scrutinised closely to understand what the circuit does, which is a major drawback. However, the symbols do allow much information regarding the behaviour of the device to be shown very concisely.

The above is a brief introduction to the symbols; more detail can be found in the references cited below.

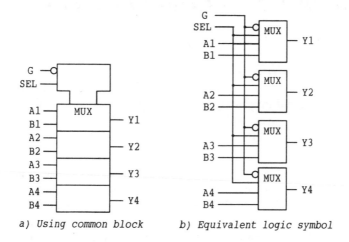

a) Using common block   b) Equivalent logic symbol

Figure A4.3 Example of symbol with common control block

References

IEEE *Standard graphic symbols for logic functions* ANSI/IEEE standard 91-1984.

IEEE *Standard for logic circuit diagrams* ANSI/IEEE standard 991-1986.

I. Kampel, *A Practical Introduction to the New Logic Symbols*, Butterworths 1985.

E. Lacy *Complete Guide to Understanding Electronics Diagrams* Prentice Hall 1989.

Appendix 5 - Logic Devices

This appendix discusses a few practical points concerning logic devices. Factors considered include the different logic families, their power dissipation and logic levels, and interfacing between logic circuits of different families.

Logic families

Modern electronic circuits can be made using the devices from many different logic families. The most common families are CMOS, TTL and ECL for simple devices (gates, decoders and flip flops, for example) and NMOS or HMOS for more complicated devices like microprocessors, UARTs and memories. The early CMOS devices consumed little power but were slow, ECL devices are very fast but consume much power, TTL devices are a compromise, but the modern high speed CMOS devices consume little power and are as fast as many TTL devices. There are many sub-families of TTL devices whose properties span from those of CMOS devices to those of the ECL family. These sub-families include standard TTL, L (low power but slow: these devices have some similar characteristics to CMOS), LS (low power Schottky: a compromise between speed and power consumption), S (Schottky: faster than LS, but consuming more power), ALS (Advanced LS: improved LS, faster and also the '0' to '1' transition time is the same as for the '1' to '0' transition), AS (Advanced S) or F (fast). The high speed CMOS families are HC, HCT, AC and ACT. The HC family provides many chips functionally compatible with both the TTL families and the early CMOS devices. However, the HC and AC families do not have the same logic levels as TTL, so the HCT and ACT families are provided which are compatible with TTL.

Properties of the logic families

In the following table a comparison is given of the characteristics of various logic families. The parameters described are the power dissipation of a gate in the various families; these are defined for the cases when the gates are static and when they are changing state, in the latter case consumption is higher as energy is required to make the switches in the gates change state. Also given is the average delay of a signal passing through a gate, the propagation delay; and the fastest changing signal that a device can follow, the maximum clock signal. The fan-out of a gate is also shown, that is, the number of devices which may be connected to the output of one gate.

Family:	CMOS	HC	TTL	LS	ACT	S	ALS	ECL
Power dissipation Static:	0.001	2×10^{-7}	10	2	0.44	19	1	30
per gate (mW) @100 KHz:	0.1	0.17	10	2	1.2	19	1	30
Propagation delay (ns)	105	8	10	10	8	3	4	1
Max clock frequency (MHz)	12	40	35	40	35	125	70	300
Fan-Out (No of LS loads)	4	10	40	20	12	50	20	3

Other factors that need to be considered are logic levels, that is, the voltages which are considered to be a logic '1' and those which are a logic '0'. These levels are defined by four values: the highest voltage input to a device which is considered to be a logic '0', V_{IL}; the lowest voltage input to a device which is a logic '1', V_{IH}; the highest voltage output by a device which is a logic '0', V_{OL}; and the lowest voltage output which is a logic '1', V_{OH}. There is a margin between the voltages for the different logic levels, so as to make the system more immune to noise. Also to be considered are the currents input and output from gates when the signals are logic '0' and '1'. The currents are the current out from an input when the input is a logic '0', I_{IL}, and when the input is a logic '1', I_{IH}; and the currents into an output when that output is a logic '0', I_{OL}, and when it is a logic '1', I_{OH}. Note, currents are defined as flowing out from an input and in to an output, as shown in figure A5.1a; this seems illogical but, for example, gates can have more current input into their outputs than output from their outputs. The voltages and currents for the logic levels for some logic families are shown below.

Family	TTL	LS/ACT	HC/AC	CMOS (5V supply)
V_{IL}	0.8V	0.8V	1.0V	1.5
V_{IH}	2.0V	2.0V	3.5V	3.5
V_{OL}	0.4V	0.4V	0.1V	0.05
V_{OH}	2.4V	0.4V	4.4V	4.95
I_{IL}	-1.6mA	-400µA	-1µA	10pA
I_{IH}	40µA	20µA	1µA	10pA
I_{OL}	16mA	8mA	4mA	1mA
I_{OH}	-400µA	-400µA	-4mA	-1mA

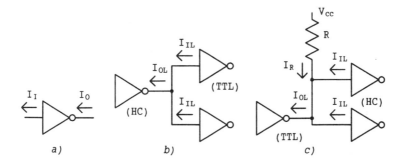

Figure A5.1 Currents and connecting gates

The currents may be used to calculate the fan-out values. Consider figure A5.1b, where a HC gate is driving two standard TTL gates. The maximum current into the output of the HC gate (I_{OL}) is 4 mA; the maximum current from the input of the TTL gate (I_{IL}) is 1.6 mA; therefore the fan-out from the HC gate is 2 TTL gates. By a similar argument, 10 LS gates may be connected to one HC gate. It should be noted that standard TTL is not recommended for new circuits; LS, HCT, ACT, HC or AC should be used.

Interfacing different logic families

Although the logic levels differ, it is possible to connect devices of different families together, though sometimes extra circuitry is required. TTL circuits may, for example, be connected directly to LS gates, and a CMOS gate may drive a TTL gate directly. However, the output from a TTL gate is too low to be connected to a CMOS gate, so a suitable pull up resistor is needed between the gate output and the positive power supply. The currents given above can be used to calculate the value of the resistor: see figure A5.1c, where two HC gates are connected to one TTL output. Sufficient current must flow through the resistor so that the voltage at the gate output is low enough to be a logic '0'. If the current through the resistor is I_R and the resistor value is R, then:

$$R = (5V - V_{OL}) / I_R$$

But the current flowing into the TTL gate is I_{OL} which must equal $I_R + 2I_{IL}$

So $$R = (5V - V_{OL}) / (I_{OL} - 2I_{IL})$$

Using the values given in the table:

$$R = (5 - 0.4) / (8 \times 10^{-3} + 2 \times 10^{-6}) = 575 \ \Omega$$

More details on these matters can be found in the books listed in the reference section as well as in relevant data books.

The logic levels of ECL device are very different. Thus suitable circuits are required to connect ECL to TTL gates. It is unusual, however, to use ECL gates in microprocessor systems, so no more will be said of ECL here.

Microprocessors and similar devices are NMOS and HMOS devices which consume little power. Such devices have TTL-compatible inputs and outputs, so they can be connected directly to TTL gates. However, they are not able to drive significant loads and they have low fan-out, hence buffers are required when connecting these devices to many gates or across buses.

References

M.Morris Mano *Digital Design* Prentice-Hall, 2nd Edn, 1990.

Thomas L. Floyd *Digital Fundamentals* Merrill, 3rd Edn, 1986.

Douglas Lewin and David Protheroe *Design of Logic Systems* Chapman and Hall, 2nd Edn, 1992.

See also relevant data books.

Appendix 6 - Answers to Exercises

This appendix contains brief answers to the exercises in the book.

Chapter 1

Algorithm for $y = x^3$ uses:

$$(x^3 - (x-1)^3 - ((x-1)^3 - (x-2)^3)) - ((x-1)^3 - (x-2)^3 - ((x-2)^3 - (x-3)^3)) = 6$$

or

$$x^3 = 3 * (x-1)^3 - 3 * (x-2)^3 + (x-3)^3 + 6$$

Chapter 2

The program for the CD player must handle the controls and displays, instigate the motors for the CD and search and play the CD. It will wait for the door open button to be pressed, open the door, close the door when the close button is pressed, cause the CD to be spun so its contents can be read and display the number and length of the tracks. It must allow the user to program which tracks are to be played or select random order. When a CD is to be played, the program should cause the tracks to be selected in the appropriate order, have them played, and maintain the display.

Chapter 3

The microcomputer hardware for the player requires interfaces for the buttons and the displays, drivers for the motors for doors and playing the CDs, and means of reading the information from the CDs. It is likely that speed control of the motor is handled by suitable circuitry. Program and data memory are also required.

Chapter 4

1. $59 = 00111011_B = 3B_H = 073_8.$ $137 = 10001001_B = 89_H = 211_8.$
       $253 = 11111101_B = FD_H = 375_8.$ ‘Z’ $= 01011010_B = 5A_H = 132_8.$
       ‘4’ $= 00110100_B = 34_H = 064_8.$ ‘#’ $= 00100011_B = 23_H = 043_8.$

2. The truth table and circuit for a full adder are given in chapter 5.

3. The four bit Gray code is as follows:

0 = 0000	1 = 0001	2 = 0011	3 = 0010
4 = 0110	5 = 0111	6 = 0101	7 = 0100
8 = 1100	9 = 1101	10 = 1111	11 = 1110
12 = 1010	13 = 1011	14 = 1001	15 = 1000

Chapter 5

1. Figure A6.1 shows configurations where NOR gates generate all functions.

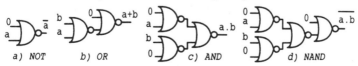

Figure A6.1 Logic functions generated using only NOR gates

2. $f = \overline{a}.\overline{b}.\overline{c}.\overline{d} + \overline{a}.\overline{b}.c.\overline{d} + \overline{a}.b.\overline{c}.\overline{d} + \overline{a}.b.c.d + a.\overline{b}.c.d + a.\overline{b}.\overline{c}.\overline{d} + a.b.\overline{c}.d$

The first 4 terms reduce to $\overline{a}.\overline{b}$; terms 5 & 7 reduce to $b.\overline{c}.d$; 1 & 6 to $\overline{b}.\overline{c}.\overline{d}$

So $f = \overline{a}.\overline{b} + b.c.d + \overline{b}.\overline{c}.\overline{d}$

3,4,5. The truth tables for these are shown in chapter 5; the circuits are in figure A6.2.

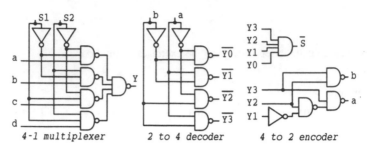

Figure A6.2 Answers to questions 3, 4 and 5

6, 7. The truth tables, expressions and circuits for comparing two 2-bit numbers and converting from 3-bit binary to 3-bit Gray code are shown in figure A6.3.

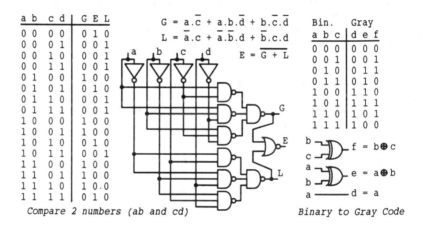

Figure A6.3 Answers to questions 6 and 7

Chapter 6

1, 2, 3. Figure A6.4 contains the truth table, expressions and circuit implementing a 3-bit up/down counter. In addition, there are the modifications to be made to each D_n input to provide synchronous clear and also syncnhronous load and clear.

4. The truth table, expressions and circuit for the Gray code counter are in figure A6.5.

Chapter 7

1. Below is shown the evaluation of the integer expressions.

a)
$$
\begin{array}{r}
00011011 = 27 \\
00111011 = 59 \\
\hline
01010110 = 86
\end{array}
$$

b)
$$
\begin{array}{r}
11100100 = -28 \\
11001000 = -56 \\
\hline
10101100 = -84
\end{array}
$$

c)
$$
\begin{array}{r}
01000001 = 65 \\
00000111 = 7 \\
\hline
01000001 \\
01000010 \\
010000100 \\
\hline
011100111 = 455
\end{array}
$$

d)
$$
\begin{array}{r}
10001 \\
111\overline{)01111001} \\
111 \\
\hline
000 \\
001001 \\
111 \\
\hline
010
\end{array}
$$

(answer is 17 remainder 2)

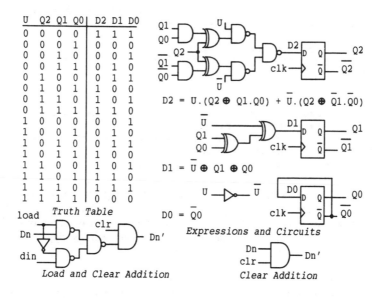

U	Q2	Q1	Q0	D2	D1	D0
0	0	0	0	1	1	1
0	0	0	1	0	0	0
0	0	1	0	0	0	1
0	0	1	1	0	1	0
0	1	0	0	0	1	1
0	1	0	1	1	0	0
0	1	1	0	1	0	1
0	1	1	1	1	1	0
1	0	0	0	0	0	1
1	0	0	1	0	1	0
1	0	1	0	0	1	1
1	0	1	1	1	0	0
1	1	0	0	1	0	1
1	1	0	1	1	1	0
1	1	1	0	1	1	1
1	1	1	1	0	0	0

load   *Truth Table*

$D2 = U.(Q2 \oplus Q1.Q0) + \bar{U}.(Q2 \oplus \bar{Q1}.\bar{Q0})$

$D1 = \bar{U} \oplus Q1 \oplus Q0$

$D0 = \bar{Q0}$

Expressions and Circuits

Load and Clear Addition

Clear Addition

Figure A6.4 3-bit synchronous up/down counter

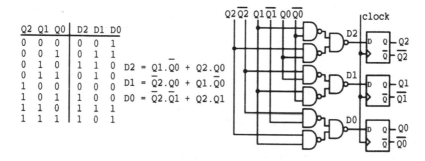

Q2	Q1	Q0	D2	D1	D0
0	0	0	0	0	1
0	0	1	0	1	1
0	1	0	1	1	0
0	1	1	0	1	0
1	0	0	0	0	0
1	0	1	1	0	0
1	1	0	1	1	1
1	1	1	1	0	1

$D2 = Q1.\bar{Q0} + Q2.Q0$

$D1 = \bar{Q2}.Q0 + Q1.\bar{Q0}$

$D0 = \bar{Q2}.\bar{Q1} + Q2.Q1$

Figure A6.5 3-bit Gray code counter

2. For adding and subtracting:
```
For smaller number, REPEAT
   Shift Right Mantissa and Increment Exponent
UNTIL Exponents of numbers equal;
If ADD and Signs of the two numbers the same
   THEN Add the Mantissae ELSE Subtract the Mantissae
IF Carry set, Rotate Right Mantissae and Increment Exponent
ELSE IF Mantissa not zero THEN REPEAT
   Shift Left Mantissa and Decrement Exponent
UNTIL Top bit of Mantissa is a 1
Set Sign of result
```

For multiplying:
```
Sign of result = Sign of first number XOR Sign of second
Add Exponents and Multiply Mantissae
IF Mantissa not zero THEN
   WHILE Top bit of Mantissa is 0 DO
      Shift Left Mantissa and Decrement Exponent
```
For dividing:
```
IF Divisor is zero THEN SetError
ELSE
   Sign of result = Sign of first number XOR Sign of second
   Subtract Exponents and Divide Mantissae
   IF Carry set, Rotate right Mantissa & Increment Exponent
   ELSE IF Mantissa not zero THEN REPEAT
      Shift Left Mantissa and Decrement Exponent
   UNTIL Top bit of Mantissa is a 1
```

3, 4. Figure A6.6 shows a circuit to provide one bit of an ALU; it assumes the full adder circuit given in chapter 5, uses M0 to invert the b input for subtract, and a multiplexer to select the add/subtract, or, and, or exclusive-or circuit. Then is shown how eight of these circuits can be connected together and circuits to generate the flags. Finally there is a circuit to detect when decimal adjust is needed.

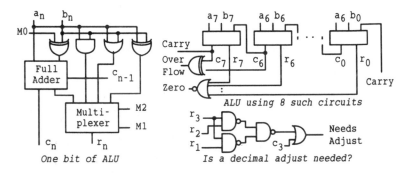

Figure A6.6 Circuits answering questions 3 and 4

Chapter 8

a) STORE DREG, (AREG): the value in the AREG is put on the address bus, that in DREG is put on the data bus, and a write operation is instigated.

b) AND DREG, (65): the microprocessor reads from address 65, the data read from there and the data in DREG are passed to the ALU which is commanded to AND them. The result is returned to the DREG and the flags set accordingly.

c) ASR (76): the microprocessor reads data from address 76, the data read are passed to the ALU which is commanded to perform the ASR operation; the result is written to address 76 and the flags are set accordingly.

d) JUMP NC, (AREG): if the carry flag is cleared the contents of the AREG are copied into the PC.

e) JUMP REL, 20: the value in the PC is loaded into the ALU together with the value 20; these are added together, the result being returned to the PC.

Chapter 9

1. Figure A6.7 shows the circuits to generate wait*.

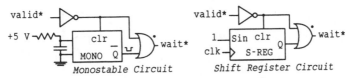

Figure A6.7 Circuits to generate wait*

2. Figure A6.8 shows the interfaces to a semi synchronous bus.

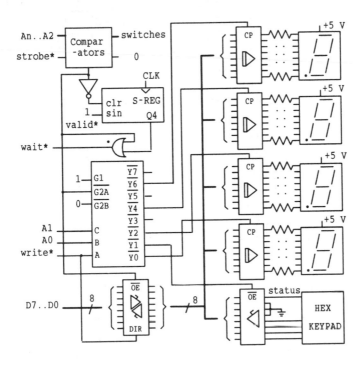

Figure A6.8 Interface of four displays and a keypad

3. Figure A6.9 show the interface of the memory to an asynchronous bus.

Chapter 10

1, 2. Figure A6.10 has the circuits for the 3-bit flash ADC and the circuit to generate RfREQ every 8 µs using a 1MHz clock.

3, 4. Figure A6.11 has the circuits for interfacing a GDC to a synchronous bus and a GDC and UART to a semi-synchronous bus (the latter uses the standard wait circuit generator as given in an earlier answer and not redrawn here).

5. Figure A6.12 has a circuit interfacing the 12-bit converters.

Chapter 11

1. Figure A6.13 has a circuit to select the appropriate memory banks. The expressions for which are given below. Note that the circuit implements the truth table given in chapter 11, and generates an active *low* signal for each of the signals $\overline{CE0}..\overline{CE3}$.

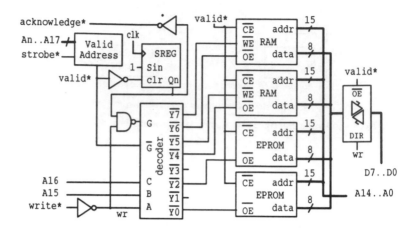

Figure A6.9 Interface of 2 EPROM and 2 RAM

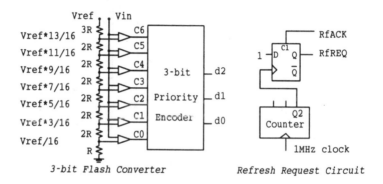

Figure A6.10 Flash converter and refresh request circuits

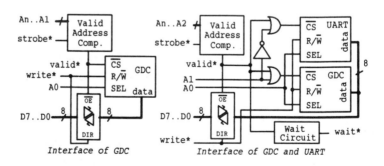

Figure A6.11 Circuits interfacing GDC and UART

$\overline{CE0} = \overline{A1}.\overline{A0}$

$\overline{CE1} = \overline{A1}.A0 + \overline{A1}.\overline{S0} + \overline{A1}.S1$

$\overline{CE2} = A1.\overline{A0} + \overline{A1}.\overline{S1}.\overline{S0} + \overline{A1}.S1.S0 + \overline{A1}.A0.S1$

$\overline{CE3} = A1.A0 + A1.S1 + A0.S1.S0 + \overline{S1}.\overline{S0}$

(note, the above are *not* hazard free; also S1 = SIZ1 and S0 = SIZ0)

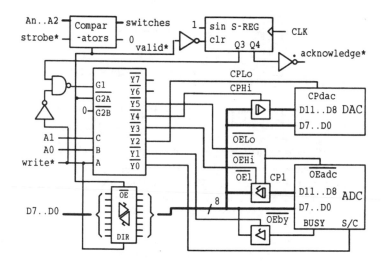

Figure A6.12 Interface of 12-bit converters

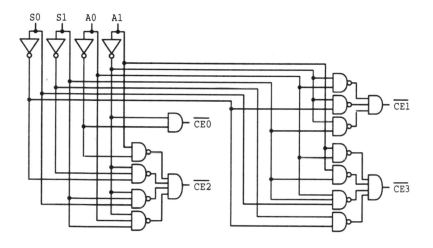

Figure A6.13 Circuit to enable the correct memory banks

2. Two things are required if the 68020 on STE is to be able to generate vector fetch cycles; a means of detecting that a vector fetch cycle is required, and the generation of such a cycle. These are achieved (in part) using the circuit in figure A6.14 together with changes to the control circuit given in figure 11.24. The circuit in figure A6.14 extends that of figure 11.25; one subtle change is that the outputs of the priority encoder are latched at the start of the data transfer cycle, before the interrupt acknowledge begins.

Here it is assumed that links are used to indicate whether the response to a given attention request is to be achieved by a vector fetch cycle, or by a local returning of a suitable vector. The links are used in the following manner. The outputs of the latch, the three bit number of the attention request being serviced, are fed to a 3-to-8 decoder, one of whose outputs will be set low. If the link is set for that output, its value is passed

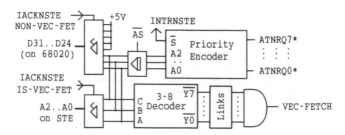

Figure A6.14 Part circuit for generating vector fetch cycles

to the AND gate, thereby generating '0' on the output of the AND gate; if the link is not set, then the output of the gate is '1'. The output of the AND gate therefore indicates if the interrupt acknowledge is to generate an STE vector fetch or just return the number of the attention request. This has achieved the first requirement.

If the circuit should just return the number, the top buffer in the figure is turned on, and the number is put on to the data bus of the STE. Otherwise, the number is put on the address lines of the STE bus, and a standard STE vector fetch transfer instigated; here ADRSTB*, CM2, etc., will be generated suitably, the vector put on the bus and DATACK* asserted by the interrupting device, and the 68020 will store the vector.

3. Figure A6.15 has the interface of the 8051 as an intelligent slave. Here the bi-directional latch is interfaced to the 8051 by direct connection to the ports, and to the STE bus using standard circuitry.

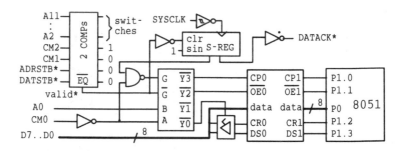

Figure A6.15 8051 intelligent slave on STE

4. Figure A6.16 has the interface of the 12-bit DAC and ADC to the 68020, STE bus and the 8051. At the bottom right of the figure is the 12-bit ADC and DAC and the signals which control them: this is used for all three interfaces.

The 8051 interface connects the devices in the manner given in figure 11.5.

The 68020 interface replaces the peripheral interface circuit of figure 11.11, and uses some signals on that figure; $\overline{VI}$ (active if the 68020 is accessing a peripheral), BDIR (the direction signal for the bi-directional buffer) and $\overline{BOE}$ (the buffers output enable).

In fact, the 68020 and STE interfaces are almost identical, so they are drawn together: the standard comparator circuit is used on the STE circuit only to generate valid*, the 68020 circuit uses $\overline{VI}$. The rest is obvious.

5. Figure A6.17 has the interface of the GDC and UART to the 68020 and the STE bus. The circuits for the two devices are again very similar, so they are shown in one figure, as in the manner used in the previous question.

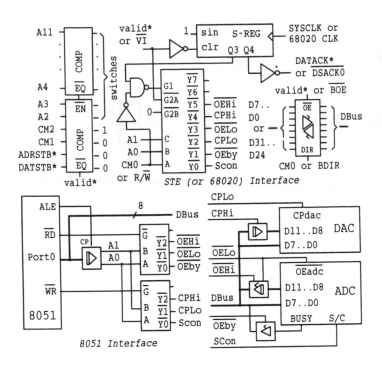

Figure A6.16 Interfaces of 12-bit ADC and DAC

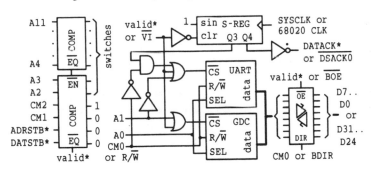

Figure A6.17 Interface of GDC and UART to the 68020 and STE

6. Figure A6.18 has the interface of the memory to the STE bus. The delay before generating DATACK* is calculated as follows (times in ns). For the EPROM: $\overline{CE}$ Access time (300ns) + Time through buffer (25) + STE set up (35) = 360 < 6 clock cycles: use Q6 output of shift register. For reading the RAM: $\overline{OE}$ Access time (120) + Delay through decoder (35) + Time through buffer (25) + STE set up (35) = 215 < 4 clock cycles: use Q4 output. Note, the $\overline{CE}$ time is shorter than the $\overline{OE}$ time + decoder delay. For writing to RAM: Delay through decoder (35) + $\overline{WE}$ Access (70) = 105 < 2 clock cycles; so turn off $\overline{WE}$ using Q2 and generate DATACK using Q3. A logic circuit selects the appropriate shift register output to generate DATACK*.

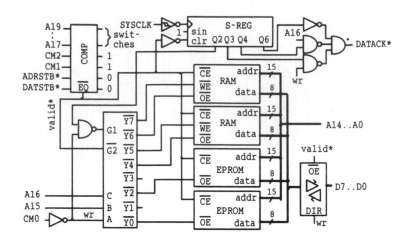

Figure A6.18 Interface of two RAMs and two EPROMs to STE

Chapter 12

1. The following forms a byte from two keypresses.

```
BYTEIN:   CALL ReadKey        ; read first byte
          ST Dreg, Temp       ; store byte in temporary storage
          CALL Convert        ; to pattern to show on 7-seg display
          ST Dreg, $FF02      ; show in first display
          CALL ReadKey        ; (ReadKey is given in chapter 12)
          PUSH Dreg
          CALL Convert        ; (Convert is given in chapter 12)
          ST Dreg, $FF03
          POP Dreg
          SWAP Dreg           ; exchange upper and lower nibbles
          OR Dreg, Temp       ; add in first byte
          SWAP Dreg           ; so first key read is in top nibble
          RTS
Temp:     DefSpace 1          ; temporary store
```

2. The following outputs a square wave whose amplitude is entered by the user.

```
          CALL ByteIn         ; read into Dreg the amplitude
          ST Dreg, Amplitude  ; store it
SqLoop:   CLR Dreg
          CALL DACOutput      ; output to DAC
          CALL Delay          ; delay for suitable time
          LD Dreg, Amplitude
          CALL DACOutput
          CALL Delay
          BRA SqLoop
Amplitude: DefSpace 1
```

3. The following reads from an ADC and puts the result in two displays.

```
AShow:    CALL ADCInput       ; read ADC: use routine given earlier
          CALL HexOut         ; display it
          RTS
```

```
HexOut:   PUSH Dreg          ; subr to o/p Dreg as two hex nibbles
          SWAP Dreg          ; so upper nibble now in lower nibble
          AND Dreg, #15      ; mask upper nibble
          CALL Convert       ; to pattern for 7-seg display
          STA %FF02          ; put in first display
          POP Dreg           ; reload saved value of Dreg
          PUSH Dreg          ; but preserve value on stack
          AND Dreg, #15      ; mask upper nibble
          CALL Convert       ; to pattern for display
          STA $FF03          ; put in second display
          POP Dreg           ; reload Dreg
          RTS
```

4. The following simulates a ramp ADC and displays the result.

```
          CALL RampADC       ; read 'ADC'
          CALL HexOut        ; and display, using the above code
          RTS
RampADC:  LD Dreg, #255      ; initialise Dreg to -1
RALoop:   INC Dreg           ; increment to the next guess
          JSR DACOutput      ;  output guess
          BIT 7, $FF01       ; test comparator bit
          BEQ RAend          ; if zero, have answer
          CMP Dreg, #255     ; check if reached top guess
          BNE RAloop         ; if not, repeat
RAEnd:    RTS
```

5. The following simulates a successive approximation ADC.

```
SAppADC:  LD Dreg, #$80        ; which bit is to be set next
          ST Dreg, WhichBit    ; store in memory
          CLR Dreg             ; guess is set to 0
SALoop:   XOR Dreg, WhichBit   ; set next bit
          JSR DACOutput        ; send to DAC
          BIT 7, $FF01         ; test comparator
          BEQ SAskip           ; skip if guess not too large
          XOR Dreg, WhichBit   ; bit is cleared
SAskip:   LSR WhichBit         ; shift WhichBit right
          BNE SAloop           ; continue unless tried all bits
          RTS
WhichBit: DefSpace 1
```

6. The keypad should be connected to the PIA as follows: the status line should be connected to HS1A, and the data lines to the lower four bits of port A. The code to use this is as follows, first the initialisation then the interrupt routine.

```
Initial:  CLR Dreg
          ST Dreg, Base+1    ; allow access to DDR of port A
          ST Dreg, Base      ; set all bits on port A as input
          LD Dreg, #%00000101; allow interrupts on edge of HS1A
          ST Dreg, Base+1
          RTS
KeyInt:   PUSH Dreg          ; reads key and puts it in memory
          LD Dreg, Base      ; read value from port A
          AND Dreg, #15      ; mask remaining bits
```

```
              ST Dreg, KeyStore      ; store value in memory
              POP Dreg
              RTI
```

Chapter 13

1. The Ramp and Successive Approximation ADCs for the 68020 are:

```
RampADC    MOVE.B #255, D0        * initialise
RALoop     ADDQ.B #1, D0          * next guess
           JSR DACOutput          * output guess to DAC
           BTST.B #7, Comparator  * test comparator
           BEQ RAend
           CMP.B #$FF, D0         * test if max value
           BNE RAloop             * loop back if not
RAEnd      RTS

SAADC      MOVE.L D1, -(A7)       * save D1
           MOVE.B #$80, D1        * which bit is in D1
           CLR D0                 * guess is in D0
SAloop     EOR.B D1, D0           * add next bit to answer
           BTST.B #7, Comparator  * test comp.
           BEQ SAskip
           EOR.B D1, D0           * remove bit
SAskip     LSR.B #1, D1           * shift which bit
           BNE SAloop             * repeat if which bit non zero
           MOVE.L (A7)+, D1       * reload D1
           RTS
```

The 8051 code is given below with an extra subroutine to test the comparator:

```
RampADC:   CLR A                  ; initialise guess to 0
RALoop:    ACALL DACOutput        ; output latest guess
           ACALL TestCmp          ; test comp.: is guess too high
           JNC RAEnd              ; exit if it is
           INC A                  ; move to next guess
           JNZ RAloop             ; if gone to 0, gone too far
           DEC A                  ; so decrement to 255
RAEnd:     RET

SAADC:     PUSH R0                ; Successive Approximation ADC
           MOV R0, #$80           ; which bit
           CLR A                  ; initialise guess
SAloop:    XRL A, R0              ; set next bit
           ACALL DACOutput        ; output to DAC
           ACALL TestCmp          ; test comparator
           JNC SAskip             ; skip if guess not too large
           XRL A, R0              ; remove next bit
SAskip:    XCH A, R0              ; swap A and R0
           RR A                   ; shift A (i.e. which bit) right
           JZ SAend               ; if zero, stop
           XCH A, R0              ; return A and which bit
           SJMP RALoop
SAend:     XCH A, R0              ; so answer in A
           RET
```

```
TestCmp: PUSH A              ; tests comparator, it sets C
         PUSH R0             ; if first voltage exceeds second
         MOV R0, #Comparator
         MOVX, A, @R0        ; read comparator
         RLC A               ; shift bit 7 into Carry
         POP R0
         POP A
         RET
```

2. The following 68020 code allow access to the 12-bit ADC and DAC.

```
DAC12    MOVE.L D0, -(A7)    * save D0, the value to be output
         LSR.W #8, D0        * shift high byte to lower byte
         MOVE.B D0, DACHi    * output to high byte of DAC
         MOVE.L (A7)+, D0    * reload D0
         MOVE.B D0, DACLo    * output low byte to DAC
         RTS

ADC12    MOVE.B D0, ADCSConv * issue start convert
A12wait  MOVE.B ADCStart, D0 * read status
         BPL A12wait         * jump back if not converted
         MOVE.B, ADCLo, D0   * read low byte into D0
         ROR.L #8, D0        * shift byte 8 times to bits 31..24
         MOVE.B ADCHi, D0    * read high byte into bits 7..0
         ROL.L #8, D0        * rotate so two bytes in bit 15..0
         AND.L #$FFF, D0     * clear upper bits
         RTS                 * with value in D0
```

The code for the 8051 is as follows.

```
DAC12:   PUSH R0             ; Value to output is in AB
         MOV R0, #DACHi      ; R0 has address of high byte of DAC
         MOVX @R0, A         ; output high byte
         DEC R0              ; R0 has address of low byte of DAC
         XCH A,B             ; now low byte in A
         MOVX @R0, A         ; output to DAC
         XCH A,B             ; return A and B to original values
         POP R0
         RET

ADC12:   PUSH R0             ; value will be read into AB
         MOV R0, #ADCSconv   ; R0 has address of busy / start con
         MOVX @R0, A         ; issue start convert
A12wait: MOVX A, @R0         ; read in busy status
         JNB A.7, A12wait    ; loop back if ADC not ready
         INC R0              ; R0 now has address of low byte
         MOVX A, @R0         ; read low byte
         XCH A,B             ; low byte in B
         INC R0              ; R0 has address of high byte
         MOVX, A, @R0        ; read high byte, result now in AB
         POP R0
         RET
```

3. The following 68020 code outputs a triangular wave.

```
TriWave  CLR D0            * initialise value to be output
uploop   JSR DACOutput     * output value to DAC
         ADDQ.B #1, D0
         BNE uploop        * keep going til incremented to 0
downlp   SUBQ.B #1, D0     * decrement
         BEQ uploop        * when reached 0 go up again
         JSR DACOutput     * output next 'down' value to DAC
         BRA downlp
```

4. The code below sets, clears and reads the values from the graphics memory. The x,y coordinates are in D0 and D1. The subroutine CalcAddress loads A0 with the address of the byte defined by x,y and D0 with the appropriate bit.

```
SetBit   CALL CalcAddress  * calculate address of x,y
         BSET D0, (A0)     * set bit in graphics memory
         RTS
ClrBit   CALL CalcAddress
         BCLR D0, (A0)     * clear bit in graphics memory
         RTS
GetBit   JSR CalcAddress
         BTST.B D0, (A0)   * return state of bit
         RTS

CalcAddress  * take x,y values in D0,D1 and calculate address
             * of byte in A0, and which bit in the byte in D0
         MOVE D0, -(A7)
         LSL #5, D1        * multiply y by 32
         LSR #3, D0        * divide x by 8
         MOVEA #MemoryStart, A0
         ADDA D0, A0
         ADDA D1, A0       * A0 has Memstart + x / 8 + y * 32
         MOVE.B #7, D0
         SUB.B (A7)+, D0
         AND.B #7, D0      * D0 has 7 - x MOD 8
         RTS
```

Chapter 14

1. The following 68020 code outputs a sine wave by reading from a table.

```
Sine     MOVEA #SineTab, A0      * load A0 with first byte of table
SineLp   MOVE.B (A0)+, D0        * load next value
         JSR DACOutput           * output to the DAC
         CMPA #SineTab+360, A0   * if reached end of table
         BEQ Sine                * reload A0 with start of table
         BRA SineLp              * otherwise just carry on
```

2. The following 68020 procedures access the 12-bit DAC and ADC.

```
         * PROCEDURE DAC12 (Value : INTEGER)
DAC12         * word to be output is at 4,a7 and 5, a7
         MOVE.B (5,A7), DACHi    * output high byte to DAC
         MOVE.B (4,A7), DACLo    * output low byte to DAC
         RTD #2                  * return popping value from stack
```

```
         * PROCEDURE ADC12 () : INTEGER
ADC12          * result should be put at 4,a7
         LINK A6, #0
         MOVE.L D0, -(A7)      * save D0
ADC12    MOVE.B D0, ADCSConv   * issue start convert
A12wait  MOVE.B ADCStart, D0   * read status
         BPL A12wait           * jump back if not converted
         MOVE.B, ADCLo, (8,a6) * read low byte into result
         MOVE.B ADCHi, (9,a6)  * read high byte into result
         MOVE.L (A7)+,D0       * save D0
         UNLK A6
         RTS
```

3. Algorithms and 68020 code for string handling are as follows.

```
Find Length:
  Load Ptr with start of string and Length with 0
  WHILE Ptr^ <> 0 DO
    Increment Length and Ptr
```

```
Length   LINK A6, #0          * on stack is address of string
         MOVEM A0/D0, -(A7)
         MOVEA (8,A6), A0     * A0 has address of string
         CLR D0               * length := 0
LenLp    TST.B (A0)+          * WHILE Ptr^ <> 0
         BEQ LenEnd
         ADDQ #1,D0           *    increment length
         BRA LenLp
LenEnd   MOVE.W D0, (12,A6)   * put result on stack
         MOVEM (A7)+, A0/D0
         UNLK A6
         RTD #4
```

```
Copy:
  Load PtrS and PtrD with start of each string
  REPEAT  PtrD^ := PtrS^ and Increment PtrS and PtrD;
  UNTIL byte copied was zero
```

```
Copy     LINK A6, #0          * on stack is addresses of strings
         MOVEM A0-A1, -(A7)
         MOVEA (8,A6), A0     * A0 has address of source string
         MOVEA (12,A6), A1    * A1 has address of dest. string
CopyLp   MOVE.B (A0)+, (A1)+  * keep copying until 0 copied
         BNE CopyLp
         MOVEM (A7)+, A0-A1
         UNLK A6
         RTD #8
```

```
Compare:   (return -1, 0 or 1 if s1<s2, s1=s2 or s1>s2)
  Load PtrS and PtrD with start of each string
  REPEAT
   IF PtrS^ < PtrD^ THEN Answer is -1, so stop
   ELSE IF PtrS^ > PtrD^ THEN Answer is 1, so stop
   ELSE IF PtrS^ = 0 THEN Answer is 0, so stop
   ELSE Increment PtrS and PtrD
```

```
Compare   LINK A6, #0              * addresses of strings on stack
          MOVEM A0-A1, -(A7)
          MOVEA (8,A6), A0         * A0 has address of source string
          MOVEA (12,A6), A1        * A1 has address of dest. string
CopyLp    CMP.B (A0)+, (A1)        * Compare bytes
          BCC SetLess              * jump if less than to set -1
          BHI SetMore              * jump if greater than to set 1
          TST.B (A1)+              * test to see if bytes are both 0
          BNE CopyLp               * if not so, look at next byte
          CLR (16,A6)              * answer is 0
          BRA CompEnd              * go and set result
SetLess   MOVE.W #-1, (16,A6)      * load -1
          BRA CompEnd
SetMore   MOVE.W #1, (16,A6)       * load 1
CompEnd   MOVEM (A7)+, A0-A1/D0
          UNLK A6
          RTD #8
```

4. The graphics procedures below use the CalcAddress function given earlier.

```
DrawDot   LINK A6, #0              * on stack are x,y,colour
          MOVEM.L A0/D0-D1, -(A7)
          MOVE (12,A6), D0         * D0 is loaded with x
          MOVE (10,A6), D1         * D1 is loaded with y
          CALL CalcAddress         * A0 has address of byte, x the bit
          BTST.B #0, (8, A6)       * test colour (is it 0 or 1)
          BEQ GoClear              * if 0, then clear the bit
          BSET.B D0, (A0)          * set dot
          BRA DDEnd
GoClear   BCLR.B D0, (A0)          * clear dot
DDEnd     UNLK A6
          MOVEM (A7)+, A0/D0-D1
          RTD #6

FindDot   LINK A6, #0              * on stack are x,y, above is result
          MOVEM.L A0/D0-D1, -(A7)
          MOVE (10,A6), D0         * D0 is loaded with x
          MOVE (8,A6), D1          * D1 is loaded with y
          CALL CalcAddress         * A0 has address of byte, x the bit
          CLR D1                   * assume result is 0
          BTST.B D0, (A0)          * test colour (is it 0 or 1)
          BEQ FDskip               * skip if is 0
          MOVE.B #1, D1            * load result as 1
FDskip    MOVE.W D1, (12,A6)       * put result on stack
          UNLK A6
          MOVEM (A7)+, A0/D0-D1
          RTD #4
```

5. In the BubbleSort procedure below A0 has the address of Data. D0 and D1 contain i and j; it is assumed the integers are 16-bit, so i and j are kept as multiples of 2, in the range 0..9; (D0,A0) is thus Data[i], (D1,A0) is Data[j].

```
BSort     CLR  DO                          * DO has i
BIloop    MOVE.B #18, D1                   * load D1 with j (2*9)
BJloop    SUBQ.B #2, D1                    * decrement j
          CMP.B D1, D0                     * end j loop if i=j
          BEQ Bnexti
          CMP.W (2,A0,D1), (0,A0,D1)    * Data[j-1] > Data [j]
          BGT BJloop
          MOVE.W (2,A0,D1), D2    * D2 has Data [j]
          MOVE.W (0,A0,D1), (2,A0,D1)   * Data[j] := Data [j-1]
          MOVE.W D2, (0,A0,D1)    * Data [j-1] := Data[j]
          BRA BJloop
Bnexti    ADDQ.B #2, D0                    * increment i
          CMP.B #18, D0                    * check it has not gone passed 18
          BEQ BIloop
          RTS
```

6. For sorting the StudentRecord problem, the above algorithm is used exept D0 and D1 are changed by multiples of the size of the record (here assumed to be 30) not 2, a different compare function is used, and different function is used to swap record. These pieces of code are as follows:

```
For comparing the integers, use the following instruction
          CMP.W (30, A0, D1), (0, A0, D1)
For comparing the strings use the following
          LEA (32, A0, D1), A1    * A1 has address of Data[j].Name
          LEA (2, A0, D1), A2     * A2 has address of Data[j-1].Name
          CALL StringComapre      * similar to one given earlier
For swapping 30 bytes
          LEA (0, A0, D1), A1     * load A1 with Data[j-1]
          MOVE.B #29, D2          * set counter for 30 loops
sloop     MOVE.B (30, A1), D3     * these 3 lines swap data
          MOVE.B (A1), (30, A1)   * at A1 and 30+A1
          MOVE.B D3, (A1)+
          DBNE D2, sloop
```

Chapter 15

1. Here it is assumed that the 8051 has external ROM and memory mapped peripherals. Initially power supplies would be checked. Then the first program to be written would just jump to itself, and a CRO would be used to view the clock, then the $\overline{\text{PSEN}}$ signal, the data and the address buses, to verify correct operation. The expected signals are those given in chapter 11. Then simple programs would be written testing the peripherals and then the RAM in the manner given in chapter 15.

2..A similar strategy would be used for the 68020. A simple jump program would be written and the bus and EPROM circuitry tested. Then the peripherals would be added gradually and then the RAM; each time adding more circuitry gradually.

Index